# Alternative Beginnings and Endings of All Things:

## Science, Religion, Politics, and Cards, Hypervolume II

# Alternative Beginnings and Endings of All Things: Science, Religion, Politics, and Cards, Hypervolume II

Maurice James Blair

Synapsid Revelations Press
Corporation

Alternative Beginnings and Endings of All Things: Science, Religion, Politics, and Cards, Hypervolume II
ISBN: 978-1-963470-08-6 (reg. distr. hardcover, incl. barcode)

ISBN: 978-1-963470-02-4 (promo. paperback, sans barcode)



Blair, Maurice James 1976-

May 21, 2024: Published: World Day for Cultural Diversity

(Note: SRPC adjusted about 0.001% of this May 23-24, 2024—subsequent to the initial May 21, 2024 transmission to a publishing database. Pbk rev. date: 5/23. H.C. rev. date: 5/24. Promo. Pbk slightly less refined. H.C. slightly more refined.)



Synapsid Revelations Press Corporation
9619 Meadowcroft Dr
Houston, TX 77063 U.S.

1. Buddhism 2. Criminology 3. Sex and Sexuality

4. Politics 5. Social Psychology 6. Science 7. Biology

8. Comparative Religion 9. Public Policy I. Title

# BOOKS BY MAURICE JAMES BLAIR

---

Fiction:

THE DIMETRODONS, THE DORIANS, AND THE MODERN WORLD

ALL THINGS UNDER AND OVER THE SUN AND STARS: ENIGMAS IN VARIOUS STAGES

---

Nonfiction:

SCIENCE, RELIGION, POLITICS, AND CARDS

---

Mixed feedback for *The Dimetrodons, the Dorians, and the Modern World*:

"An imaginative but jumbled journey through the mysteries of earthly existence." –*Kirkus Reviews*

---

Praise for *All Things under and over the Sun and Stars: Enigmas in Various Stages*:

"... both extravagant and grounded, part convoluted history, hypothetical events, and parallel worlds..."
–E. Lee Caleca

"A quizzical, nonlinear journey through complicated SF plotlines involving philosophy and epistemology."
–*Kirkus Reviews*

---

Following up those fiction works, Maurice James Blair authored the nonfiction work *Science, Religion, Politics, and Cards*. Here is one reaction to his arrangement for complimentary copies to go to select public figures:

"...Justice Gorsuch is not able to accept gifts in these circumstances..." –Ethan V. Torrey, Legal Counsel to the Supreme Court of the United States

Note: Tracking indicated one complimentary copy each to have been delivered in the third quarter of 2023 to all nine justices of the U.S. Supreme Court, yet among those there was only one instance of a return received by the author. To be clear, there was also only one letter received by the author from that court's legal counsel—the letter that accompanied the aforementioned return.

This would appear to indicate three main possibilities:

a) Perhaps Justices Alito, Barrett, Jackson, Sotomayor, Kagan, Thomas, Kavanaugh, and Roberts *were able* to accept gifts in these circumstances.

b) Perhaps those other eight were unable to accept gifts in these circumstances yet *chose an alternative method* of refusal; for example, by immediately giving received copies of it away to charity.

c) An extremely unlikely scenario would involve at least one return package in connection with one or more of the other eight getting lost in the mail/delivery, thereby mysteriously found by recipient(s) unknown.

* Although there appear possibilities beyond (a), (b), and (c), it may seem, from outside of the SCOTUS processes looking in, that (a) was most likely, (b) the second most likely, and the others, though not completely ruled out, a stretch, at a mere trace of a percentage chance.

In much the same vein as the earlier nonfiction work *Science, Religion, Politics, and Cards*, this sequel nonfiction work *Alternative Beginnings and Endings of All Things: Science, Religion, Politics, and Cards, Hypervolume II* continues the many quests to inform, enlighten, and empower sentient beings, thereby enhancing abilities to steer reality toward the good, the better, and the best.

*Portions of this work include open discussions of religion, sex, sexuality, ethics, criminal activities, law enforcement activities, science, and investigations. Here is a recommendation for you to trust yourself to a major degree regarding if and when to proceed.*

* * * * * * * * * * * *

Consider anywhere and everywhere that it ever has or ever will be written,

"LONG AGO, *HOMO SAPIENS*

ARRIVED ON THE SCENE.

HOW DID THEY ARRIVE?

WHY DID THEY ARRIVE?

WHERE NEXT FOR THEM?

WHAT NEXT FOR THEM?"

* * * * * * * * * * * *

Consider anywhere and everywhere that it

ever has or ever will be written,

"EXTINCTION?"

Sending complimentary copies of this to select foreign embassies is not intended as an act of diplomacy, because if it were, given the context, then the author and the publisher would be violating The Logan Act. Even devoid of telling any countries associated with those U.S. embassies what to do, what to refrain from doing, when to do what, when to refrain from doing what, etc., I, nevertheless, believe this helpful to the long run prospects for the well-being of the living beings of the species known as *Homo sapiens* and living beings of other species. Although some embassies, the U.S. FBI, the U.S. CIA, business leaders, theologians, attorneys, and others who might receive complimentary copies might exhibit skepticism toward the value they would obtain from studying it, consider how this work addresses criminology, comparative religion, sexual ethics, geopolitics, physics, metaphysics, social psychology, business ethics, public policy, the ethics of possible human survival, the ethics of possible human extinction, and the relationships between human beings and the totality of reality. *In case there was ever a doubt in the minds of any readers about the seriousness and sincerity of the author and the publisher, the composition process of this project took into account that lying to the FBI by U.S. persons is a crime. The author plans to send at least one copy of it directly to the FBI. There is absolutely no intentional lying in this book. A commitment to the intentional telling of truth uniformly appears throughout this book.*

# PREFACE:

Although many may best study *Science, Religion, Politics, and Cards* before possibly starting to study *Alternative Beginnings and Endings of All Things: Science, Religion, Politics, and Cards, Hypervolume II*, others might best start with the latter rather than the former, and yet another set of adventurers might best study both works concurrently.

When the years, decades, centuries, and millennia in this work are not otherwise specified in relation to occurrences, the temporal identifiers are with the modern global convention of most often labeling temporal identifiers by Gregorian Calendar means.

However, neither the author nor the publisher advocate via this work for beholders to ascribe to ultimate reality any type of absolute, inherent, unequivocal supremacy of the Gregorian Calendar over Chinese Calendars, Hebrew Calendars, the Julian Calendar, extraterrestrial calendars, the Muslim Calendar, Tibetan Calendars, the Mayan Calendar, or any other one calendar or collection of multiple calendars.

Praise be to all true awareness of duration, time, space, space-time, sight-and-sound-and-mind, and the combinations of space, time, space-time, mind, matter, energy, matter-energy, space-time-mind, and beyond. Praise be to all true awareness.

# Alternative Beginnings and Endings of All Things: Science, Religion, Politics, and Cards, Hypervolume II

CONTENTS:

Chapter Ten has Its own Table of Contents on pp. 280-281.

# INTRODUCTION

Both the author and the publisher recognize at the time of first going to print with this work that profound humility is appropriate. *This is largely due to how, after the author joined X (formerly known as Twitter) on April 1, 2024,* believing the odds low that within the first few weeks he would either wind up with many followers or zero followers, *the reality encountered was that he wound up with zero followers up to shortly before the initial publication of this book.*

*As of each time checked from April 1, 2024 until just before the May 21, 2024 sending of finalized files to facilitate going to print, that number persisted at zero. This is clear-cut rebuke of us, and we accept its reality.*

Whatever the prospects might be for that lack of traction ever changing or not, beware that we are choosing to be very humble at the time of this book going to print and factoring that lack of traction into our decisions of what to include and what to exclude from the corridors of these pages. – a joint statement from Synapsid Revelations Press Corporation & M.J.B.

* * *

*With this book, to the best of abilities, I show all due respect to all beings. In some cases, this is by rather fully exposing things that others might prefer not to become public knowledge, and I do it anyway. This is part of honoring a duty to all truth and all total levels of absolute reality, as well as all relative realities. In other cases, this is by choosing massive omissions in between what shows.* There are many competing ideas regarding what might make something relevant. The publisher and I are doing our utmost to present all that is relevant and nothing else. – M.J.B.

*　*　*　*　*　*　*

On another note, although there have been cases in which the author and his next of kin have alienated people due to his and his next of kin's ineptitude, there have also been many cases in which others have felt alienated by the author and his next of kin due to the others' ineptitude. There have also been gray areas of interpretation about who to blame for what with this. Similarly, in much intercultural, interfaith, international, etc., interaction, different cultures, faiths, and nations have often disagreed about how much praise and blame to attribute to whom, as well as what the best courses of action would be. *Yes, you—or at least some of you—might react* with thinking something along the lines of, *Tell me something I don't know. I already knew the stated-just-now perspective regarding virtually anyone, including those of various faiths, cultures, and nations. This is blatantly obvious to almost anyone who's been around many blocks, and I've been around tens of thousands of blocks. Come on, man! What's with you? Tell me something I don't already know!*

Here is part of how I can respond to that line of thinking: *Yes, if you already felt very well aware of that, then more power to you! Congratulations! At least a few other readers might still benefit greatly from being informed or reminded of that, nevertheless. This kind of parallels sometime when I was around 8-13 years old, and some church gathering had a bunch of very young people in a class, and an adult then discussed things, including some math that was extremely basic to me, yet which was a relevant part of instructing some percentage of the students. At that time, I expressed annoyance, and the instructor correctly pointed out to me that although that math seemed unnecessarily simple to me for the instructor to mention, it was something that at least some of the others could truly benefit from hearing pointed out then and there.*

Extending this type of approach further, before I go into repeated, sharp criticisms aimed both at myself and others, including details that may have the potential to lead to criminal prosecutions that otherwise would never have seen the light of day, I will express a mixture of praise and criticism:

1. The United States of America is quite an extraordinary country, and I am fortunate to be an American citizen. The First Amendment is one of the finest compositions of practical idea structures ever to arrive anywhere, and its profundity and ambiguity have inspired a great many people, both in the U.S.A. and elsewhere. That being acknowledged, though, it does seem that many Americans, including many U.S. political leaders, have taken many things way too far on many occasions.
2. Each of the other nations, in its own way, exudes mysticism, flexibility, and austerity, presenting much danger and opportunity to

everyone and everything. It can be helpful for the ready to debate the ethics of both the U.S. and the set of all other nations in terms of how to best regulate sexual activities, the balance of power between genders along various dimensions, and risks associated with accuracy of communication versus inaccuracy of communication, and issues involving transcendental aspects of communications and interactions.

3. Each former employer, each former peer-level coworker, each former subordinate, and each former supervisor can be thought of as having proven helpful, harmful, or both, based on the choices of cognition. Each who has been of extensive interaction may exhibit what many of the religious and many self-improvement gurus might characterize with such sayings as, "All fall short of the glory of God" and "Everyone has room for improvement."
4. Ancestors have often proven helpful in many ways, yet it can be best for descendants to be freely aware of both the more favorable of the ancestral influences and the less favorable of the ancestral influences.
5. The U.S. Military-Industrial Complex is quite a mystery, even unto itself, and a great many of its aspects are interwoven in many cases with the previous four categories listed.

*In Memory of President George Washington, Teacher Yeshe Tsogyal, Warrior Padmasambhava, Physicist Moo Young Han, Athlete Jim Thorpe, Occultist P.D. Ouspensky, Musician Jimi Hendrix, Eschatologist John of Patmos, Zen Patriarch Bodhidharma, Martial Artist Bruce Lee, Performer Anita Ekberg, Tantric Interpreter John Woodroffe, Host Rod Serling, Visual Artist Pamela Colman Smith, Advocate Olivia Newton-John, and Inventor Arthur C. Clarke*

# CHAPTER ONE: ALTERNATIVE SYMBOLIC TIMETABLE PATTERNS

## CREATION, SEXUALITY, PRESERVATION, DESTRUCTION, COMMERCE, REVELATION, ANATOMY, BIOLOGY, MILITARY SCIENCE, CHEMISTRY, PHYSICS, THEOLOGY, GEOLOGY, AND METEROROLOGY

THIS CHAPTER PRESENTS IN RELATIONSHIP WITH VARIOUS DATES FROM THE EIGHTY-YEAR PERIOD FROM NOVEMBER 4, 1922 TO NOVEMBER 3, 2002, CONCEIVED VIA A CARD DECK CONSISTING OF ACE THROUGH ONE HUNDRED EIGHT FOR EACH OF FOURTEEN SUITS (i.e., patterns featuring 1,512 cards with which to symbolize what happened, how it continues to affect reality in the present, and how it could potentially continue to affect reality in the future) & SUPPLEMENTED IN SOME CASES BY what many residents of English-speaking countries have oft considered THE MOST STANDARD 52-CARD deck since about two or three centuries before the U.S. Declaration of Independence.

NOV. 4, 1922 (per Gregorian Calendar) / (with three main Tibetan Calendar Year numbers for it being 2049, 1668, and 896) / (earlier in the year as measured by the Tibetan Calendar than as measured by the Gregorian Calendar) (Tibetan Calendar Year Symbolism: Water Dog)

North: Ace-to-95 of Biology.

East: 24-to-78 of Geology, Ace of Sexuality, and 12 of Commerce.

Center / shared-in-common cards: 18 of Sexuality, 20 of Sexuality, 27-to-54 of Meteorology, 71 of Physics.

South: 88-to-108 of Commerce, Ace-to-5 of Commerce, 85 of Meteorology, and Ace of Geology.

West: Complete suit (Ace through 108) of Military Science.

Northwest: 27, 48, 53, 58, 65, 87, 89, 93, and 98 of Theology.

[Note 1: Subsequent pages with symbolic cartomancy of dates label the directional hands with the abbreviations C, N, NE, E, SE, S, SW, W, and NW. To which set of spreads and/or games the metaphors apply is intentionally left wide open to interpretation(s)—be they allegedly-right, allegedly-whatever-else, &c. Skipped listing = free of possession; of an empty status. (e.g., NE, SE, and SW in the above.)]

[Note 2: Some subsequent pages representing dates in this manner abbreviate the introductory identification in the pattern of "NOV. 4, 1922 (per G.C.) / (T.C. Yr #'s 2049, 1668, & 896) (earlier in T.C. yr than in G.C. yr) (T.C.Y.S.: Water Dog)." Others use other abbreviations.]

Nov. 11, 1922 (per G.C.) / (T.C. Yr #'s 2049, 1668, & 896) (earlier in T.C. yr than in G.C. yr) (T.C.Y.S.: Water Dog)

C: Complete Suits (Ace-108 each) of Sexuality, Preservation, Anatomy, and Chemistry.

E: Ace, 2, 5, 12, 18, 93, 96, 97, and 99 of Creation; Ace of Destruction; and a Complete Suit (Ace-108) of Military Science.

W: 2-100 of Destruction; 5 of Geology; 2, 8, 12, and 15 of Commerce.

---

Nov. 30, 1922 (per G.C.) / (T.C. Yr #'s 2049, 1668, & 896) (earlier in T.C. yr than in G.C. yr) (T.C.Y.S.: Water Dog)

N: All Fourteen Aces

C: All Fourteen 100s

S: All Fourteen 88s

---

December 7, 1922 (per G.C.) / (T.C. Yr #'s 2049, 1668, & 896) (earlier in T.C. yr than in G.C. yr) (T.C.Y.S.: Water Dog)

N: Ace of Creation, Ace of Destruction, Ace of Preservation, Ace of Geology, and Ace of Military Science

S: 2 of Creation, 5 of Destruction, 3 of Sexuality, 4 of Sexuality, and 108 of Geology

E: 12-16 of Commerce

W: 4-8 of Commerce

December 22, 1922 (per G.C.) / (T.C. Yr #'s 2049, 1668, & 896) (earlier in T.C. yr than in G.C. yr) (T.C.Y.S.: Water Dog)

C: Full Suit of Destruction

E: Full Suit of Creation

SE: The Ace-54 set of Preservation

S: Ace of Biology

SW: Ace of Commerce

W: 9 of Meteorology

NW: The 55-108 set of Preservation

N: The Aces of Theology, Physics, Military Science, Spades, Hearts, Clubs, and Geology

---

May 1, 1925 (per G.C.) / (T.C. Yr #'s 2052, 1671, & 899) ((earlier in T.C. yr than in G.C. yr) (T.C.Y.S.: Wood Ox)

Ace of Destruction, Ace of Creation, Ace of Commerce, 108 of Sexuality, 108 of Destruction, 108 of Creation, 5 of Preservation, 10 of Theology, 11 of Theology, 12 of Theology, 19 of Meteorology, and 108 of Military Science

(When all layout cards are of a single set, as in the above spread and/or game starting position, this work declines to label that set as being of any one of the nine categories that it uses to organize the spreads and/or game starting positions that consist of two or more sets.)

---

HERE IS A PAGE WITH SEMISIMPLIFIED WAYS OF PRESENTATION:

April 3, 1936 /////// Rat

8 of Geology, 22 of Theology, Ace of Commerce

November 24, 1948 (as meas. by G.C.) /////// Rat

---

April 19, 1936 ///////// Rat

27 of Sexuality, 27 of Biology, 27 of Theology, 27 of Military Science

---

April 22, 1949

Ox

All Fourteen Aces, All Fourteen Deuces, All Fourteen 3s, All Fourteen 4s, and All Fourteen 5s

---

Intermission: An Adjacency of Association for portions of April 22, 1949 to August 27. 1950, for analytical consideration: Ohio, Texas, Nevada, London, Dallas, and Oxford.

---

August 27, 1950

Tiger

THE COMPLETE DECK

THIS PAGE CONSISTS OF FIVE SIMPLIFIED PRESENTATIONS:

—

September 28, 1951

Hare

---

October 31, 1952

Dragon

—

+...........................................................

..............................................................

..............................................................

.......................................+

---

October 20, 1987

Hare

---

September 1, 1995

Boar

— -------------------------------- —

October 7, 1998

Tiger

November 20, 1954 (per G.C.) / Year #s 2081; 1700; & 928 per some alternatives of T.C.)

(earlier in the year as measured by the Tibetan Calendar than as measured by the Gregorian Calendar) (Tibetan Calendar Year Symbolism: Horse)

The full set of odd-numbered cards.

---

October 19, 1986 (per G.C.) / (Year #s 2113; 1732; & 960 per three versions of year tracking by T.C.)

(earlier in the year as measured by the Tibetan Calendar than as measured by the Gregorian Calendar) (Tibetan Calendar Year Symbolism: Tiger)

The half from Ace through 54 of each of the suits.

---

October 19, 1987 (per G.C.) (Yr #s 2114; 1733; & 961 per some alternatives of T.C.)

(earlier in the year as measured by the Tibetan Calendar than as measured by the Gregorian Calendar) (Tibetan Calendar Year Symbolism: Hare)

The full set of even-numbered cards.

November 1, 1952 (per G.C.) (Yr #s 2079; 1698; & 926 per some alternatives of T.C.)

(earlier in the year as measured by the Tibetan Calendar than as measured by the Gregorian Calendar) (Tibetan Calendar Year Symbolism: Dragon

Center: The one-third of the deck with each card a multiple of three (i.e., 3, 6, 9, 12, 15, 18, 21, 24, 27, 30, 33, 36, 39, 42, 45, 48, 51, 54, 57, 60, 63, 66, 69, 72, 75, 78, 81, 84, 87, 90, 93, 96, 99, 102, 105, and 108).

North: The one-third with Ace, 4, 7, 10, 13, etc.

South: The one-third with 2, 5, 8, 11, 14, etc.

East: The spades combined with clubs half of the standard 52-card deck.

West: The hearts combined with diamonds half of the standard 52-card deck.

September 17, 1953 (per G.C.)

(earlier in the year as measured by the Tibetan Calendar than as measured by the Gregorian Calendar) (Tibetan Calendar Year Symbolism: Snake. The 14 ea. w/ 2-21.

July 4, 2000 (as meas. by G.C.)

(T.C. Year #s: 2127; 1746; 974) (earlier in the year as measured by the Tibetan Calendar than as measured by the Gregorian Calendar) (Tibetan Calendar Year Symbolism: Dragon)

A set of all fourteen of the Aces

..................................

........................................

..............................................

November 23, 2001 __///__ 2128 __//__ 1747 _//_ 975.

In the Year of the Snake. __ ////__. The complete deck.

..........................................

..................................

........................................

..............................................

..................................

........................................

..............................................

October 4, 1929 __//__ 2056 __//__ 1675 _//_ 903.

In the Year of the Snake.

Ace of Sexuality. Ace of Biology. 10 of Military Science.
25 of Geology. 108 of Meteorology.

..................................

...............................

........................................

....................................................

October 24, 1929 _/_ 2056 _/_ 1675 _/_ 903. / Snake.

5-108 of Destruction. 2-25 of Sexuality. Ace-101 of Creation. 5 of Commerce.

....................................

..........................................

..................................

....................................

..............................................

August 9, 1945 _/_ 2072 _/_ 1691 _/_ 919. / Bird.

Complete Suit of Revelation. Complete Suit of Physics. Complete Suit of Destruction. The Aces of Each of the Other Eleven Suits.

....................................

..........................................

..................................

....................................

..................................

..............................................

November 3. 2002 _/_ 2129 _/_ 1748 _/_ 976. Horse.

Ace-25 of Creation. 28-34 of Sexuality. 2-12 of Biology. 5, 25, 105, 106, and 108 of Destruction. 5 of Geology.

North: Ace of Spades, 2 of Clubs, 5 of Hearts, 3 & 4 of Diamonds. Also, 6 & 10 of Clubs, and Jack, Queen, and King of Spades.

East: 10, Jack, Queen, King, and Ace of Diamonds. Also, Queen of Hearts.

South: 10, Jack, Queen, King, and 5 of Hearts. Also, Ace of Hearts.

West: 6, 7, 8, 9, and 10 of Spades. Also, 8 of Diamonds.

# CHAPTER TWO: NARRATIVES

Exhibit A, Pt. 1: Transcription of the first fourteen sentences of the revised-after-feedback version of a paper from my first undergraduate semester University Writing Course:

(which occurred in portions of Q4 of Year 1994 as measured by the Gregorian Calendar / in portions of Year 2121 as measured by one version of the Tibetan Calendar / in portions of Year 968 as measured by another version of the Tibetan Calendar)

(Please note that the instructor wrote a recommendation to replace "the f-word" in the first version with "fuck" in the second version, and I chose to agree with that recommendation.)

(Further revision in transcription here of early sentences, besides spacing, pagination, and line-breaking, was the addition of two commas.)

## The first 14 sentences of the 4Q 1994 essay "The Crucial Importance of the Rights of the Accused"

The American criminal justice system provides that an accused person is innocent until proven guilty in order to minimize the chances of doing innocent persons wrong (United Nations, 1959, p. 242). This would provide little insurance against the wrongful imprisonment of innocent persons, though, without a number of our legal system's other provisions. Abuse of powers must be held in check in each part of the criminal justice system for justice to be maintained. If any parts of the system were allowed to abuse their powers, then they could make a mockery of justice in spite of efforts to uphold justice in the other areas.

I gained a sense of the need to insure the rights of the accused long before I knew a thing about our legal system. Specifically, an incident in first grade brought the issue to my attention. In PE class one day the coach noticed that a girl was crying as she ran her lap. Immature as I was back then, I thought it might be funny to say that the reason why she was crying was that she feared failing PE. The problem was that I decided to apply the word "flunk," which I had learned recently, and my enunciation was not very good. I tried to say, "Maybe she thinks she's going to flunk," but my coach thought she heard me say, "fuck." Coach immediately sent me to stand against the wall for the rest of class. I pleaded with her, explaining that I never meant to say such a thing, but she refused to consider my "excuses."

---

Exh. A, Pt. 2: On the next set of pages shall appear an exhibit of an actual scanning of the paper itself (what I typed way back then and gave to the instructor, and which show two brief, handwritten notes of praise from the course instructor).

(As a caveat, some of its characterizations may be considered dated, whereas other of its characterizations may be considered timeless, and different beholders might disagree about which is which.)

Exhibit A, Part 2 (a 1994 essay), Section 1 (most of p.1):

Jim Blair
Armstrong - UWC 5
Portfolio - Assignment 7B

The Crucial Importance of the Rights of the Accused

The American criminal justice system provides that an accused person is innocent until proven guilty in order to minimize the chances of doing innocent persons wrong (United Nations, 1959, p. 242). This would provide little insurance against the wrongful imprisonment of innocent persons, though, without a number of our legal system's other provisions. Abuse of powers must be held in check in each part of the criminal justice system for justice to be maintained. If any parts of the system were allowed to abuse their powers, then they could make a mockery of justice in spite of efforts to uphold justice in the other areas. The rights of the accused are crucial to holding the powers of police officers and prosecutors in check, and they ensure defendants the due process of law (i.e., procedural guarantees). These rights also play an important role in defending our right to privacy.

I gained a sense of the need to insure the rights of the accused long before I knew a thing about our legal system. Specifically, an incident in first grade brought the issue to my attention. In PE class one day the coach noticed that a girl was crying as she ran her lap. Immature as I was back then, I thought it might be funny to say that the reason why she was crying was that she feared failing PE. The problem was that I decided to apply the word "flunk," which I had learned recently, and my enunciation was not very good. I tried to say "Maybe she thinks she's going to flunk," but my coach thought she heard me say "fuck." Coach immediately sent me to stand against the wall for the rest of class. I pleaded with her, explaining that I never meant to say such a thing, but she refused to consider my "excuses." The entire time I stood against the wall I wondered why in the world I deserved to be punished. It was simply unfair. Coach thought I deliberately used

Exh. A, Pt. 2 (A Q4 1994 Essay), Sec. 2 (end of p.1, most of p.2)

foul language, but I knew that in reality I did nothing of the sort. All I had done was to

try using a new, "appropriate" word in my vocabulary, and why should a child be discouraged from doing that?

In the years since that incident I have been very concerned about what my prospects of being found innocent would be if I am someday falsely accused of a crime. I have occasionally imagined scenarios in which I was found guilty of crimes I did not commit and scenarios in which I was found innocent. I did this in the desperate hope of reassuring myself that it was unlikely for the former outcome to ever prevail, but I soon figured out that the probability of an innocent verdict versus the probability of a guilty verdict depends on a number of factors that vary from case to case *and* one constant factor: the pertinent laws. Since I knew little about our legal system at the time I was pondering all these scenarios, I realized that I would need more legal knowledge to understand the issue any better.

I gained this additional legal knowledge from a course at Baylor University on American National Government and a high school course on US Government. From these courses I learned many details about the rights of the accused. In addition to building my knowledge of how certain laws are designed to reduce the chance of punishing innocent people for crimes they did not commit, these courses brought to my attention another important aspect of several of these rights: they protect our rights to privacy and private

Exh. A, Pt. 2 (a 1994 essay), Sec. 3 (part p.2 & part p. 3)

property. Since taking those courses, I have been involved in several arguments with people over the worth of the rights of the accused. These arguments taught me that many people in this country fail to appreciate the ways in which our legal system protects them from arbitrary arrest, detainment, and search and seizure, and how it tries to minimize the chances of their wrongful conviction.

To fully appreciate how our legal system protects us in these ways, we must have a basic understanding of the rights of the accused. So, what exactly are these rights? First, there are limits on the conduct of police officers and prosecutors (Schmidt, Shelley, & Bardes, 1993, p. 129). Freedom from unreasonable search and seizure is provided for

under the Fourth Amendment (Ibid). The so-called exclusionary rule, which forbids the admission at trial of illegally seized evidence, is necessary because internal disciplinary actions within the police force and prosecution or suits against the police do not effectively protect against unreasonable search and seizure (Farkas, 1977, p. 124). The reasoning behind the rule is that it forces police to properly obtain evidence (Schmidt, et al., 1993, p. 132). The Fourth Amendment also provides that no arrest can be made except on probable cause (Schmidt, et al., 1993, p. 129). Except under specified conditions, a person can only be taken into custody with a properly issued warrant of arrest, and a judge will only issue a warrant to a police officer if (s)he decides that there is "probable cause" (United Nations, 1959, p.242). Probable cause means that, given the

Exh. A, Pt. 2 (a 1994 essay), Sec. 4 (part p. 3 & part p. 4)

facts known to the police officer, a person of reasonable intelligence would think the accused probably committed the crime. The conditions under which an arrest can take place without a warrant are 1) while the suspect commits a crime, 2) when police are in hot pursuit, and 3) when police have reason to believe that a crime has or will take place and the suspect will escape unless arrested (Allen, Friday, Roebuck, & Sagarin, 1981, p. 317). Coerced confessions and illegal interrogation are prohibited by the Fifth Amendment, and entrapment is disallowed (Schmidt, et al., 1993, p. 129). Entrapment occurs whenever police cause someone to commit a crime (s)he would not have otherwise committed, solely for the purpose of making an arrest (Allen, et al., 1981, p. 336). In a key ruling, "the Supreme Court ...stated that it is not the function of law enforcement to manufacture crime" (Ibid, p.337). Finally, a suspect must be informed of his/her rights upon questioning, as a result of *Miranda v. Arizona*, in which the Supreme Court ruled that:

> Prior to any questioning, the person must be warned that he has the right to remain silent, that any statement he does make may be used against him, and that he has a right to the presence of an attorney, either retained or appointed (Schmidt, et al., 1993, p. 130).

---

This requirement was imposed in response to many cases where police resorted to brutality, trickery, and other illegal means to obtain confessions (Allen, et al., 1981, p. 317). Legislation and rulings since the time of *Miranda* have limited its impact, though, by providing that *Miranda* does not apply to certain cases (Schmidt, et al., 1993, pp. 130-131).

Second, defendants have pretrial rights, which are critical to securing our personal liberty, because, as the UN notes:

> The greatest single threat to the individual's personal security throughout history has been the exercise of government authority arbitrarily to take into custody and indefinitely imprison any person without granting him, as a right, an opportunity to be heard and to have a speedy and impartial public hearing (1959, p. 245).

The writ of habeous corpus is an order requiring jailers to bring a prisoner before a court in order to determine whether or not his/her detainment is legal (Ibid, p. 246). The Sixth Amendment provides for prompt arraignment, which means the suspect must be brought to appear in court without delay after probable cause is determined (Ibid, p. 243). The right to counsel is guaranteed by the Sixth Amendment in conjunction with a number of Supreme Court rulings, the most significant being *Gideon v. Wainright*, in which the court said that accused persons unable to afford a lawyer must be given a lawyer at the government's expense (Schmidt, et al., 1993, pp. 130-131). According to the Eighth Amendment, the arrested person has the right to be released on reasonable bail, which means the amount of bail must be reasonably related to the severity of the offense charged (United Nations, 1959, p. 243). Also, the defendant must be informed of his/her charges, and the Fifth Amendment guarantees her/him the right to remain silent (Schmidt, et al., 1993, p. 130).

Third, defendants have trial rights. The Sixth and Seventh Amendments provide the right to a speedy and public trial before an impartial jury selected from a cross section of the defendant's community, and the trial atmosphere must be free of prejudice, fear, and outside interference (Ibid). The accused also has the privilege against self-incrimination;

Exh. A, Pt. 2 (a 1994 essay), Bonus Adjacent to Sec. 5

The writ of habeous corpus is an order requiring jailers to bring a prisoner before a court in order to determine whether or not his/her detainment is legal (Ibid, p. 246). The Sixth Amendment provides for prompt arraignment, which means the suspect must be brought to appear in court without delay after probable cause is determined (Ibid, p. 243). The right to counsel is guaranteed by the Sixth Amendment in conjunction with a number of Supreme Court rulings, the most significant being *Gideon v. Wainright*, in which the court said that accused persons unable to afford a lawyer must be given a lawyer at the government's expense (Schmidt, et al., 1993, pp. 130-131). According to the Eighth Amendment, the arrested person has the right to be released on reasonable bail, which means the amount of bail must be reasonably related to the severity of the offense charged (United Nations, 1959, p. 243). Also, the defendant must be informed of his/her charges, and the Fifth Amendment guarantees her/him the right to remain silent (Schmidt, et al., 1993, p. 130).

Exhibit A, Part 2 (a 1994 essay), Section 6 (page 5)

without this right, defendants might suffer torture or coercion despite any other laws expressly forbidding such practices (Farkas, 1977, p. 131). Another trial right is to adequate, or competent, counsel; if a defendant's trial lawyer's conduct is deemed incompetent, then the accused is entitled to another trial (Ibid, p. 136). If acquitted, the accused cannot be retried later for the same offense; if convicted, the accused has the right to have the case reviewed by an appellate court (United Nations, 1959, p. 243). Finally, no "cruel and unusual" punishment is permitted under the Eighth Amendment (Farkas, 1977, p. 136; Schmidt, et al., 1993, pp. 130, 133). There has been great controversy over whether capital punishment is cruel and unusual (Schmidt, et al., 1993, p. 133), but that issue is beyond the scope of my discussion here.

Many people object to the rights of the accused, saying these rights come at too great a cost to the rights of society and actual or potential victims (Schmidt, et al., 1993, p. 129). Some point to the fact that the United States has one of the highest violent crime rates in the world and question whether suspects should have any rights at all. While it may be true that 1) most of the accused either plead guilty or are convicted, 2) the vast majority of prisoners are guilty of the crimes they were convicted of doing, and 3) taking away these rights would greatly reduce the number of criminals escaping the clutches of the law, the rights of the accused are needed to avoid 1) convicting innocent people, 2) inhumanely torturing suspects, and 3) arbitrarily searching and seizing property (Allen, et al., 1981, p. 345). Without substantial rights of the accused, the United States would be a much less desirable place to live.

To see why this is so, consider the plight of many accused persons in South Korea, a typical example of a country not guaranteeing these rights. Under the nation's National Security Law (NSL), people are banned from associating with North Koreans without government permission (Paisley, 1994, p. 16). Before Kim Young Sam became president in February 1993, the generals preceding him used the NSL to force confessions out of spies and political dissidents, often resorting to cattle prods and brutal beatings. After

## Exhibit A, Part 2, Section 7 (i.e., p. 6 of a 1994 essay)

Kim's inauguration, many hoped for improved human rights, but torture allegations have continued. Kim Sam Sok and Kim Un Ju, arrested in September 1993, claim to have been brutally beaten:

> Kim Sang Sok, 27, claims that during his 17-day interrogation session, he was forced to stay awake for several days at a stretch and had his limbs twisted and contorted by interrogators to force a confession. Down the corridor, his younger sister, Kim Un Ju, 24, alleges that her interrogators asked: "Should we take your clothes off and investigate if you're a virgin?"
>
> She [said]...that interrogators also twisted her limbs and banged her head against a soundproof wall during a 48-hour stint without sleep. Both signed confessions that linked them to an "anti-state organization" in Japan with ties to North Korea (Ibid).

The government disputes the charges of torture, but there is good reason to believe that many such claims are true. These human rights abuses in South Korea are a direct consequence of the nation's failure to provide persons accused of crimes with adequate rights.

Quite a few people in this country agree that the rights of the accused in general are necessary, but object to the extent of the exclusionary rule, which has always been controversial (Farkas, 1977, p. 125). Byron White, one advocate of narrowing the scope of the exclusionary rule, helped create the "good-faith exception" while he served as a Supreme Court Justice (Dripps, 1993, p. 71). The good-faith exception allows prosecutors to use evidence seized under technically incorrect search warrants, provided that the police acted in good faith (Schmidt, et al., 1993, p. 133). One argument against this exception is that "excluding illegally obtained evidence deters police misconduct even when it is unintentional" (Dripps, 1993, p. 72). As evident in many areas of both criminal and civil law, negligence *can* be deterred by punishing negligent actions. An argument in favor of the good-faith exception and other exceptions to the exclusionary rule, is that warrant searches tend to be reasonable even without the exclusionary rule because of the burdensome nature of obtaining a search warrant. However, the good faith exception represents a serious curtailment of our freedom from unwarranted search and seizure.

Exhibit A, Part 2, Section 8 (i.e., page 7 of a 1994 essay)

Basically, it means that we are not guaranteed freedom from unreasonable searches and seizures in which officers intended to be reasonable and were able to obtain an invalid search warrant (Ibid, pp. 72-73). My high school US government teacher illustrated the dire implications with an example:

> Imagine a police officer gets a search warrant but accidentally has the wrong address put on it. He shows up at your house in the middle of the night, breaks in, and while half-asleep you pull your gun out from under your pillow and point it at him, thinking he's an intruder. He shoots and kills you--but that's all right, because he was acting in good faith.

As you can see, the rights of the accused are a key feature of our criminal justice system. They help maintain justice by reducing innocent people's chances of being convicted and provide for the humane treatment of suspects. Although perfect justice is unattainable, it is a worthwhile endeavor to pursue better justice (Allen, et al., 1981, p. 349). Because the only way to be absolutely certain that no innocent person will be imprisoned is to abolish prisons and the only way to imprison all guilty persons is to imprison everyone, our police and courts must delicately balance the rights of the accused with the rights of society. Many people in this country suggest that the rights of the accused be eliminated, or severely limited. They are all-too willing to trade off these safeguards--which protect us from arbitrary arrest, search and seizure, detainment, and conviction--for stronger law enforcement. The next time someone around you complains about a suspect being set free for an apparent legal "technicality," or that our legal system is way too soft on crime, keep in mind the importance of the rights of the accused and carefully consider the issues raised.

nice!

---

May 07, 2024 Reminder: After the typed conclusion by yours truly, the handwritten comment was by the UWC instructor.

Exhibit A, Part 2 (a 1994 essay), Section 9 (consisting of page 8 (of 8) of that University Writing Course essay)

References

Allen, H. E., Friday, P. C., Roebuck, J. B., & Sagarin, E. (1981). *Crime and punishment: An introduction to criminology.* New York: Macmillan.

Dripps, D. A. (1993). Justice White and the rights of the accused. *Trial, 29,* 71-74.

Farkas, T. (1977). *Criminal justice: Cases, readings, and comments.* Washington, DC: University Press of America.

Paisley, E. (1994). Rights of the accused: Government's human right's record assailed. *Far Eastern Economic Review, 157,* 16.

Schmidt, S. W., Shelley, M. C., & Bardes, B. A. (1993). *American government and politics today.* New York: West.

United Nations. Bureau of Social Affairs. (1959). *Freedom from arbitrary arrest detainment, and exile. Yearbook on human rights, first supplemental volume.* New York: United Nations.

Exhibit B: 2024 commentary on the Exhibit A essay

First and foremost, something that has occasionally bothered me in recent years is that it eventually hit me that, although I had for decades believed the elementary school PE instructor to have thought that I said "fuck" when I had actually said "flunk," I do not actually know if punishment for the perceived use of vulgar speech at an elementary school playground during physical education class was what actually went through that instructor's mind. From my perspective, what I observed and intuited about the situation might have been compatible with if that instructor heard "flunk" correctly and judged the combination of my pronouncement, with other factors, to justify punishing me for unnecessary callousness and viciousness.

Also, that line of thinking could mean that the situation might not have involved anywhere near the amount of unfairness toward me that I had previously perceived it to have involved. Actually, with esoteric insights from multiple religious and philosophical traditions, I recognize a kind of transcendence across the board with respect to concepts of "this was fair," "this was not fair," "that was fair," "that was not fair," and "this and that transcend fixed notions of fairness versus unfairness."

* * *

This could lead to interesting thought experiments.

Attempting to place myself in her shoes for a moment to better understand that situation, how might I handle an almost exactly identical situation, and how might I handle an almost-but-not-quite-as-exactly-identical-that-is-with-one-key-detail-changed situation?

As a thought exercise, first, let's consider if a PE student poked fun at a crying classmate from a distance in a similar manner, yet used the word "fuck" in contrast with how I used the word "flunk," and let us place me in the role of PE instructor.

(Setting: Multiple phys. ed. students and a phys. ed. instructor witness one of the students, at a distance of about 30 or 40 yards suddenly crying profusely while attempting to perform the assigned run.)

PE Student who recently learned the word flunk, yet chooses to speak in a saucier manner, chuckling lightly: Maybe she thinks she's going to fuck PE class!

PE Instructor (MJB in this hypothetical): What did you say?

PE Student: Maybe she thinks she's going to flunk PE class!

PE Instructor: I'm quite sure I heard you say a different word, one which students at this school are not permitted to say in class. *However*, whether you actually used that vulgarity or actually said "flunk" as you claimed a moment ago, you were cruel and inappropriate. You deserve to be punished! Go stand by the wall as punishment!!

...

Next, consider a hypothetical more exactly matching how I as a student had actually said "flunk."

(Setting: Multiple phys. ed. students and a phys. ed. instructor witness one of the students, at a distance of about 30 or 40 yards suddenly crying profusely while attempting to perform the assigned run.)

PE Student who recently learned the word flunk, and chooses to practice speaking that newly-learned word, chuckling lightly: Maybe she thinks she's going to flunk PE class!

PE Instructor (MJB in this hypothetical): What did you say?

PE Student: Maybe she thinks she's going to flunk PE class!

PE Instructor: I'm quite sure I heard you say a different word, one which students at this school are not permitted to say in class. *However*, whether you actually used that vulgarity or actually said "flunk" as you claimed a moment ago, you were cruel and inappropriate. You deserve to be punished! Go stand by the wall as punishment!!

...

Sidenote: If you wish to know the identity of the instructor for the 1994 UWC course, way back then a literary grad student who taught undergrads as part of paying her dues, and who later became a PhD, then consider exploring available information regarding Dr. Dorsey Armstrong, a Purdue University professor during much of the early Twenty-First Century A.D. / C.E.

...

On another note, in the decades after that course, experience and extra thought eventually led me to become aware how priceless an acceptance of the multiple-truths-transcending-rigid-perspectives type of approach can be when dealing with complex inter-personal statics and dynamics.

***********************************

Exhibit C: A few occupational hazard stories that my father told me about long ago, to the best of my ability to remember and transcribe them here.

Occupational Hazard Story #1

M.A.T. Blair, sometimes known as Ted Blair, sometime in his youth, decided to enter a rodeo contest. Although he made an admirable effort to perform well, it resulted in sustaining a broken bone.

He declined to make any further attempt at a rodeo career.

---

## Occupational Hazard Story #2

A ways into attending college in pursuit of a bachelor's degree, Ted Blair considered his entire situation and the United States' need for soldiers to enlist, train, and ship off for Korea. He decided to drop out of college in order to join the U.S. Army.

After basic training and related steps, he joined many other military people in what some call The Korean War (though others prefer to use the word "Conflict" with it, rather than the word "War"). A ways into the fighting, his position became overrun by Chinese soldiers who teamed up with North Korea against the American soldiers who teamed up with South Korea.

Ted and another soldier decided to lay low and hope for the Americans to reclaim the position as soon as reasonably possible. Much time went by. The other soldier grew impatient and stepped out from hiding and laying low. In the remainder of his life, Ted never again met the soldier who had wandered out from hiding in that precarious situation. Fortunately, for Ted Blair, the Americans stormed back to reclaim that portion of territory. When he could tell that the coast was reasonably clear, he stepped out from where he was hidden and rejoined the other American soldiers.

## Occupational Hazard Story #3

Although Ted Blair served in the army for over twenty years in total, several times he stepped away from it before returning.

On one such occasion, whether motivated by safety concerns, money, romance, all of the above, or none of the above, he worked as a member of a team of electricians.

They were collaborating on high voltage equipment one day, and Ted noticed one of the other men starting to walk toward an area with powerful live electricity.

With things like that posing an extraordinary risk, paying attention was often paramount. People were supposed to know not to go into that area unless the power situation would be right for it. Seemingly inexplicably, the other guy continued to walk toward that danger anyway.

Ted screamed out to his co-worker, “Stop! Wait!!”

Soon, however, it was too late.

Ted Blair witnessed one of his co-workers die right in front of him by accidental electrocution.

# CHAPTER THREE: EXTENDED EDITION OF LIST COMMENTARIES

There are so many different awards shows and so many different cultural critics who advise the general public about notions of which movies, music albums, television shows, etc. to explore.

In this chapter, I shall act as a movie critic, a music critic, and a television critic in a peculiar way: by providing lists of what my vote would have been in five categories as of most of the March-to-May 2024 period. This involves two top four lists, two top three lists, and a top six list.

---

"Best Actor in a Leading Role in a Motion Picture Film"

1. Richard Burton (in *Where Eagles Dare*)
2. Tim Robbins (in *The Shawshank Redemption*)
3. Ryunosuke Kamiki (in *Godzilla Minus One*)
4. Daniel Craig (in *No Time to Die*)

"Best Actress in a Leading Role in a Motion Picture Film"

1. Bette Davis (in *Hush...Hush, Sweet Charlotte*)
2. Claudia Cardinale (in *Once Upon a Time in the West*)
3. Letitia Wright (in *Black Panther: Wakanda Forever*)
4. Angelina Jolie (in *Salt*)

"Most Benevolent Mainly-English-Lyric Album"

1. *Grace and Gratitude* (by Olivia Newton-John)
2. *Innervisions* (by Stevie Wonder)
3. *Stones in the Road* (by Mary Chapin Carpenter)

"Most Confrontational Mainly-English-Lyric Album"

1. *The Great Milenko* (by Insane Clown Posse)
2. *The Chronic* (by Dr. Dre)
3. *Lovelife* (by Lush)

"TV Episodes Most Helpful with Understanding the Controversies of the 2020s"

1. "Freedom of Expression" / *Law and Order* / first aired: January 18, 2024
2. "Somehow, Satan Got Behind Me" / *Millennium* / first aired: May 1, 1998
3. "Osama bin Laden Has Farty Pants" / *South Park* / first aired: November 7, 2001
4. "An Occurrence at Owl Creek Bridge" / *The Twilight Zone* / first aired in the English-speaking-oriented television episode format: February 28, 1964 {though it was mostly a republication with added intro, &c., of the French short film *Occurrence at Owl Creek Bridge* (1961)}
5. "Archie Is Branded" / *All in the Family* / first aired: February 24, 1973
6. "Riding the Tiger" / *The Vietnam War* / first aired: September 18, 2017

# CHAPTER FOUR: COMPARISONS AND CONTRASTS

A person sometimes of the alias Radically Transformed sent me a March 11, 2024 Facebook message consisting of a link to: https://www.facebook.com/reel/302222842404218.

On March 14, 2024, after careful consideration, I sent this rejoinder to her: Thanks for sharing that. Although at first look, it is easy for everyone to join together into a laugh about the idea that a very high percentage of people would consider the woman who claimed to have a possibility of being pregnant and appearing generally very physically unappealing to most of the populace most of the time to definitely not be pregnant, we cannot know that with absolute certainty. For example, consider how guys sometimes get drunk and have sex with women whom they would not have sex with when sober. Also, consider how some guys some of the time will juggernaut (i.e., decide to adjust their minds to allow women they would otherwise find ugly to be deemed acceptable to them for dating, romancing, and, in some cases even having sex with and/or marrying). Here's one more thing to consider: a set of perspectives in and adjacent to the Jewel song "Pieces of You" (Cf. https://www.youtube.com/watch?v=5umlhGtetxY as accessed at the time of sending this e-mail).

After that, also on March 14, 2024, she responded: LOL that's so true

---

(The transcript stayed as-is, copying her omissions of a comma and a period that otherwise would have been present if it had been in-keeping with standard punctuation.)

At many levels that interaction can illustrate the idea that Robert B. Cialdini clearly elucidated in portions of *Influence: The Psychology of Persuasion* that a combination of reams of psychological studies point toward how a large percentage of people a high percentage of the time have a huge bias in favor of those whom they find physically attractive and against those whom they find physically unattractive. Among other things, it sometimes makes a major difference in how much people trust others, their propensities to vote for a given candidate, their likelihood to buy a given product, their tendencies to find people credible in a court of law, etc.

This is not, by any means, an unqualified endorsement of that nonfiction work, though, because in it Cialdini on some occasions veers into going too far into sidestepping and rejecting the deeper and more profound levels of religious experiences and practices (e.g., taking too much of a circumspect and academically-ivory-towered approach to things like ferocious manifestations of religious zealotry in *both* (!) the Abrahamic religions *and* the Dharmic religions).

Indeed, although this in some ways touches on issues of comparing and contrasting different beholders, etc., we should be honest with ourselves and others about many relevant trends. If I had understood this type of deep critical thinking better at various earlier stages of my life, perhaps I might have declined more of the employment offers that I received rather than accepting so many of them. Also, maybe I would have majored in a STEM field at Duke instead of majoring in Economics. *Water and blood under bridges and elsewhere: much of this relates to much of that.* More regarding this in Chapters Six and Ten.

****

Next, consider a set of 187 from years ago and a set of 187 either now or at another time much later than back then.

In recent years, I would often think of ranking cultural artifacts as greatest by virtue of how helpful they might be to boosting the enlightenment of sentient beings, especially emphasizing perceptions of utility toward improving resiliency.

However, as time went by, I shifted in portions of 2023 toward recognizing that my perception had previously been perhaps a bit skewed toward over-emphasizing psychological warfare training when performing such evaluations.

* * *

*Reflecting now on your life*, think a little while about if some number of years ago you had set out to make a list of who and what you would vote for in several categories of film criticism and music criticism. Maybe you already did this exercise a few years ago or maybe you did not. In any case, think about it for a while, if you will.

For example, you could consider what you might have voted for in the following four categories:

I) 100 Greatest Motion Picture Films of All Time

II) 29 Greatest Music Albums to Feature Lyrics Mainly of Your Primary Spoken Language

III) 29 Most Powerful Music Albums to Feature Lyrics Mainly of Your Primary Spoken Language

IV) 29 Most Enjoyable Music Albums to Feature Lyrics Mainly of Your Primary Spoken Language

..........................................................................

*Next, observing your present situation, consider how you might compose answers to the very same aforementioned four categories as of the time of studying this book.*

How have you changed in the intervening years? How has this affected your perceptions of what cultural artifacts you would esteem highly enough to honor with voting for them?

Do you have a clear sense of the possible reasons for your voting choices then and your voting choices now?

# CHAPTER FIVE: ALTERNATIVE SYMBOLIC TIMETABLE PATTERNS II

This chapter has a nonlinear sequencing of dates, and only two of them have symbolic card spreads shown.

The symbolism also features mixtures of simple geometric/punctuation with creative blank space, supplementing the chronological arrangements' more obvious patterns.

January 1, 1953 /// 2079 / (1698) / (926).

(Later in the Tibetan Calendar Year than in The Gregorian Calendar Year.)

In the Year of the Dragon.

A Complete Deck of the 14-suit deck described, An Additional Complete Suit of Spades, and An Additional Complete Suit of Hearts.

..........................................................................

..........................................................................

..........................................................................

..........................................................................

..........................................................................

..........................................................................

..........................................................................

..........................................................................

..........................................................................

..........................................................................

..........................................................................

..........................................................................

..........................................................................

..........................................................................

..........................................................................

January 1, 1924. // 2050 / 1669 / 897.

Year of the Ox.

Charles T. Munger (1924-2023) was born.

March 31, 1927. // 2054 / 1673 / 901.

Year of the Hare.

Cesar Chavez (1927-1993) was born.

April 23, 1993_ /_ 2120 / (1739) / (967). // Bird.

Cesar Chavez (1927-1993) died.

November 8, 1994 _///_ 2121 / (1740) / (968).

In the Year of the Dog.

Former Governor of Missouri John Ashcroft won an election for a U.S. Senate seat in Missouri.

---

September 11, 2001 _///_ 2128 / (1747) / (975).

In the Year of the Snake.

Notable events: Multiple Al-Quaeda attacks upon the United States occurred. Osama bin Laden, President George W. Bush, Attorney General John Ashcroft, New York, and Pennsylvania figured prominently in the unfolding of events on that day. A very large number of people transitioned into binge-watching television news.

---

.............................................................................

.............................................................................

---

October 31, 2001 _///_ 2128 / (1747) / (975). Snake.

Notable events: 1) In the state of Massachusetts in the United States, an adjustment happened to that state's legal relationship with witchcraft. 2) In New York, NY, there was a planned reduction in the number of firefighters assigned to recover human remains at the World Trade Center (as part of the aftermath of what happened there a little over seven weeks prior).

---

* * *

February 28, 2003. _///_ 2130 _/_ 1749 _/_ 977. Sheep.

* * *

* * *

April 27, 2004. _///_ 2131 _/_ 1750 _/_ 978. Monkey.

* * *

* * *

* * *

* * *

June 14, 2006 _///_ 2133 _/_ 1752 _/_ 980. Dog.

* * *

* * *

* * *

* * *

* * *

January 31, 2023 (per The Gregorian Calendar) / (Later in the Tibetan Year than in the Gregorian Year.) / (In the Year of the Tiger as measured by The Tibetan Calendar.) /// Three versions of what year number it was, as per interpretations of what The Tibetan Calendar can be: 2149; 1768; & 996.

---

NOTE: THE NEXT SET OF SEVERAL GREGORIAN CALENDAR DATES OF THE RANGE FROM APRIL 20 TO DECEMBER 31, 2023 EACH CORRESPOND WITH THE YEAR OF THE HARE IN THE TIBETAN CALENDARS, OF WHICH ONE HAD THOSE DATES IN THE YEAR 2150, ANOTHER HAD THEM IN THE YEAR 1769, AND ANOTHER STILL HAD THAT RANGE IN THE YEAR 997.

---

November 28, 2023

Charles T. Munger (1924-2023) died.

---

................................................................

................................................................

---

................................................................

April 20, 2023

A Complete Suit of Destruction, Ace-101 of Creation, 5 of Commerce, 8 of Sexuality, 4-108 of Geology, A Royal Flush of Diamonds, Ace-5 of Spades, Ace-5 of Hearts, and Ace-10 of Clubs.

................................................................

July 19, 2023

October 5, 2023

October 6, 2023

September 13, 2023: Tensions between Israel and Hamas escalated dramatically.

---

October 7, 2023:

Islamist militants among Hamas and other people associated with Hamas attacked Israeli civilians and Israeli Defense Forces military personnel. The attack upon civilians included how Islamist militants brutally tortured and killed many of them, while capturing many of the others as hostages. That shocked Israel and most of the rest of the world.

---

October 8, 2023

---

---

December 31, 2023

---

May 19, 2024 (per The Gregorian Calendar) / In the Year 2151 per one version of The Tibetan Calendar / In the Year 1770 per another version of The Tibetan Calendar / In the Year 998 in yet another version of The Tibetan Calendar: Iranian President Ebrahim Raisi (1960-2024) died in a helicopter crash.

............................................................
............................................................
............................................................

# CHAPTER SIX: SELECT RECONCILIATIONS

FEBRUARY 22, 2024 RECONCILIATIONS BETWEEN THE AUTHOR AND THE RADIO SHOW THAT HAD ENTERED AN APRIL 9, 2023 CONFLICT WITH HIM; AUGUST 2023 RECONCILIATIONS WITH THE FORMER BUSINESS ASSOCIATE WHO HAD INSTIGATED SOME JANUARY 2021 CONFLICTS WITH HIM AS A REACTION TO U.S. POLITICAL DEVELOPMENTS; AND RELATED IDEAS AND OCCURENCES

## PART 1

*Science, Religion, Politics, and Cards* included several references, copies of correspondence, and explanations informing readers about the April 9, 2023 conflict between Emily of *The Michael Berry Show* and me. However, on February 22, 2024, the way that the morning show was going, I decided to call in and offer the possibility that the show and I could get back onto reasonably mutually benevolent terms with each other, by discussing what had happened, some of its background, and its aftermath.

When I called in, Ramón chose to give me a chance to hold while the show might find an appropriate time to bring Michael and me back together for a new phone call. As the show reached the end of its scheduled morning edition for that day, and I heard the concluding music playing, I anticipated to soon hear the phone change into a busy signal, to indicate them to have hung up. However, as the morning show closed, suddenly Michael Berry and I started speaking with each other on the telephone again.

Indeed, as I had envisioned, we shared a conversation in which we came to understand each other better, to comprehend better the background, occurrence, and aftermath of the Resurrection Sunday 2023 conflict, and adjacent stuff. As a pleasant surprise, briefly Emily Bull joined in on the conversation and spoke with me in a reasonably friendly manner. By the end of the phone call, I knew that some elements of reality had changed for the better by virtue of both their graciousness toward me and my graciousness toward them, and whatever other factors helped facilitate that reconciliation.

Sometime went by with uncertainty about if and when it might air, then, on March 15, 2024, portions of it broadcast in the morning edition of *The Michael Berry Show*. We exhibited a degree of agreeing to disagree about some things, a degree of agreeing about some things, and a reasonable amount of mutual respect—with neither side cowering to the other.

************************************

## Ch. 6, PART 2

Next, here is an update about a degree of reconciliation between my former business associate Bill Walker and me. The new, rather friendly direct messaging occurred near the end of when I was working for Goodwill Houston, and consisted of using LinkedIn.

The date-and-time stamps for the following transcription shall be using Houston, TX time, and every effort will be made to preserve any typos, missing punctuation, etc. as is, without bothering to place [sic] in spots, etc. as a formalized printing corrections process.

William Crockett Walker, AUG 21, 2023; 7:27 PM

Congrats on the promotion man

Maurice Blair, AUG 23, 2023; 7:44 AM

Bill,

Thank you for the sentiment, but it was not what it appeared to be to you.

On Thursday, 8/17/23, a combination of things were such that I requested early on the next day to be voluntarily demoted from Merchandising Specialist to Donation Specialist. They granted me that request, effective Sunday, 8/20/2023. Then, on Monday, 8/21/2023, a problem happened with a furniture carryout team effort (for clarification, furniture carryouts are a somewhat common duty shared by both the merchandising specialist role and the donation specialist role, sometimes involving a team of one of each or two of either, at other times involving one worker, and at yet other times involving three or more workers), no humans were harmed, one furniture item was harmed, and I followed Goodwill Houston's legal protection guidelines by not stepping into the bed of the pickup truck we were loading into (though the merchandising specialist who teamed with me on that carryout was not previously familiar with that guideline and suddenly instructed me at a critical juncture to step completely onto the pickup truck bed, at which point I stated forcefully the truth of how that is absolutely prohibited under the guidelines due to the organization's concerns for potential legal liabilities if a worker gets completely into any vehicle, with getting completely onto a truck bed being one form of that).

{Of course, someone may need to go outside that guideline if there arrives an emergency situation with serious physical risk of injury or death to a human being potentially averted by someone going against the guideline, which was clearly not the case with that incident, since no human beings sustained physical injury of any kind from how the incident unfolded.}

However, the nature of the ensuing discussion at the management office, together with all factors present at that time, was such that I chose to give them two weeks notice in writing somewhat early during that meeting.

The upcoming Labor Day is scheduled to be my last day of work with that organization. I still feel favorable toward each of my GWH co-workers and former co-workers, including each of my GWH supervisors and former supervisors, though I considered several aspects of several incidents and trends to be such that it would be best for me to remove myself from the environment, either temporarily or permanently. I have already indicated to GWH clearly that although it is a longshot, I am open to the possibility of someday returning to working for that nonprofit organization, if enough months or years were to go by and they and I were to mutually agree upon such a return to them at that time.

I am considering both the possibility (a) of going for a while with the change from three jobs to two simply staying at a level of two jobs and (b) of relatively soon after the change from three jobs to two going back to having a total of three jobs.

Take care, and best wishes with making changes and improvements how and when appropriate.

Regards,

Maurice

William Crockett Walker, AUG 24, 2023; 10:12 AM

Hey thank you for the update - I miss hanging out with you and I'm sorry for introducing politics into our relationship. I have since learned that certain personal topics are better left personal, and are really none of my business. I like you as a person, period and if you want to grab lunch sometime I would like to catch up

Maurice Blair, AUG 27, 2023; 2:18 PM

How about if sometime we meet at a large, public venue for a meal... and continue for a little ways the blindfold chess game that we started circa late 2015 with you playing as white and me playing as black, which started with 1.e4 c6 2.Ne2 d5 and then became adjourned, then converting it into a full, regular, pieces-and-board-visible game? Or we could leave that game adjourned and talk about movies and careers, still steering clear of those things that caused us such conflicts before.

(Either way, as a caveat, I'm no longer nearly as serious about chess itself now as I was in much of the mid-2010-to-early-2020 period, since much of competitive enthusiasm transferred to other pursuits.)

Or if those things come up a little, we could and probably should both go into some kind of carefully-walking-through-a-minefield mode.

Ah, on a related note, some chess authors communicate about some endgame situations as including how certain squares become "mined squares," meaning that if a given king lands on such a square at the wrong time for the player with that king, then the position automatically converts to being a lost game for that player with proper play by the other player, who then has a won game if playing precisely and accurately. Oh, either way, we could talk about sports, too... or, to be more precise, if we meet again, then it is obvious that no matter which way things go, we will almost definitely talk about sports part of the time.

William Crockett Walker, AUG 28, 2023; 10 AM

That sounds good man. Let me know your schedule, Sunday afternoons are generally good for me, maybe we could meet at a coffee shop. I can look to see if my chess set is still around

Maurice Blair, SEP 1, 2023; Noon

Maybe Sunday the 17th at 3 PM might work. I can plan to bring a chess set, and if you also bring a set, then that would be fine, yet either way, we could be prepared to possibly play casual chess on the side of participating in conversation. We could start considering, also, which coffee shop. How about Minuti Coffee, near the Southwest corner of Gessner and Fondren?

Maurice Blair, SEP 4, 2023; 6:30 AM

Although the Minuti Coffee location that I mentioned to you recently is near the Southwest corner of Gessner and Fondren, to be more specific, it and its parking lot together are virtually at the Southeast corner of Gessner and Fondren.

An alternative could be the Starbucks located at 1801 Richmond, which I've just now looked up on the Internet, though I'm not very familiar with that location. That would be much closer to being equidistant from your home (if it's still located where it was a few years ago) and my current home (which is located a little further from I-610 than where my previous home was located).

Maurice Blair, SEP 10, 2023; 3:45 PM

Bill,

Since you've been silent for a while in this communication thread, I'll suggest an alternative in which we let the started-and-adjourned-in-2015 blindfold chess game stay adjourned, leaving it uncertain whether or not we'll ever continue it and/or convert it into a regular chess game. Also, I'll suggest that we could consider skipping playing chess with the meeting in the near future, if that meeting actually happens. What are your updated thoughts and suggestions on this meeting possibility that we've been discussing?

Maurice

---

Footnotes to the Walker-and-Blair conciliatory communication thread just presented:

1. On December 5, 2014, he and I played two chess games (i.e., one each way for color coordination), and I won both games in convincing fashion. Those were in a very informal setup, with no specific time control, but trying not to move way too slowly.
2. Although he and I expressed interest in meeting each other again, we have not met each other again, from the time of the copied correspondence to the time of the initial publication of this book.
3. Bill Walker went silent toward me for about seven months, until starting about one-fourth of the way into 2024 a new step toward a possible new meeting. Early in that period of silence I published an article onto

LinkedIn—specifically, it was on September 1, 2023, soon after he started to go silent for a while. Here is a revised version of that article (including alteration to the title):

**Regarding Degrees of Work, Retirement, Semiretirement, Etcetera**

By Maurice James Blair, Multiprofession Worker

September 1, 2023; Subsequently Revised

Version Date: May 18, 2024

Around mid-1997 to mid-1998 or thereabouts a strange booklet by an author going by the name Timothy Righteous circulated in portions of Durham, NC. I happened to read major portions of it, maybe even the entire work, and had mixed feelings about the ideas presented. That author expressed that in the interests of curbing the use of natural resources, curbing carbon emissions, and enhancing quality of life, it could be desirable for many people to use a radical work-life-balance approach: sometimes working in blitzes of activity, taking substantial breaks from working, using part-time schedules, having much less ambition toward careers than the levels encouraged by most western cultural norms, and having much more leisure time than most conformist situations would usually allow for people in the early-20s-to-mid-50s range. To the best of memory, the title was, "For the Destruction of Human Society."

Of course, if people were to consider possible titles that could be similar to that, yet with the third word changed, then two possibilities could be, "For the Preservation of Human Society" and "For the Creation of Human Society."

In the past three years, many employers in the U.S. have struggled with how, due to some combination of many reasons, a large percentage of the potential U.S. workforce has tilted significantly in the direction of the foot-mostly-off-the-throttle approach toward availability for work hours. To what degree this has been influenced by a sequence of dominoes emanating from Timothy Righteous' efforts from decades ago to steer things in that direction may be unknown, though it is generally agreed-upon by many observers that something about how the governmental pandemic-based restrictions on business activities in portions of March 2020 to mid-2021 were a huge part of what caused many workers to shift their work-life balance orientations away from work. From the perspective of humanity as a whole or a given nation as a whole, these things can have many pendulum effects, and for each worker individually it can also have such effects.

In my case, I often did not set out to become a workaholic or a slacker, yet there have been many times that I found myself at each extreme on that range, as well as many levels between each end. As I have set the wheels in motion to change from having three jobs to having two jobs within a few days after the publication of this article, with the most time-consuming job being the one I am letting go of having, and plan to most likely go into a long-term semiretirement mode (even if going back to three jobs and/or more rigorous work scheduling someday), I find myself again returning to vividly remembering that free booklet that circulated circa 1997 and reached me around that time. I do not know who was mainly behind the printing and distribution of that item and what motives may have been beneath the surface.

Another oddity about that free literature item was that it recommended that people gather in small groups who could live together to spread living costs, which seemed like a 1990s attempt by the distributors to steer American society in the direction of stuff like 1960s communes.

Well, now seems as good a time as any for me to share publicly the identities of three of the playlists that I legally burned to CD from music downloads long ago, with the following arrangements, to somehow provide additional context to this discussion.

(Note: The second playlist identified below is something that I publicly half-identified in two separate places online in 2010, yet I am here fully and clearly identifying publicly it in one spot for the first time. Also, on that list, the sequencing of tracks #8 through #13 came directly from the listing of tracks #1 through #6 on a then-already-existing album, without altering the sequence copied from their source album.)

{For each song, the listing format here is: "Song/Track Title" (Officially-Stated Performer(s) and/or Other(s) Attributed in Main Listing / *Name of the Source Album or Single that the song/track recording download came from*).}

...

*Augustus Intensity Mix*

(arranged on August 25th, 2010)

1. "I Believe" (Diamond Rio / *16 Biggest Hits*)
2. "Stand By Your Man" (Tammy Wynette / *16 Biggest Hits*)
3. "Toughen Up" (Olivia Newton-John / *Soul Kiss*)
4. "Reflections of My Life" (The Marmalade / *Ultimate Collection*)
5. "This Wheel's On Fire" (The Band / *Music from Big Pink [Bonus Tracks]*)
6. "Point of Light" (Randy Travis / *Trail of Memories: The Randy Travis Anthology [U.S. Release]*)
7. "Stranglehold" (Ted Nugent / *The Ultimate Ted Nugent*)
8. "You And Tequila" (Deana Carter / *I'm Just a Girl*)
9. "Whiskey Girl" (Toby Keith / *35 Biggest Hits*)

10. "Wasted" (Carrie Underwood / *Some Hearts*)
11. "Easy Come, Easy Go" (George Strait / *Easy Come, Easy Go*)
12. "Our Town [Album Version]" (Iris DeMent / *Infamous Angel*)
13. "A Little Less Talk And A Lot More Action" (Toby Keith / *35 Biggest Hits*)
14. "Physical (Glee Cast Version) [feat. Olivia Newton-John]" (Glee Cast / *Physical (Glee Cast Version) [feat. Olivia Newton-John] - Single*)
15. "There's No Limit" (Deana Carter / *I'm Just a Girl*)
16. "The Twilight Zone" (Marius Constant / *Sci-Fi's Greatest Hits Vol. 2: The Dark Side*)
17. "Help Me Make It Through The Night" (Sammi Smith / *Help Me Make It Through The Night & Other Country Hits [Album]*)
18. "Why Shouldn't We" (Mary Chapin Carpenter / *The Calling*)
19. "That's My Job" (Conway Twitty / *Gold*)

...

*A Music CD Arranged on August Twenty-Second, Twenty-Ten*

1. "India" (Anthems Orchestra / *The National Anthems, Volume 3*)
2. "Germany" (Anthems Orchestra / *The National Anthems, Volume 3)*

3. "Tales From The Darkside" (Donald Rubenstein, Erica Lindsay / *Sci-Fi's Greatest Hits Vol. 2: The Dark Side*)
4. "Il Triello (The Trio - Main Title) (2004 Digital Remaster)" (Ennio Morricone / *The Good, The Bad & The Ugly [Soundtrack]*)
5. "The Miracle of the Ark" (John Williams / *Raiders of the Lost Ark [Soundtrack]*)
6. "Israel" (Anthems Orchestra / *The National Anthems, Volume 3*)
7. "Point of Light" (Randy Travis / *Trail of Memories: The Randy Travis Anthology [U.S. Release]*)
8. "Mahakala" (Gyuto Monks of Tibet / *Pure Sounds*)
9. "Heart Sutra" (Gyuto Monks of Tibet / *Pure Sounds*)
10. "Jis Pai Bhum Chung (Original)" (Gyuto Monks of Tibet / *Pure Sounds*)
11. "Mandala Offerings" (Gyuto Monks of Tibet / *Pure Sounds*)
12. "Dedication Prayer" (Gyuto Monks of Tibet / *Pure Sounds*)
13. "Dalai Lama Long Life" (Gyuto Monks of Tibet / *Pure Sounds*)
14. "Great Britain" (Anthems Orchestra / *The National Anthems, Volume 3*)
15. "Haiti (Republic of Haiti)" (Anthems Orchestra / *The National Anthems, Volume 3*)
16. "Italy" (Anthems Orchestra / *The National Anthems, Volume 3*)

...

*Songs & Wakefulness*

(Arranged on October 28th, 2011)

1. "Uncertain Destination" (Power of Zeus / *The Gospel According to Zeus*)
2. "Help Me Make It Through The Night" (Sammi Smith / *Help Me Make It Through The Night & Other Country Hits [Album]*)
3. "Everything Is Beautiful" (Ray Stevens / *Everything Is Beautiful*)
4. "Get Together" (The Youngbloods / *The Essential Youngbloods*)
5. "November Rain" (Guns N' Roses / *Use Your Illusion I*)
6. "Turn! Turn! Turn! (To Everything There Is A Season)" (Pete Seeger / *The Essential Pete Seeger*)

... ... ...

On another note, here is an approximation of how an August 22nd, 2023 conversation between a former nuclear power plant worker and me happened, when I met him for the first time:

M. James Blair: Hi, you must be Michael, Justin's father.

Former Nuclear Power Plant Worker: Yes, I am. With whom do I have the pleasure of speaking?

MJB: My name is Maurice. Justin has said much about you to me. Probably most of it is true, though I wouldn't know for sure. Glad to actually meet you in person.

FNPW (jokingly in a mocking manner): Mary! That's a woman's name!

MJB: I said, "Maurice." It has the variation "Maury," like in "Maury Povich." Also, with the same spelling it can be pronounced several ways, including like how people normally pronounce "Morris."

FNPW (continuing to tease): Maury is also of a women's kind of style.

MJB: Even with how I'm a man and often go by "Maurice," as it's part of my legal name, I also sometimes go by "Jim" as a nickname for my middle name "James," and I occasionally go by "James."

FNPW: Yes, "Jim" is a more manly name.

MJB: "Maurice" and "Maury" are clearly able to be men's names. On a related note, you're aware, aren't you, that "Merry," spelled "M-E-R-R-Y" used to be a popular name for men and boys in the

English language, but for some reason it isn't used much of all as a name anymore.

FNPW: That's because 'Mary' is a woman's name!

MJB: Well, people can use their minds in flexible ways. Still, I wonder sometimes about names becoming more popular or less popular over time.

FNPW: I also have another name, by the way.

MJB: Oh, and what would that be?

FNPW: Sir.

MJB: Yes, you mean using that as a title because of how you're Justin's father. I wonder sometimes about if someone already received the given name "Sir" and then became knighted, then the person would be "Sir Sir."

FNPW: Yeah.

MJB: Ah, but then that sounds similar to the name of that infamous guy Sirhan Sirhan.

..............................................................................

(Michael Haynes and Maurice Blair continued a somewhat-cordial and somewhat-combative set of dialogue for a while after that.)

..............................................................................

On another note, returning to the theme of levels of work ethic, comparing and contrasting various coursework and other experiences from the mid-to-late 1990s, much of it ran the full gamut from very, very favorable toward ramped-up global economic activity to very, very unfavorable toward ramped-up global economic activity. Thus it is unsurprising that the aforementioned strangely-alternatively-themed booklet circulated during portions of the last few years of the twentieth century.

---

Here is another playlist idea; this time, something I arranged in my mind while working on parts of this book:

1. "The Ballad of the Green Berets" by Sgt. Barry Sadler
2. "Forlorn Spirits of Smallville" by Terry G. Reed
3. "Amos Moses" by Jerry Reed
4. "Grace and Gratitude" by Olivia Newton-John
5. "When You Leave That Way You Can Never Go Back" by Confederate Railroad
6. "He's Misstra Know It All" by Stevie Wonder
7. "Suicide Is Not The Way" by Maurice John Vaughn
8. "You Can't Always Get What You Want" by The Rolling Stones

---

## Ch. 6, PART 3

Another mysterious thing which has an unknown degree, if any, of relationship with my publication of that article: how someone purportedly of the name Corrine Biduaya seemed intent on sowing hostility against me by sending me multiple *vague* e-mail messages with *an ominous tone.* As demonstrated next, I handled that situation with a continuation of the kinds of psychological warfare strategies and tactics that appeared in *Science, Religion, Politics, and Cards.*

(In each of the messages in the following correspondence, the quoted times are in accordance with U.S. Central Time as observed via Houston, Texas.) (The first message copied thoroughly mentions the caveat of uncertainty about whether that person really had the name presented. After that, the text presents that name repeatedly with less-complete warning of that, yet it should be understood by the reader that the caveat remains, unless somehow someday some reader were to actually know whether the allegedly-Corine-Biduaya sender really has that name or not.) (This includes an attempt to copy/transcribe all typos, unorthodox grammar, missing punctuation, other omissions, etc. as-is, without inserting [sic] or other standard corrections, letting the records be, for your consideration, with whatever additional reality you might happen to glean from this mayhem.)

---

From: (Person allegedly/ presenting as having the name) Corine Biduaya

To: Maurice Blair

Date and Time: September 11, 2023 at 1:31 PM

Subject: Maurice

Mother Fucker

---

From: Maurice Blair

To: Corrine Biduaya

Cc: hpd.communityaffairs@houstonpolice.org

[same thread, in response directly to the previous message]

September 16, 2023 at 4:53 AM

Corine,

What is your message about?

That was an extremely bizarre first introduction of an e-mail message from you to me.

At a literal level, I am not a mother fucker in terms of a multitude of possibly immoral acts that could be associated with that phrase.

However, if you are stating that I am willing to fight back against any and all authority figures when they deserve for me to fight back against them, then hell yes I am willing to fight back against any and all authority figures when they deserve for me to fight back against them. That is, in ways that I believe to be ethical in terms of the most profound levels of reality.

As both your first and second introductions to me involve your use of what appears to be an extreme hostility suggestive that either you or someone spoofing you and/or your e-mail address (or hacking your e-mail address if not spoofing it) are somehow likely very directly involved with criminal behavior (though the surfaces of your messages are probably well within your First Amendment rights if you are using that phrase metaphorically and also neither being spoofed nor hacked), I believe it is well within my First Amendment rights to place one of the non-emergency e-mail addresses of the Houston Police Department on the cc line of this message.

Regards,

Maurice

---

From: (allegedly) Corine Biduaya

To: Maurice Blair

[continuing the same thread of messaging]

September 18, 2023 at 5:17 PM

Maurice mother fucker from duke what's up mother fucker

---

(From that same allegedly-Biduaya e-mail account I received a separate message that led to a parallel thread. I chose to let go of responding on the above thread, yet focused closely on methods of responding to the other thread.)

---

From: (allegedly) Corine Biduaya

To: Maurice Blair

(No Subject)

Mother fucker from duke university

September 11, 2023 at 1:32 PM

---

From: Maurice Blair

To: (allegedly) Corine Biduaya

Cc: hpd.communityaffairs@houstonpolice.org, newstips@abc13.com, investigates@cbsnews.com, FOX26HoustonNews@fox.com

September 16, 2023 at 5:26 PM

Corine or Whoever Might Be Spoofing a Person Allegedly of the Name Corine,

As stated in the previous message, although I do not know to what degree you might be referring to what, there are multitudes of levels at which your use of the phrase "mother fucker" to address me could be suggestive of defamation of my character, though there are other levels at which it could relate to complimenting my character at a metaphorical level involving how: 1) I sometimes fight authorities in recent years with legitimate reasons for doing so (for example, as in interpersonally criticizing and refuting the expressions of persons who sometimes have a degree of authority and abuse some of their access to authority) and 2) I sometimes act legitimately as an authority in recent years to some degree, especially as part of pushing back against some of those people who at times abuse their use of access to authority.

As with the earlier message that you sent to me, I am choosing to include one of the non-emergency e-mail addresses of HPD on the copy concern line.

On this second strange introduction from you, suggestive of a likelihood of your involvement with criminal activity, much like the message you sent me earlier on that same day (five days ago), in contrast with my response a little while ago (today)

to your earlier message, I have decided to include three news tips e-mail addresses on the cc line next to the HPD nonemergency address. This way, just in case I suddenly turn up dead in the near future or a while later in the future and there turns out to either be definite foul play involved or a major suspicion of foul play, then your suspicious e-mail messages could be part of the investigations into candidates of who or what might have perpetrated whatever.

Regards,

Maurice Blair

---

From: (Person presenting to be) Corine Biduaya

To: Maurice Blair

September 18, 2023 at 6:37 PM

I'm not reading those long ass paragraphs mother fucker

---

From: Maurice Blair

To: (person presenting as allegedly being) Corine Biduaya

Cc: hpd.communityaffairs@houstonpolice.org, FOX26HoustonNews@fox.com, newstips@abc13.com, investigates@cbsnews.com, (& an alternate address for Maurice J. Blair, with that address withheld from the copy in this book, to protect reasonable privacy)

September 26, 2023 at 5:55 PM

Being who is presenting with the name Corine Biduaya,

Given that you seem to indicate not giving a damn about my having already provided some of your communication (demonstrating a degree of hostility from out of the blue from you to me with my having no knowledge of prior contact under your name/alias) to media and law enforcement authorities via the cc line, I do not know what's up with you and your reason(s) for contacting me.

If you wish to be more specific, then go for it, yet bear in mind that I'm about two millimeters away from deciding to walk into a police station to discuss with them what in the world is or might be going on with your strange introductory e-mail communications.

Also, I noticed that "Corine Biduaya" (with quotes) on DuckDuckGo did not give any search results a little while ago.

Even with your choice of figures of speech and seemingly-threatening tones, best wishes for the possibilities of enlightenment/salvation/conscience

/soteriology processes for all sentient beings, including you, whoever you might be behind what appears to be an alias.

Maurice Blair

---

---

2024 Commentary: It seemed rather remarkable, but whoever was communicating from the other side of that correspondence continued with the same m.o. even after that, and I dealt with the situation carefully.

---

From: Corine Biduaya

To: Maurice Blair

Bald headed motha fucka u don't scare me

October 3, 2023 at 4:29 PM

---

From: Maurice Blair

To: Corine Biduaya

Cc: FOX26HoustonNews@fox.com, newstips@abc13.com, investigates@cbsnews.com, nbcnewsdigitalcontact@nbcuni.com

October 12, 2023 at 3:43 PM

Corine or Whoever Is Presenting as Having that name and using odd and interesting though potentially abrasive as considered by some observers slang phraseology from {EMAIL ADDRESS REDACTED},

A few minutes ago, I finally found your message from October 3rd (nine days ago). You clearly have virtually no clue about me or my life or my mind, and you possibly know little about your own mind.

The idea was not to attempt to scare you in the previous rounds of this communication; the idea was to stand up for truth, accurate perceptions of reality, and the processes of soteriology (which can include any religion and/or philosophy, insofar as any of them may have any amount(s) of reality and truth to them). Whether you would become scared or not is not a main goal, it is fine either way, much as the whether anyone anywhere dies or not at any given time is not a main goal; all of that can help to serve truth, accurate perceptions, soteriology, & cetera.

However, if we define things from different angles, then imbuing anyone with proper respect for relations between sowing and reaping could relate to whether you fear or refrain from fearing as considered in any given definition of fear, with or without fearing as considered in any other given definition of fear.

Perhaps to get a better grip on reality, consider the mirror imaging of this sentence. ecnetnes siht fo gnigami rorrim eht redisnoc ,ytilaer no pirg retteb a teg ot spahreP

I made a small change on the cc line. If you proceed from here with silence, fine. If you proceed in a somewhat ridiculous manner, then maybe I'll ignore you and walk away from the written dialogue. However, if you go further into vaguely-seemingly-intending-to-threaten pathways, then I might choose to engage in a new round of whatever I might choose to improvise as a response.

Life is much bigger than the idea of people posturing forcefulness and superiority to whomever they perceive to be antagonists and people displaying meekness to whomever they perceive it best to be meek toward.

I stand here at this very instant with neither you nor anyone else as a living enemy, whether or not you or anyone else perceives himself/herself/itself to be a living enemy toward me.

Of course, everything could change in the blink of an eye. That includes any instant after I hit send for this message.

Relationships of enmity come and go. Relationships of friendship, too, may come and go, at least some of the time. Many scientists believe that entire universes come and go, as well.

Whatever issues, if any, you might happen to have, at another level you lack those issues; that is why it can be said that you have those issues. (Credit for that type of going beyond normal conceptual limits should go to various ancients of over one-and-a-half millennia ago. For example, *The Diamond Sutra.*)

# CHAPTER SIX, PART 4

Here is a list of three songs, two movies, and two television episodes, presented here for your consideration:

- "Big and Strong" as performed by Olivia Newton-John
- "Anything Could Happen" as performed by Ellie Goulding
- "Are You Experienced?" as performed by The Jimi Hendrix Experience
- *Dalai Lama Renaissance, Volume 2: A Revolution of Ideas* (2009)
- *Godzilla vs. Kong* (2021)
- "Jose Chung's 'From Outer Space'" (1996) (an episode of *The X-Files*)
- "The Masks" (1964) (an episode of *The Twilight Zone*)

...

Note: Something potentially helpful to readers as providing insights adjacent to that set of back-and-forths would be page 15 of the article "The *Rimé* Activities of Shabkar Tsokdruk Rangdrol (1781-1851)" by Rachel H. Pang (Davidson College) ... ... (as accessed at http://himalaya.socanth.cam.ac.uk/collections/journals/ret/pdf/ret_30_01.pdf 31 DEC 2023 and 18 MAR 2024).

*****

Although I feel very favorable toward how Shabkar expresses transcending sectarianism in a manner that to some could be reminiscent of things involving the relationship between Benjamin Franklin (1706-1790) and Michael Welfare* (1687-1741), I also recognize that he had a role in the dietary controversies of Buddhism, and that some Buddhists consider True Buddha School's practices of believing it ethical and justified for humans to eat meat as problematic. As some readers may have known before encountering this book, and others may find out via it, I officially joined True Buddha School in October 2003 by taking refuge in Grand Master Sheng-yen Lu.

* Technically, that M.W. was of the name Michael Wohlfahrt, per multiple corroborating sources (of which this work declines to name any specific instance but which readers with access to reasonably diverse and thorough historical records should be able to corroborate on their own).

Next, consider a revised, expanded, and updated version of the article that I published on December 9, 2023. Previous version title: "Why I Support Tibetan Sky Burial." Publication of the original happened via LinkedIn. As of 3/19/2024 it was accessible at https://www.linkedin.com/pulse/why-i-support-tibetan-sky-burial-maurice-blair-ckbqc.

The revised version here has the adjusted title, "Support For Sky Burial."

---

# Support For Sky Burial

by Maurice James Blair

---

Among the many controversies about the interactions between *Homo sapiens* and other categories of sentient beings, some of the most interesting concern the dynamics of various food chains.

Next, consider an overview of possible ethical theories regarding this (including the use of "human-centric" in place of the more standard "anthropocentric" in order to be more absolutely straightforward and blunt, deliberately, as part of making contrasts about as sharp as they can be):

- *Human-centric One-Way Street:* People[1] should have clear dominion over the Earth except for when forces more powerful and legitimate[2] than the human race ethically supplant people from that role. Therefore, people should be able to impose a double standard of enforcing in the vast majority of cases allowance for humans to practice the hunting, food preparation, and eating of the flesh of animals[3] while banning animals from practicing the hunting, food preparation, and eating of the flesh of humans.
- *Anti-Carnivorous Human-and-Animal Two-Way Street:* Although various animals eat other animals as part of nature and other animals refrain from eating other animals as another part of nature, people should refrain from eating the flesh of animals while also imposing upon animals for them to refrain from eating the flesh of humans.
- *Animal-centric One-Way Street:* Animals should have clear dominion over the Earth, except for when forces more powerful and legitimate than either the human race or the animals ethically supplant animals from that role. Therefore, animals should be able to impose a double standard of enforcing in the vast majority of cases allowance for animals to practice the hunting, food preparation, and eating of the flesh of humans while banning humans from practicing the hunting, food preparation, and eating of the

flesh of animals.

- *Pro-Carnivorous Human-and-Animal Two-Way Street:* A single standard is appropriate; namely, that there should be a high degree of open acceptance toward both the practice of humans hunting, preparing, and eating the flesh of animals and the practice of animals hunting, preparing[8], and eating the flesh of humans.

*****

Although I agree that there should be significant legal restrictions enforced regarding corpse management, in recent decades I have tended to find the Pro-Carnivorous Human-and-Animal Two-Way Street policy to be the most practical and realistic approach to ethically dealing with this issue. Combining this with a) how circa October 2003 I learned of methods, ideas, and practices involving some Vajrayana means of blessing beings whose remains present nourishment to those eating their flesh and b) how circa 2004 I learned about the practice of Tibetan sky burial, the cognitive approach to this has on some occasions proven a centerpiece of tension between myself and other Americans.[4,5,6]

Repeatedly, when considering the United States of America and how in this lifetime I was born an

American citizen by blood while overseas, on many occasions there is a striking sense of degrees to which American exceptionalism seems legitimate and degrees to which American exceptionalism seems illegitimate. Even if we take some amount of American exceptionalism to be true, real, and legitimate, there can be a notion that its exceptionalism is greatly curtailed by how its laws and practices in general have held on tightly to the aforementioned Human-centric One-Way Street policy.

Although the use of the First Amendment to the U.S. Constitution is possibly the best evidence placing weight on a scale of judgment in favor of American exceptionalism, and there can be much other evidence also contributing to that side, there are various factors providing weight on the other side of that scale, the side against that exceptionalism. For example, contemplate the historical presence of racism by any race (or combination of races) against any race (or combination of races) (whether by any given race toward any other given race, by any race against itself, or of any other possible manifestation of those types of distortions).

If any jurisdiction (whether national, state, or local) that in a prior age outlawed sky burial chooses to transition into legalizing sky burial, then such a jurisdiction affords its residents enhanced religious and ecological liberty.

---

---

Endnotes:

1 i.e., humanoids who either have bodies identifiable as being of the *Homo sapiens* category or materially close enough to that category such as to be generally considered indistinguishable from it

2 e.g., according to religious doctrines, when divine power(s) overwhelm situations such that humans are not much in control compared to divinity/divinities

3 here defined as those with bodies observationally, biologically classifiable as among Kingdom Animalia and yet scientifically distinguishable from what people generally consider to be the humans, in accordance with how many regular folks in regular conversations communicate with the use of that definition; although many scientific expressions categorize humans as among the categories of animals

4 Sometimes the terms "sky burial," "Himalayan sky burial," and "Tibetan sky burial" can be used synonymously.

[5] Cf. the "Manjusri Rebirth Mantra" chapter of *Dharma Talks by a Living Buddha* (Lu, Sheng-yen; translated by Janny Chow; 1995; Amitabha Enterprises, Inc.; ISBN 1-881493-05-9).

Although some former business associates at more than one prior place of work exhibited discomfort and/or derision toward the basic idea of this upon learning of it, and although I have worked hard to circumscribe my presentation of it to others based on True Buddha School advice to carefully limit the dissemination of its information, I believe that everything has aligned perfectly for me to present this article at this time to the general public. Of my former employers in the 2004-2023 period, I perceive that Goodwill Houston was best and CMCD LLC (as located in Houston, TX) second best at overall demonstration of respect shown by co-workers toward my use of those practices, whereas The Financial Advisory Group, Inc. (as located in Houston, TX) was the worst at that, and KPMG LLP (a multinational firm) was somewhere in the middle. However, all three organizations are perhaps better now for having encountered me, and I am myself better now for having encountered everyone I have ever encountered up to the time of the publication of this book.[12]

[6] Prior to the December 9, 2023 publication of the original version of this article, the most extreme ex-

ample to date of my support for sky burial involved a combination of December 11, 2021 and April 7, 2022.

Emboldened by great success with intense interpersonal, interorganizational, and interfaith dynamics over a period of nearly five months[13], on December 11, 2021 I set out to strategically promote the legalization of sky burial in the United States of America, and especially in Texas.

As part of that endeavor, I stopped inside Legends Poker. On that occasion, I refrained from competing in poker, yet I chose to order combination fried rice, which included cooked flesh from the remains of cattle, poultry, and shellfish. Specifically, that dish was beef, chicken, and shrimp fried rice.

At the gambling joint I refrained from imbibing in alcohol and refrained from directly bringing up the issues detailed in this article; however, as I have almost always done since learning about it, I used the we-can-bless-the-beings-whose-remains-provided-the-meat method promulgated by True Buddha School (Cf. footnote 5), simply not initiating conversation about it. Meanwhile, other people present also refrained from initiating conversation about it.

Having arrived there on foot, I walked out the door and continued walking along to find the next joint at which to aim not only toward a generalized enlightenment of sentient beings, but also with extra energy specifically toward legalization of sky burial in Texas. The intention included that whether or not legalization would actually be achieved within a given era, the effort to push people in that direction would contribute toward the enlightenment of sentient beings.

(This is not merely some academic exercise, mind you. For many years I have preferred that when I someday die, I could arrange for my remains to be prepared by sky burial, such that my corpse could then be made available to nourish animals with portions of those remains, returning the favor that many previous animals conferred on me by supplying, via their remains, meat that I have eaten.)

Next, I walked into Bluto's Sports Bar and discovered that it had a ten-dollar minimum for if people would choose to pay by credit card.

(Although I had reasonable cash on hand, I wanted to pay by credit card in order to impose on the analysts at the bank issuing the card an awareness of my patronage on that occasion of that specific bar, as a method of being territorial, not only on my behalf, but on behalf of all affiliations and affinities involved.)

While at the bar, as if magically occurring, I overheard a conversation veering into exactly a perfect opportunity for me to strategically impose upon others awareness of issues that would later become outlined in this article.

A light-skinned woman said to a white man something very much like, "I've heard that if you hunt an animal, then you really should eat all its remains, out of respect for the life that you have taken from that animal."

I deliberately budded in with something like, "Although there could be much truth to that view, there are other ways of dealing with these kinds of issues. I respect how various people, including Ted Nugent, have presented the practice that you just mentioned. However, I believe that there is potential value at times with if a human being, after killing an animal, rather than choosing to seek to fully eat that animal, chooses to leave some portion of the remains for whichever scavenger animals might happen to come along and eat that remainder of the remains.

"*Furthermore, there is a practice of Himalayan sky burial, in which priests can prepare a human corpse such that it can nourish animals who come along.*"

"I support the legalization of Himalayan sky burial in the United States of America, including in Texas."

The white man said, either verbatim or nearly verbatim, "*You,* get back over there and stay over there. Don't come back to this section of the bar!"

I walked back over to where I had been seated, beneath a San Francisco 49ers helmet (that was part of a row of NFL helmets on display), and I said to him essentially identical to, "You don't own this bar! If I later believe that the season, time, and purposes align themselves for it to be right for me to walk back over to that section of the bar where you're at, then I probably will."

Immediately after that, I looked right at him and sang the chorus of the Grateful Dead song "Casey Jones" loudly enough to be audible for all or nearly all present.

(Between the lines I was attempting to convey to him that I care enough about the value of the cultures that emerged in and emerged from the Himalayan region, including Vajrayana Buddhism and much else, that, if and when push comes to shove, I am willing to fight another being to the death over those issues.)

While on that visit to that bar, I had three drinks of alcohol.[9]

With that year's edition of the Army-Navy game broadcast on television in that bar, and with various patrons occasionally ordering up songs on the juke box, things proceeded for a while without incident.

I did notice, though, that at some point how a Hispanic man said to the aforementioned white man, "You're the only white guy in here, and you don't have any rhythm!" The white man responded with what seemed like dead silence.

(My racial background is mixed, by the way.[10])

I remained silent and observant while those two men had that interaction and for a while after, feeling fine that it made sense for the Hispanic man to consider me in that case to not be white, much as I feel fine about people in general in different cases considering me to be white, nonwhite, Asian, Nonasian, mixed, and/or nonmixed. Most of the time I feel completely outside the entire seemingly-ridiculous-at-times viciousness that all-too-often goes back and forth between different identity groups.

A very long time later, something like an hour and a half after the initial verbal skirmish that seemed mainly driven by differences over the issue of sky burial, I paid my tab.

While seated under a 49ers helmet, I then placed the 49ers cap that I had been wearing down on the counter and placed the glasses that I had been wearing down on that portion of the counter as well.

That was strategic.

Around the same time, I decided to take off an outer T-shirt to reveal the T-shirt underneath it.

On full display on my chest for anyone to see was the message of that shirt: "My Opinion Offended You? You Should Hear What I Keep To Myself."

On account of gratitude for how Vajrayana skillful means, goals, and trainings have proven helpful to me since early this century, how they hold promise to help others, how sky burial can offer a way for people to return ecological favors with balance, a commitment to honor gateways to truth, and a strong commitment to the orientation of "Death before dishonor," I decided that the best way to defend the honor of the entire Himalayan region and great swathes of the entirety of reality would be to psychologically fully throttle the rival territoriality, with absolute clarity. I walked over to about two feet in front of that man, looked right at him in his face, and walloped my left pectoral muscle with my right fist, then turned and walked away from him.

He started to try lunging at me, while other patrons tried to hold him back.

I walked back over to the area under the bar's 49ers helmet, calmly prepared both for the scenario of walking out without incident and the scenario of a possible fight to the death.

The man who had tried lunging at me broke free from the patrons who had been restraining him.

I saw him running right toward me as I had premeditated would be one of the possible scenarios and remembered studying in 2002 how Bruce Lee (1940-1973) in writing somewhere stated that in a no-rules-street-fight kind of scenario, it is generally best to stand in a strong-arm-lead position, in contrast with how professional boxing typically proceeds with people standing in a weak-arm-lead position. I also remembered having taken a basic double-martial-art (i.e., Jeet Kune Do and Kali) class over the span of about six weeks in Austin under the direction of Larry St. Clair in mid-2002, having done some extremely basic boxing training under the direction of Jesus Poll in Houston in later portions of 2002 into early portions of 2003, having received some very basic hand-to-hand combat pointers from my father (Maurice A.T. Blair, 1931-2015, who had served in combat in both Korea and Vietnam during portions of his U.S. Army duties in portions of 1950-1972), and other resources helpful with how to conduct a fight.

The guy who charged at me came with such speed and such an evident intent to kill that on the spectrum from a scientific boxer to a wild puncher, he acted as a wild puncher.

He landed a bunch of punches onto my face in a very short span of time, then I landed one solid and explosive right straight lead punch, immediately followed by a second right straight lead punch that made a less-solid impact onto his face.

Immediately after landing the second blow to that rival, I fell onto my back, then almost-instantly bounced back up to pick up the eyewear and cap that I had left on the counter.

I started to walk out, and overheard someone say, "You better leave."

It was not like I had any intention of hanging around longer, anyway.

Although I did not look toward the guy who had thrown the first eight or seventeen or whatever-number-they-were punches and against whom I had retaliated with landing two punches, I was thankful that he was no longer charging after me in any way whatsoever.

As I left I said, either word-for-word or nearly so, "I would like to thank everyone here for this exciting draw that we just experienced. Vaya con Dios!"

Although I had a moderate amount of bleeding from portions of my scalp, I walked along and thought to myself that if I were to walk straight home or straight to medical care, my detractors could easily interpret me as less manly than the minimum level of manliness that they would have to concede to me if I were to continue walking along while eschewing both home and potential medical treatment for quite a while.

Therefore, I walked over to a location of O'Reilly Auto Parts and sought something to buy and display to others as a kind of participation trophy. I found a small toolset that seemed suitable for that purpose and purchased it.

Next, walking along the side of the road, I held up the "trophy" while looking toward motorists who drove by, and I asserted support for sky burial (without most of the motorists consciously knowing it), employing an Arsenio Hall style of a "Whoop! Whoop!" motion of the right arm while holding the toolset trophy with the left arm.

After buying and eating food at a Pizza Hut, I walked over to a location of Roostar Vietnamese Restaurant and ordered some food. However, very soon at Roostar both the Houston Police Department and the Houston Fire Department arrived to interview me.

After some initial pleasantries, someone from HPD asked me if I would like to press charges against the guy who had thrown the first punch in the bar fight. I thought for only a few seconds and responded, "No."

(You see, although the other fellow and I evidently had a strong disagreement on public policy, I believed then and I believe now that there was something fundamentally fair about how the fight played itself out. As a general rule, it is best for people to work out policy differences by methods like agreeing to disagree and choosing to later reconsider issues rather than getting into a bare-knuckle brawl, yet there are exceptions to rules.)

For a long time, I believed it best for me to avoid returning to that bar.

However, on April 7, 2022, my evaluation of all factors, intuitions, sensory data, knowledge, the unknown, and everything else were such that I arrived at a combined solution (i.e., Zen Buddhism, Vajrayana Buddhism, Esoteric Christianity, Noahidism, Nondenominational Esoteric Abrahamic Religion, Nondenominational Esoteric Dharmic Religion, common sense, uncommon sense, and everything else found unified agreement within my field of consciousness and decision making)[11] to return to that bar.

A major factor was that there is an idea in the judgment of evaluating some officially-sanctioned fights that for someone to complete a win or a draw properly, sometimes the competitor has to step back into the ring from which that competitor had exited.

Another factor was that I thought it might be possible that stepping back over there could be conducive to someone revealing something useful.

I noticed that the woman who had been the bartender a little less than four months prior was now present as a patron. She seemed to recognize me, but did not bring up the previous incident.

Soon, I ordered one Skyy vodka, preparing to pay by cash. Also soon, the bartender-turned-patron mentioned that she would be stepping outside for a little while, and she stepped outside.

I looked at some Major League Baseball 2022 opening day developments on television inside the bar. There was a decision to be made: to volunteer to mention the incident or not to volunteer to mention the incident. Though my father and other military people have at times spoken the mantra, "Never volunteer," some of my fraternity brothers and other people involved with some charity work have at times spoken the mantra, "Volunteer." I considered the situation and recognized no clear answer, somewhat the opposite of arriving at a combined solution. At some stage I decided to volunteer to identify myself as having had the role that I did in the earlier incident.

Thereupon the male bartender said, "This will be the last drink that you have at this bar."

I said to him, essentially, "But back in that incident, I did not throw the first punch. The other guy threw the first so-many punches and then I punched back."

He said to me, essentially, "It makes no difference. You caused trouble."

After silently thinking briefly, I said something very much like, "I respect that you made this decision. Although there have been other people in recent years who set out to reject me in ways that I believed to be unjustified, I believe that your establishment in this case is acting within its range of justifiable actions.

"Though I believe you could be justified in this case either to banish me or to refrain from banishing me, and you have chosen to banish me, I appreciate your hospitality in allowing me to finish this drink and then pay my tab before I head out."[7] I finished the drink, paid my tab, and headed out.

On my way out, I saw in the front porch area the bartender-turned-patron lady, and she said to me something like, "Be safe."

Unperturbed by everything, I nonchalantly said to her something like, "You, too. Take care."[15]

[15] Ch. 10, Sec. 5, Pt. R circles back to that.

[7] To reduce the risk of casual readers carelessly stereotyping me as some ne'er-do-well who nearly

universally alienates people and becomes banned from many places, I shall inform you that few have ever banned me from revisitation.

Also, as a tonic to how people at times have tendencies to blow things out of proportions, here is an example of when something truly weird happened and I did not get banned: One day in approximately October or November 2021 I drank and dined at a location of Outback Steakhouse and shared several interesting conversations.

Some mixture of people seated to my left received an inquiry from me at some stage about whether they were familiar with the TV series *Night Gallery* (1969-1973), and at least one of them answered that he did not previously know that it even existed. I said a few favorable and moderately-analytical words about that series.

Later, somehow the controversies swirling around the murders of Nicole Brown Simpson (1959-1994) and Ronald Goldman (1968-1994) came up in conversation.

A black man seated to my right soon spoke aloud and endorsed a theory that one of O.J. Simpson's sons had been the real murderer and that O.J. Simpson's legal team, at his instruction, had set out to avoid pursuing at all the possibility of that son having been the perpetrator.[14]

I indicated major uncertainty and having never heard or read about that theory anywhere else. (Later, on April 11, 2024 I heard William Dear present that theory on *The Michael Berry Show.*)

At some stage I asked the restaurant to give me the strongest vodka that they had, without asking them to name what that would happen to be.

Earlier, I had slipped on part of the floor and, within a split-second, caught myself from falling by using the left index finger and left middle finger to press against a nearby chair. That sprained both of those fingers, and I spent much of the remainder of that visit with a glass of water resting on those two fingers to help them to heal.

Not very long after the fellow seated to my right expressed the aforementioned bizarre theory about a controversy from very long ago, although there were no high-frequency operatic singers performing opera nearby, the glass of water tipped over from the fingers, from a height of about one centimeter, *and it shattered loudly on the counter into many pieces.*

The bartender closest to me said, "You need to leave now!"

I said, "But I haven't even paid my tab, and I would really like to pay my tab before I go,"

That bartender responded, "It doesn't matter. Go, now!"

I immediately left, recognizing how the way that a glass in good condition tipping over from a height of about four-tenths of an inch and suddenly shattering, without any loud, high-frequency background sounds audible as a rational explanation for why it would happen had evidently freaked out the bartender.

Before I left, though, I decided to adjust the energy dynamics somewhat, with a statement approximating to, "Just before I leave, here's a toast. To the late, great director Sergio Leone and to the late, great chess grandmaster Evgeny Sveshnikov."

Since then, I returned to that location of Outback Steakhouse, dined, paid for my tab, left, and re-turned again, and left again, without incident, multiple times.

[8] The reference to the preparation of human flesh by animals could be broadened to also include the preparation of human flesh by humans in connection with morgues, cemeteries, and other places, whether without sky burial or with sky burial.

[9] That was calculated based on how two drinks would have been insufficient to reach the ten dollar credit card minimum threshold and factoring the

pedestrian travel method of that trip, consisting of Stella Artois and Bud Light. Although some readers might have preferred it if I had omitted any reference to Bud Light on account of some controversies from April 2023, I believe it best with this article that I tell everything like it is while holding very little back, and therefore, there it is. It was specifically two glasses of Stella Artois and one glass of Bud Light. Additionally, although that bar as of that time neither offered for anyone to be able to buy solid food nor offered complimentary solid food, it did offer at the time free soft drinks to anyone purchasing alcoholic beverages. I chose to utilize that feature and ordered up two free soft drinks.

[10] Although I have not sought out genetic testing for ancestral analysis up to the time of composing this article, my family's records indicate that if we equally weigh male and female branching, then I am about 50% (i.e., half) Chinese (from my mother's side of the family), about 40.625% (i.e., 13/32) white (from my father's side of the family), and about 9.375% (i.e., 3/32) Native American (also of father's side), and that there is no sizable quantity of Hispanic ancestry within that. Therefore, if I get a form that lets me opt out of selecting to answer about race, I often consider that my best option; if I get a form that lets me choose "multiracial" without specifying, then that is sometimes the best option; and if a form allows

specification, then sometimes I choose Asian and White while omitting Native American, whereas on other occasions I choose White, Asian, and Native American. However, the most difficult forms for me to deal with in terms of asking me to identify by race are those that force everyone into an exercise of multiple choice and separate White and Asian from each other on the form, while not presenting Multiracial as an option and refusing to let the person filling out the form from opting out from choosing a race. In those types of cases, when I was very young, my father established a precedence that I would count in the category of White. In contrast, one of my former primary care physicians had a computer system in which he and his staff would select race for the patients without letting patients select it for themselves, and he chose to count me as Asian. In case some government people look at this article and compare it with their records, I shall inform them that when in recent years I get backed into that kind of a corner and I go with my father's precedence, the main rationale is that portions of religious literature–both East and West–place an emphasis on males being of lineages from their forefathers as a primary aspect of their realities.

Nevertheless, the vast majority of the time, I use mindsets completely devoid of the basic racial identity cognitive structure, "I am a (fill-in-the-blank-with-a-specified-racial-identity-category-of-a-person)." To the degree that anyone anywhere uses the mind in an absolutely pedantic manner of cognizing everyone as having to conform to that cognitive structure, they set themselves up for instant discomfort with the very presence of my mind upon meeting me to the extent that they might intuitively sense that the vast majority of the time my mind is devoid of that cognitive structure.

[11] Cf. The free book *An Encyclopedic Survival Guide for Navigating Normal and Paranormal Experiences* (edited by yours truly, M.J. Blair) (ISBN: 979-8-9859094-8-7 paperback; free, not for initial sale / 979-8-9859094-9-4 ebook available at https://mixam.com/share/655c27abd6df672f5fc02e04 as a flipbook).

[12] There are many favorable and unfavorable things I could say about any of the employers I had from 1994 to September 4, 2022, and there are many sides to many issues with virtually everyone.

Repeatedly, on many occasions, from early 2023 to the present, I have returned to a state of transcending any clinging toward considering anyone to be an enemy.

An example of a gateway into that mindset is how I concluded a 3:43 PM Houston time, October 12, 2023 e-mail message to culminate a set of September-to-October 2023 correspondence with someone from the general public (who may have been spoofing possession of the name presented on the electronic server) who had repeatedly initiated correspondence by sending ambiguously-threat-ening messages to me. Here are the last few paragraphs of that concluding message from me:

Life is much bigger than the idea of people posturing forcefulness and superiority to whomever they perceive to be antagonists and people displaying meekness to whomever they perceive it best to be meek toward.

I stand here at this very instant with neither you nor anyone else as a living enemy, whether or not you or anyone else perceives himself/herself/itself to be a living enemy toward me.

Of course, everything could change in the blink of an eye. That includes any instant after I hit send for this message.

Relationships of enmity come and go. Relationships of friendship, too, may come and go, at least some of the time. Many scientists believe that entire universes come and go, as well.

Whatever issues, if any, you might happen to have, at another level you lack those issues; that is why it can be said that you have those issues. (Credit for that type of going beyond normal conceptual limits should go to various ancients of over one-and-a-half millennia ago. For example, *The Diamond Sutra.*)

[13] Besides appearing on *The Michael Berry Show* twice in the first half of August 2021 and twice in the second half of October 2021, there were many other examples of the referenced success in my life. Another part of that was that I layered the quest to influence in the direction of sky burial legalization in the U.S. with trying to run for Texas Governor, with it to-be-determined which party to affiliate with for that purpose. For example, if running such a campaign in a manner reminiscent of Kinky Friedman's gubernatorial campaign of a few years ago, then it would bring more awareness to the sky burial issue. However, after both the bar fight and a series of other extreme difficulties that landed on me one after another, I called off that gubernatorial attempt after something like fifty-and-a-half hours.

[14] Consider this 11 APR 2024 cropped screenshot from X (formerly known as Twitter):

Maurice Blair @M_James_Blair · Now
Although I posted (~11:30 AM U.S. CDT, 11 APR 2024) regarding having maintained a nonjudgment toward whether-beyond-reasonable-doubt-or-not O.J. Simpson (1947-2024) had murdered N.B. Simpson (1959-1994) and R. Goldman (1968-1994), consider ECCLESIASTES 12 & THE DHAMMAPADA 1&2.

Maurice Blair @M_James_Blair · 42m
Although folks' perceptions of O.J. Simpson (1947-2024, "OJ Simpson") as beyond a reasonable doubt guilty vs. not guilty of murder, I have maintained a nonjudgment toward him on that. I have often perceived a likelihood he had hired a hitman whose hand fit the glove. #OJSimpson

1

12:24 PM
4/11/2024

## CHAPTER 6, PART 5

Although I do not know the famous author David Grann personally and have not, to the best of my knowledge, received any direct message from him, I sent to him an e-mail on January 27, 2023 at 4:57 PM U.S. CST. As part of introducing myself, I gave him extra information adjacent to *The Dimetrodons, the Dorians, and the Modern World: Revised Edition* (2022):

The book I published on 10/10/2022 mentions near the end of its "About the Author" section a man named Dale and a man named Nick having had a then-recent major conflict with each other and that as of that time I was on reasonably good terms with both of them. Although I did not reveal the more complete names of either of them in that book, I will now reveal to you that their more complete names are Dale Siegel and Nick Rinchiuso. I am still on good terms with Nick, though I have rarely met him and have never shared telephone or writen correspondence with him to the best of my knowledge. Meanwhile, as another update, the potential blowing up of relations with Dale that I recognized when meeting him on 10/6/2022 eventually resulted in actually blowing up. That specific Siegel set out to attempt to market a T-shirt that, by his own admission, is derogatory toward the prophet generally regarded as the founder of Islam, and he was showing it to people at the diner where he and I met. Later, he put together a text mailing list of people to try to get to consider sending him money and/or buying the T-shirt that he's trying to sell. I expressed moderate criticism toward him repeatedly regarding this, even upon first seeing what he was trying to do, yet he and I did not get into a sharp conflict for quite a while. Finally, a few days ago, that specific Dale Siegel sent another group text message, this time layering the crude shirt image advertisement with other messages, including an attempt at absolute-or-nearly-absolute condemnation of Islam. I found out yesterday. On account of how I think and feel various degrees of criticism, praise, and respect toward all five of the main religions of this planet (i.e., Judaism, Christianity, Islam, Hinduism, and Buddhism), I decided enough was enough regarding that guy's behavior; I responded with a major degree of criticism toward his going over the top with what I perceived to be excessive harshness toward the entirety of Islam and expressed multiple perspectives, including sending (per records at 10:50 AM CST yesterday) to him and the rest of his group text messaging list's recipients the message, "Dale, I respect your right to focus on some negative (or apparently negative) trends in Islam, and your First Amendment right to attempt South Park-style humor with tongue-in-cheek allegations against its fonder (or alleged founder), yet I believe that there is a major mixture of positive and negative trends in each religion. I also wonder if karma in connection with much of this might be heading in some precarious directions for your possible future(s). Jim" ... After that, he and I had additional text messages back and forth, and other people in that list sent a few messages. At 2:28 PM CST yesterday per text records, he sent me a text message that included a reference to his plan to block my cell phone number immediately after sending me that message.

*********************************************

As a footnote to that excerpt of that Blair-to-Grann message, let it be known that somehow the include-ed transcription of the 10:50 AM CST, January 26, 2023 Blair-to-Siegel text message was missing one letter (the "u" in one instance of "founder").

Consider this expression: "Dale, I respect your right to focus on some negative (or apparently negative) trends in Islam, and your First Amendment right to attempt South Park-style humor with tongue-in-cheek allegations against its founder (or alleged founder), yet I believe that there is a major mixture of positive and negative trends in each religion. I also wonder if karma in connection with much of this might be heading in some precarious directions for your possible future(s). Jim"

---

.............................................................................

---

## CHAPTER 6, PART 6

Next, as a supplement to Part Four of Chapter Seven, and as a prelude to that part of that chapter, here is a copy of a Facebook direct message that I sent to a friend and acquaintance of the name Ustinya Shevtsova on March 10, 2024 at 12:54 PM Houston time:

FYI: Justin Haynes's Facebook profile in connection with ID "jay.haynes.102" evidently became hijacked months ago and became long-term inaccessible to him; whereas, he recently started a new Facebook profile in connection with ID "61555658505496" (per his descriptions to me about his situation).

..........................................................................

As yet another prelude to Chapter 7, Part 4, consider this: Dale Siegel expressed being a Jew believing in Agnosticism and similar approaches rather than a Jew believing in a Judaism-based metaphysical reality or any other religiously-based metaphysical reality, and he expressed belief in extremely harsh condemnation toward the entirety of Islam. In contrast, a friend named Aron Silberg, in mid-2023, expressed being a Jew who believes—at least somewhat—in Judaism and spiritual levels of reality in general, and he expressed belief in showing reasonable respect toward Islam and toward possible peaceful coexistence between the various major religions.

---

… … … … … … … … … … … … … …

---

Sometime in mid-2023, in a conversation with Aron, I briefly mentioned salient facts from some of the October-2022-to-January-2023 interactions between Dale Siegel and others.

That Jew named Aron Silberg sharply criticized that Jew named Dale Siegel, in keeping with how that Jewish Aron strongly supported benevolence and tolerance in general.

As with many of the people referenced in this book by what I would generally consider bad behavior, I do not know with certainty how much, if any, Dale Siegel might have learned and grown as a spiritual being since the times when I interacted with him. Maybe he might have already transformed into doing a great deal of what I would generally consider good behavior, or maybe he might not have.

Something I do know is that it seems very possible—maybe almost definite—that any or almost any sentient being just might have the chance to become a better sentient being in the future.

# CHAPTER SEVEN: ALTERNATIVE SYMBOLIC TIMETABLE PATTERNS III, SELECT QUOTES, VERY TRANSFIGURED SYMBOLISMS, AND HIGHLIGHTS FROM TWO EPIC PHONE CONVERSATIONS BETWEEN JAMES BLAIR AND JUSTIN HAYNES

# Ch. 7, Pt. I: Alternative Symbolic Timetable Patterns III

Version A of Tibetan Calendar Symbolism alignment is from offsetting calculations by Michael Erlewine's program *Tibetan Astrology* (2002, Matrix Software, ISBN: 092518231-1; alternatively, 9780925182319) to line up with "Tibetan Calendar Mathematics" article by Svante Janson (Cf. the URL: https://www2.math.uu.se/~svantejs/papers/calendars/tibet.pdf as accessed on May 15, 2024), in terms of New Year's Day differences b/w the software output and Table 1 of the pdf article.

Version B of Tibetan Calendar Symbolism is straight from calculations by Erlewine's *Tibetan Astrology* (2002) computer software. Note: Some animal names here are of a different variation than the software.

Here is what this book's setup is using as its standard:

• Sheep • Monkey • Bird • Dog • Boar • Rat
• Ox • Tiger • Hare • Dragon • Snake • Horse

---

November 5, 2029 (per G.C.) / (T.C. yr #'s 2156, 1775, & 1003)
(T.C. Symbolism, ver. A: Year of the Bird, Month 9, Day 29)
(T.C. Symbolism, version B: Y: Bird, M: Dog / M#: 9,
Day of the Snake / Day #: 28)

April 30, 2045 (per the G.C.) / (T.C. yr #'s 2172, 1791, & 1019)
(T.C. Symbolism, ver. A: Year of the Ox, Month 3, Day 15)
(T.C. Symbolism, version B: Y: Ox, M: Dragon / M#: 3,
Day: Monkey / Day #: 13)

(The remaining four entries of this set include for their Tibetan Calendar sections the Version B symbolism method only. (Note: The latest New Year's Day shown in Table 1 of the article pdf was February 6, 2046.)

---

November 11, 2047 per G.C. T.C.yr #s 2174, 1793, & 1021. T.C. Symbolism, version B, Year: Hare, Month: Dog, M#: 9, Day: Snake, Day #: 22.

---

December 30, 2048 per G.C. / T.C. yr #'s 2175, 1794, & 1022. T.C. Symbolism, version B: Year of the Earth Dragon, Month of the Rat / Month #: 11, Day of the Ox / Day #: 24.

---

December 31, 2048 per G.C. / T.C. yr #'s 2175, 1794, & 1022 T.C. Symbolism, version B: Year of the Earth Dragon, M#: 11 Month: Rat, Day: Tiger, Day #: 25.

---

January 1, 2049 per G.C. / T.C. yr #'s 2175, 1794, & 1022 T.C. Symbolism, version B: Year of the Earth Dragon, M#: 11 Month: Rat, Day: Hare, Day #: 26.

---

## Ch. 7, Pt. II: Select Quotes

"Thus, one should know all the tenets of the religions of Buddhism and non-Buddhism—for example, other religions, Bönpos, the Chan Buddhists, the Nyingma, the Kagyus, the Sakya, the Geluks, and so forth—to be the emanations of the buddhas and bodhisattvas." –Shabkar Tsokdruk Rangdrol (1781-1851)

"Relationships of enmity come and go. Relationships of friendship, too, may come and go, at least some of the time. Many scientists believe that entire universes come and go, as well."
–Maurice James Blair, October 12, 2023

"This too shall pass." – Anonymous, ancient times

"Clothes make the man. Naked people have little or no influence in society." –attributed to Mark Twain [pseudonym of Samuel Longhorne Clemens] (1835-1910), though there is some uncertainty about whether he actually stated that

"To every argument, an equal argument is opposed." –Pyrrhonist School [of philosophy], ancient times

Ch. 7, Pt. III: Very Transfigured Symbolisms

April 9, 1993, Exhibit A: 1. Structure to Chemistry Four. Structure to Chemistry Five. 2. Enforcement to Forensics Three. Enforcement to Forensics Six.

April 9, 1993, Exhibit B: 1. Structure to Ethical Economics Four. Structure to Ethical Economics Five. 2. Enforcement to Forensics Three. Enforcement to Chemistry Six.

April 9, 1993, Exhibit C: 1. Structure to Divinity Four. Enforcement to Forensics Six. 2. Structure to Chemistry Four. Structure to Ethical Economics Six.

October 12, 1903: 1. Structure to Ethical Economics Four. Structure to Ethical Economics Five. 2. Structure to Forensics Four. Structure to Divinity Six. 3. Enforcement to Forensics Three. 4. Subjective to Biology Five. Subjective to Geology Four. 5. Objective-Side Industrialization. Structure to Anatomy Six. 6. Subjective to Anatomy Four. Structure to Biology Five. 7. Subjective to Biology Three. Enforcement to Divinity Four. 8. Subjective to Divinity Five. Structure to Chemistry Six. 9. Enforcement takes Divinity Four. Subjective takes Divinity One. 10. Subjective takes Chemistry Six to Present a Mortal Threat. Objective to Ethical Economics Seven. 11. Enforcement to Chemistry Three. Structure on Ethical Economics takes Divinity Four. 12. Enforcement to Divinity Five to Present a Mortal Threat. Objective to Ethical Economics Six. 13. Structure to Forensics Five to Present a Mortal Threat. Objective to Ethical Economics Five. 14. Structure to Divinity Three. Structure to Geology Five. 15. Structure to Geology Three. Subjective to History Six. 16. Structure to Chemistry Three. Structure to Geology

Four. 17. Subjective to Forensics Four to Present a Mortal Threat. Subjective takes Forensics Four. 18. Structure takes Forensics Four, Mortally Trapping The Second Mover's Objective, Achieving a Victory For The First Mover's Objective.

August 29, 2015: 1. Structure to Divinity Four. Enforcement to Forensics Six. 2. Structure to Chemistry Four. Structure to Geology Six. 3. Enforcement to Chemistry Three. Subjective to Geology Seven. 4. Structure to Ethical Economics Four. Structure to Divinity Six. 5. Enforcement to Forensics Three. Objective-Side Industrialization. 6. Subjective to Ethical Economics Five. 7. Objective-Side Industrialization. Enforcement to Chemistry Six. 8. Structure to Divinity Five. Enforcement to Ethical Economics Seven. 9. Enforcement to Ethical Economics One. Enforcement to Divinity Seven. 10. Structure to Forensics Three. Structure to Forensics Five. 11. Subjective to Ethical Economics Three. Structure to Forensics Four. 12. Subjective to Forensics Two. Structure to Geology Five. 13. Enforcement to Divinity Three. Enforcement to Geology Six. 14. Structure to Chemistry Five. Enforcement to Forensics Six. 15. Industry to Chemstry One. Industry to Forensics Seven. 16. Objective to History One. Structure to History Five. 17. Structure on Chemistry takes Divinity Six. Structure on Chemistry takes Divinity Six. 18. Enforcement to Biology Five. Structure to Anatomy Six. 19. Enforcement to Anatomy Three. Structure to Biology Five. 20. Industry to Chemistry Six. Structure to Geology Four. 21. Motive to Chemistry Two. Motive to Forensics Eight. 22. Industry to Chemistry One. Subjective to Divinity Seven. 23. Industry to Chemistry Seven. Subjective to History Six. 24. Subjective to Ethical Economics One. Structure to History Four. 25. Structure on Forensics takes Geology Four. Structure to Forensics Three. 26. Structure on Geology takes Forensics Three. Enforcement takes Ethical Economics Four. 27. Industry to Divinity One. Industry takes Forensics Three. 28. Industry takes Divinity Seven. Industry to Forensics One to Present a Mortal Threat. 29. Objective to Geology Two. Subjective to Ethical Economics Three. 30. Subjective to Geology Three. Structure on History takes Geology Three. 31. Industry takes Forensics One. Enforcement to History Four to Present a Mortal Threat. 32. Objective to History Three. Motive to History Six. 33. Structure to Geology Five. Enforcement takes Geology Five to Present a Mortal Threat. 34. Objective to Geology Four. Enforcement from History to Forensics Three. 35. Enforcement to Forensics Two. Motive to History Four to Present a Mortal Threat. 36. Objective to Forensics Five. Industry to Forensics Eight to Present a Mortal Threat. 37. Objective to Geology Six. Industry to Forensics Six to Present a Mortal Threat. 38. Objective takes Forensics Six. 39. Objective to Geology Six. Motive to Geology Five, Mortally Trapping the First Mover's Objective, Achieving Victory for the Second Mover's Objective.

Many Unspecified Dates: 1. Structure to Ethical Economics Four. Structure to Chemistry Five. 2. Enforcement to Forensics Three. Structure to Divinity Six. 3. Structure to Divinity Four. Structure takes Divinity Four. 4. Enforcement takes Divinity Four. Enforcement to Forensics Six. 5. Enforcement to Chemistry Three. Structure to Anatomy Six. 6. Subjective to Ethical Economics Three. Structure to Ethical Economics Six. 7. Structure to Forensics Three. Structure to Biology Five.

8. Motive to Divinity Two. Enforcement from Biology to Divinity Seven. 9. Structure to Geology Four. Structure to History Six. 10. Motive-Side Industrialization.

Many Unspecified Dates: 1. Structure to Ethical Economics Four. Structure to Chemistry Five. 2. Enforcement to Forensics Three. Structure to Divinity Six. 3. Structure to Divinity Four. Structure takes Divinity Four. 4. Enforcement takes Divinity Four. Enforcement to Forensics Six. 5. Enforcement to Chemistry Three. Structure to Anatomy Six. 6. Structure to History Three. Structure to Ethical Economics Five. 7. Enforcement from Divinity to Ethical Economics Two. Structure to History Five.

Many Unspecified Dates: 1. Structure to Ethical Economics Four. Structure to Ethical Economics Five. 2. Enforcement to Forensics Three. Enforcement to Chemistry Six. 3. Subjective to Biology Five. Structure to Anatomy Six. 4. Subjective to Anatomy Four. Enforcement to Forensics Six. 5. Objective-Side Industrialization. Subjective to Ethical Economics Seven. 6. Industry to Ethical Economics One. Structure to Biology Five. 7. Subjective to Biology Three. Structure to Divinity Six. 8. Structure to Chemistry Three. Objective-Side Industrialization. 9. Structure to History Three. Subjective to Biology Seven. 10. Structure to Divinity Four. Industry to Ethical Economics Eight. 11. Enforcement to Geology Five. Industry to Forensics Eight. 12. Enforcement to Forensics Three. Industry to Ethical Economics Eight. 12. Enforcement to Geology Five. Industry to Forensics Eight. 13. Enforcement to Forensics Three. Drawn by three-fold repetition of a position.

## CHAPTER SEVEN, PART FOUR:

## HIGHLIGHTS FROM TWO EPIC PHONE CONVERSATIONS BETWEEN JAMES BLAIR AND JUSTIN HAYNES

On March 15, 2024, at about 1:15 PM CDT in Houston, TX, USA, a man named Justin Haynes called this James Blair. Much later, the handheld wireless landline receiver that Blair was using started beeping to indicate that it was running low on its battery. Blair mentioned that to Haynes, then the two agreed to end the call, with a plan for Blair to use a cellphone to initiate a call to Haynes with which to resume the conversation, a little while after ending the first phone call.

Blair and Haynes brought that plan to fruition. James called Justin at 2:27 P.M. CDT. That second call's duration was 55 minutes and 33 seconds (i.e., a little over fifty-five-and-a-half minutes).

FOR YOUR CONSIDERATION:

A SEMBLANCE OF PORTIONS OF THOSE DIALOGUES, WHICH INCLUDED TREADING INTO REVELATORY TERRITORIES

[James Blair picks up the phone, already seeing by caller ID clues with which to be nearly certain of Justin Haynes being the caller.]

James Blair: Is there at least one Justin Haynes in the house or houses or whatever contributing to the telephone line?

Justin Haynes [in a falsetto]: Mmmmeeoow, Hssss, Mmmheeeee-eeee-eeeeee-oooooooowwwwwwwww, Hmmm, Mmmmmeeeeeeooowwwwww.

James Blair: What is going on? Justin, is that you? What are you doing with your voice?

Haynes [in a normal voice]: I was just imitating almost every cat I've ever known, bro.

Blair: Oh, that makes more sense now.

Haynes: Hey so what's up?

Blair: Things are going well...

...

---

...

...

---

...

Blair: Sometimes lately I think about this situation in the country, in which things have changed enough that over and over again many people think that if their side of the politics wins, then great, but if their side loses, then its somehow the end of liberty in the country, or almost the end of liberty in the country. Many people have that idea that their side must be so thoroughly right and the other side so thoroughly wrong that it's going to be a disaster if the other side wins. I know that in general you're tending to be somewhat liberal, and I'm tending to trend lately in the range from moderate to conservative, but I really have to wonder about all the doomsday predictions from both sides. Theoretically, like you and I have discussed before, if we could someday have technology advance to an extraordinary level, then maybe it could be like that idea that Roddenberry and Clarke expressed of a society where people could still negotiate who provides what to whom, yet the entire redistribution-versus-competition dynamic could be "solved," such that it would be like Adam Smith and Karl Marx shaking hands, with an announcement that the war is over. However, the reality is that we are a long ways away from the possibility of reaching that state of such advanced technology, and, in the meantime, the controversy about how much to redistribute, how much to let competition be free, and so on, it's such a huge problem.

Haynes: Yes, it's a problem. I miss the Mitt Romneys and the John McCains who would be conservatives but would do a whole lot to reach across the aisle and do things in a sensible way to make more bipartisan stuff happen. Now, it seems more like many of the conservatives are focused on something like, "To hell with what you think. To hell with what many liberals and moderates believe are worthwhile programs to benefit the future. We're going to stand our ground, and we don't care about the poor getting stomped on. We care about getting the system to help support the rich." I mean, some folks like Biden are trying to do what they can to make the country better, but Trump and a bunch of the MAGA crowd are putting up roadblocks over and over again.

Blair: I think your view is skewed. Although I am not completely on board with how the Trump and MAGA movement folks are doing things, and I'm not fully on board with how many of the hardcore conservatives of recent times criticize the John McCain and Mitt Romney types of conservatives as not being conservative enough, and although I believe myself to in many ways transcend the entire political spectrum, I believe that your forthright liberal expression is also quite off-base to a major degree.

Haynes: How so? Biden and many of the other liberals are not at the extreme of how some Sanders supporters dive right into Marxism or something almost Marxist.

I'm liberal in a way that agrees with many of the people in the Democratic Party who are weary of how some of the most extreme on the left are too enthusiastic—going overboard for redistribution. I believe that Biden is also of that more careful liberal type. I am aware that in history it's never worked when the people of the mindset of total redistribution and having the government get totalitarian completely take over. But, bro, that's not really liberalism... I mean, if you just think about the word, "liberal." It's supposed to mean that the people support liberty. How is that supposed to be compatible with if you take away all or almost all property rights and then have a totalitarian government force everyone to not have much freedom at all?

Blair: Yes, part of what you said with that is on track, but I still believe that there are major threats from much of the left—not only the extremists of the left, but also many of the people you perceive to be more moderate liberals, and I've experienced some of that directly in my life.

Haynes: What do you consider to be so bad about The Democratic Party in general?

Blair: Part of that goes to how when I worked for The Financial Advisory Group in Houston; I believe that part of how the whole fiasco happened could be traced back to Saul Alinsky, and that Alinsky and others arranged for The Democratic Party to unleash an environment of intimidation against many people—both liberals and conservatives. Are you familiar with the history involving Saul Alinsky?

Haynes: That name does not really ring a bell.

Blair: Let me tell you a summary of some stuff involving him and how it relates. When I called in to *The Michael Berry Show* on August 6, 2021, and his open-line Friday that morning ended up becoming a conduit through which he walked into letting me thermonuke The Financial Advisory Group, I mentioned to him on air that I had not yet read Alinsky's *Rules for Radicals* as of that time, though I'd heard Mark Levin mention a whole bunch about that book when Levin was talking on *The Mark Levin Show* on talk radio.

Of course, I followed up the live broadcast phone call with Michael Berry by going to the Facebook page for *The Michael Berry Show*, kind of paralleling when a military operation has an air attack followed up by sending the ground forces. But, you see, soon after all that, I checked out from a local library a copy of Saul Alinsky's *Rules for Radicals*, to finally get around to studying that thing.

Now, does that title *Rules for Radicals* bring to mind anything you might remember about it as a book?

Haynes: No, I don't remember anything specific about that from before.

Blair: Well, then let me tell you something like a brief summary of some of the relevant stuff about that. There was a guy named Saul Alinsky, and though he was born into Judaism, which many people consider to make a person permanently a Jew, whether the person likes it or not and whether the person keeps believing in Judaism as a religion or not, at some stage he went over to telling people that he was an atheist. His largest concern after a while, it seems, revolved around stuff like fighting back against the ways that many of the rich and powerful rigged systems to make the poor and other underprivileged often unable to make much hedgeway into improving their lives, especially if and when such improvement would come at a high price for the rich and powerful. Also, he fell in with the crowd who supported radical redistribution, sometimes proclaiming himself to be a communist—even in the midst of that entire Cold War thing between The United States and The Soviet Union back then.

For a while, he experimented with organizing groups aimed toward fighting back against powerful people they believed to be suppressing the abilities of the poor to improve their lots in life. At some stage, very near the end of his life, he wrote *Rules for Radicals.*

Something like mid-August 2021 I checked it out, and over the span of several weeks I read it carefully from cover to cover.

In that book, he harshly criticized and condemned just about everyone he thought deserved it, and he provided blueprints for how he believed people fighting for stuff like redistribution and the taking down of those they believed to be unjustified should proceed.

Some of what he presented I believed to be way over-the-top, some of it off-base, and there were some things that could be very helpful to some people. I became absolutely infuriated at the book's passages many times, yet I believe in that thing like Voltaire about how even when strongly disagreeing with a presentation believing in the right to make it part of the public discourse, such that we can all in the long run become more enlightened.

Another thing is that in the very early pages, he gave special thanks to a couple of regular-world human beings, and then—get this—he stated something along the lines of, "And, at least as an over-the-shoulder nod, let us thank the original rebel, who, according to legend, rebeled so strongly that he was able to earn his own kingdom: Lucifer."

Haynes: You mentioned that he called himself an Atheist, and, you know, some Atheists choose to become Satanists, but it is not like they are treating Satan as some kind of deity. Instead, it is like they want to say to the traditional religious people, "Hey, we don't believe in any of your stuff. We'll point this out to you by making our ceremonies celebrate and honor The Devil whom many of you consider to be so terrible. It's not like we really believe that The Devil is completely real and is going to supernaturally do things on our behalf to help out like some deity pattern with prayers and such. Rather, it is the way that we can symbolize how we do our Atheism and how thoroughly we think of your religion as having so much bullshit involved with it.

Blair: Ah, there are probably many different kinds of Satanists, though. Some may be like what you described; others may have very different ideas. Also, although there can be some valid points at times about criticizing the foundings of major religions, sometimes people can experience those kinds of things in which mysterious levels of reality do to us stuff way beyond what anyone would typically believe is humanly possible to do to our reality. *And I've experienced that kind of stuff multiple times, as I've mentioned to you before.* Some people who hold on tightly to being so dead-set against traditional religion may have to someday deal with those kinds of ultra-mysterious experiences and have a day of reckoning.

Haynes: I hear ya, bro.

.............

---

.............

Blair [continuing a while later in the conversation]: Unfortunately, many people in the Democratic Party have an overblown attachment to heavy reliance on Alinsky's *Rules for Radicals*, such that they are unaware of how much they overvalue the perspectives and methods expressed in that book.

This also ties in to something mysterious I saw on the Internet that seems suggestive of several things. You are familiar with how Conservapedia exists as a competitor to Wikipedia, yes?

Haynes: Yes, I know about that.

Blair: Well, one day something like a couple of years ago, I looked up the Conservapedia entry for Saul Alinsky. Oddly enough, it provided a quote from the *Playboy* article from very near the end of

Saul Alinsky's life—after *Rules for Radicals* had been published, and only a short amount of time before he died. I don't know if Conservapedia correctly quoted the source article in its having a most peculiar typo or if Conservapedia might have inserted that typo into attempting to quote from the source article. Either way that typo is suggestive of if some author or editor somewhere decided to use a kind of publishing black ops method: an intentional typographic error that therefore is not so much a typographic error as a deliberate typographic anomaly aimed at conveying something between the lines. In that case they were interviewing Alinsky about various of his ways of supporting communism and expressing his opinions and beliefs on many subjects, and at some stage there was a reference to The Great Depression, yet the Conservapedia transcription, as accessed on the Internet about two years ago, indicated that "Depression" in that case had the "r" replaced by an "i." How much do you know about the history of the Russian alphabet?

Haynes: Not much.

Blair: You do know about how the letters look weird, including what looks like a backward "R" and what looks like a backward "N," yes?

Haynes: Yes.

Blair: Well, when there was that October 1917 revolution, and then the Marxists took over Russia, they tried to act out the Karl Marx gameplan stuff. A bunch of ideas about how capitalism having seeds of destruction leading to the have-nots overturning it and replacing it, and that the communist advice to the new leaders would be to make a clean break from history. Therefore, they look for how to force the people to disconnect from the weight of history and set up a new society, believing they can somehow make it into a paradise.

Although my knowledge of this is limited, I found out that there were several variations of their alphabet in use, and they decided to standardize it while also forcing people to make a break from the old versions of their written language. The Russian Alphabet changed per Soviet stipulation effective 1918 for those who had allegiance to Soviet authorities, and part of that was that they banned some of the letters in their alphabet! They made some complicated rules about which new letters would substitute for which old letters, and in which ways. An example is that they used to have a letter that looks just like how when we use The Roman Alphabet to write our Modern English language we have the letter "I," and before the Soviet-stipulated change to The Russian Alphabet, they used to have a letter that looked like our letter "I," both the capital "I" and the lowercase "i." The communists actually had the nerve to tell the people that in new writings they could no longer use that letter! It seems that they were pulling out many stops with which to get new generations of Russians to be unable to very fully connect with the old writings and the old cultural awareness of Russia.

Actually, although I'd seen the page on the inside back cover of a large dictionary that my family acquired in mid-1991 a number of times over the decades, yet I had not bothered to look and consider carefully that page until around early September 2021. Looking at it again, after all I'd experienced, I suddenly understood. It was like a live action version of Charlton Heston in that iconic scene in which his character sees The Statue of Liberty and suddenly he *knows* where he is, and he kneels down and pounds the ground.

A huge part of this was recognizing through relating that dictionary to using online translation stuff… *that one of the main ways of writing Jesus in Russian used to look like what in the Roman alphabet would transliterate into the spelling pattern I-I-C-Y-C, and therefore they would be forcing their people to no longer be able to connect with their previous traditional written word for that.* Although I don't know how much of what happened was like what I'm about to describe to you, clearly either it or something very similar happened in connection with all of this. Ya know, sometimes people in history have burned books. But burning a book takes such an effort, it takes time, it takes setting up a fire, and all of that. *However, if you change what letters are allowed or not, then you don't have to bother to burn old books.* Also, imagine this: You're in Russia in January 1918, and authorities send out communist enforcers to go from door to door and find Christian families' treasured Bibles. They then take out pens, and they go looking for references to Jesus. Over and over again, they then mutilate those Bibles by changing the old version I-I-C-Y-C spelling and changing it into a different name missing one letter compared to how they would spell Jesus: starting with only one Backward-N and followed with the C-Y-C. It would only take a little while with a pen to mutilate every or almost every occurrence of the old-Russian-alphabet name of Jesus by, with just a stroke or two of the pen, in each case taking the old version's double-I and changing it into a new single backward-N, and they could then hand those Bibles back to Christian families in Russia and say to them something like, "You might not be fully on board with the Marxist agenda wiping out how the aristocrats used portions of your Christian heritage to brainwash and hold down the proletariat class—religion being the opiate of the masses—but you should remember what we just did to your allegedly holy book here today. You can have your bible, you can have your opium back, now that we have adjusted to de-poison it. Also, here again is a reminder: be sure with your new writings to abide by the new law in which several old letters are banned, and in which some new letters replace them."

However much or little anyone might believe in Christianity and its values, I have discovered over recent decades that there is at least some significant legitimacy about the conscience, compassion, and love expressed by those legends about Jesus of Nazareth, as handed down to posterity primarily through the Christian Bible. Although I often have varying degrees of belief at various times with respect to elements and proclamations of Christianity, Buddhism, Esotericism, and other sets or alleged sets of beliefs and practices, there is some almost unspeakable tragedy about that scenario I just described, a scenario that may or may not have happened quite like that in Russia in the early 20th century, but which was clearly, at a minimum, very similar to a bunch of the tragic intercultural brutality that happened under the Marxism and totalitarianism of Soviet Russia.

Whoever introduced the typo with an "i" in place of an "r" in "Depression" in quoting Saul Alinsky in transcribing that interview, whether introduced in its original publication by *Playboy* or subsequently in its transcription process by Conservapedia, I wonder if it might have been an intentional typo—someone deciding along the lines of, "*You know what, this Saul Alinsky guy rather clearly does not get it with how much of a brutal violation of life itself happens when totalitarian governments use redistribution as a pretext for taking away nearly all the rights of the citizens.* As a subtle way to give readers who can read enough between the lines a message, we can introduce a typo pointing toward the Soviet outlawing of the letter "i" and how it ties into many Soviet totalitarian atrocities, though to many casual readers it will look like just a little unintentional typo." Not very long after that, Saul Alinsky died.

The liberal sentiment of redistributing wealth by aiming to use extremely vicious and at-times very deceptive means to target the rich and powerful, history shows us, every-so-often leads to a cruel and dehumanizing totalitarian form of government.

Haynes: Dude, I know that's very extreme, but of course that's not what most Democrats are trying to make happen here in America!!

Blair: Yes, but it is a very real threat that history shows repeatedly with how the very-redistribution-oriented people can get so carried away that they trample on people's rights.

You know what, though, this discussion does also bring to mind, if we flip things a bit, the risk on the other side: how having way too much of a laissez-faire capitalism can lead to some rich and powerful people setting up their niches in which underlings can be stuck in what are de facto mini-totalitarian states. Some examples of this could go back to 19th century robber barons and stuff like that.

Before the Theodore Roosevelt reforms to regulating big business, there were many tragic situations in which a powerful business leader would have an empire in which the low level workers were trapped by their employers in situations where it's like, "You're not officially a slave, and officially you have plenty of rights to liberty in this country, but actually, in terms of substance over form, you really, de facto, are an economic slave to your employer. Don't step out of line much at all, you're basically in some kind of totalitarian mini-country. Watch out about how your family acts, also." Although there's still some of that going on today for some folks, getting government involved with clamping down on those kinds of abuses helped reduce the severity of those tragedies happening in this country.

Also, there were some of those gut-wrenching stories from way back when with the robber barons. In a high school history class, an instructor told the people in the class, including me, sometime in the early 1990s, about something reflecting this. He said something like, "Back then, many children were basically born into economic servitude. Once the child might reach the age of six, the child could go to work in a factory, with many dangerous challenges. Some people even had a macabre joke back then: In a factory where a child slipped and fell into a machine to die, what was the main first impression that the foreman had upon the discovery? A small inconvenience to replace a little worker, but, as a silver lining, the blood and guts will help lubricate the gears of the machines!"

Callous, excessively-profit-oriented, excessively power-hungry mindsets among the rich in a very capitalist society could be a huge threat to people.

Haynes: Now you're sounding like a Social Democrat!

Blair: Ah, this could be again like that ancient story about the dangers of the Scylla and the Charybdis, with a huge danger on one side and a huge danger on the other side. And it's very much what we're facing in this country for the future, with the very redistribution-and-regulation-oriented people posing threats in some ways, while the very-anything-goes-taken-to-the-extreme-oriented people posing threats in some ways.

.............

---

.............

[Much later in the first phone call.]

James Blair [hearing the handheld receiver beeping]: The landline wireless phone is beeping; its battery must be almost out. We'll need to end this call soon, so it can go back onto its stand and charge up. I'll plan to call you back in just a little while from my smartphone.

Justin Haynes: Great! Then we'll talk again soon.

Blair: Bye.

Haynes: Bye.

.............

---

.............

[A moderate amount of time later, arriving at 2:27 P.M. U.S. Central Daylight Time]

[Maurice James Blair initiates a call to Justin Monroe Haynes.]

Haynes: Hello there!

Blair: Hi! Good to be talking with you again.

Haynes: Yeah. Good.

.............

---

.............

James Blair: Have you heard about something called The Zelda Complex?

Justin Haynes: I think I kind of remember hearing about something called that.

James Blair: What do you remember about it?

Justin Haynes: Not much. Pretty much just that it was something that had that name.

Blair: Well, then I'll tell you more. Some psychologists a while ago came up with a theory or model in which sometimes people for whatever reason—maybe trauma or thrill-seeking or something else, or some combination—wind up in their romantic relationships with feeling some kind of addiction to sharp conflicts with their partners. It's something like if things become really calm and peaceful for a while, a person with a Zelda complex can't stand for it to keep going like that very long. The person then does something to force the situation into having a new big conflict happen with his or her partner. It's like folks with that feel that in the absence of a rough roller coaster of a relationship with lots of major fights, they get the feeling that maybe the relationship isn't real enough or isn't exciting enough, so they do something to upset things and start a new argument.

Haynes: Wow, that sounds like my relationship with Erica!

Blair: Also, there was some famous couple long ago. The guy was some kind of major celebrity, and his wife was also some kind of major celebrity, and the woman had the name Zelda. So this has little or nothing to do with that video game *The Legend of Zelda*. The name of the complex came from the name of the woman in that celebrity couple.

Haynes: Yes, I think I kind of remember now.
The man in that couple might have been F. Scott Fitzgerald.

..............

---

..............

Justin Haynes: There was a study where some people came to the conclusion that very religious communities tend to become more violent. What do you think about that?

James Blair: Social scientists come up with studies that point all over the place. You get a result that says something. You get a result that says something else. They're all over the place!

That said, there are times when some set of situations could exhibit precisely what a given study's conclusions indicate, though, of course, another set of situations could exhibit precisely what some contradictory study concluded with. Letting go of that way of looking at it, though, and thinking about actual religious communities, they're all over the place, too! All over the place in terms of how peaceful or violent they can be in different ways and on different occasions.

Yet all of this reminds me now of a couple of additional things.

..............

---

..............

Blair: This could also tie in to the truly weird stuff that happened with a guy I only met one time, back in early October 2022. It started over at one of the restaurants on Westheimer. A few people arrived, and I hadn't met any of them before, but they knew each other. One of them, a guy named Dale Siegel received a warning from another person among them, a woman named Juana. She warned him about how his behavior in other bars and restaurants had led him into trouble several times before, and she hoped that he could adjust his behavior to not get into so much trouble again.

Well, I told him a bunch of stuff about some of the challenging interpersonal relations of recent years, and he told me about some of his life's challenging interpersonal relations of times leading up to when he and I happened to meet. We evidently did not really know each other even existed until we happened to be at the same venue at the same time.

Things generally seemed to go smoothly, but there was a very disturbing thing about his approach to Jewish-Muslim relations. That Dale was evidently between jobs as some kind of swimming pool repairman or a similar swimming-pool-themed worker, and he decided to do some entrepreneurship that involved what he believed... yet it reflected an extreme viciousness toward the entirety of Islam. You see, that Dale had a belief system that flexed between Agnosticism and Atheism, kind of like you do, but he was also born a Jew, so the situation somewhat complicated things for him. Yet, of all the things in the world he could choose to do with his life, he decided he should try to advertise the Internet availability for sale of a T-shirt that's very derogatory toward the entirety of Islam, especially toward its founder, Muhammad.

Haynes: Oh?!

Blair: What that Dale Siegel did was to advertise that T-shirt, the image of which he showed several people at the restaurant to have something very shocking. Remember how there've been so many controversies in recent times involving this kind of stuff? Well, what that T-shirt included was: a cartoon-style image of what looked like an Arabic man, a caption that included the four-letter word that, in its capitalized form, can be a nickname for Richard, featuring that as the final word in a sentence accusing The Prophet Muhammad of performing fellatio on other men, and showing a rainbow-style background pattern suggestive of the Gay Pride Flag.

Haynes: Something's wrong with that guy!

Blair: You see, that Dale Siegel also went on to tell several people there, including myself, that he planned to wear one of those shirts into one of the largely-Muslim areas of Houston, for example, maybe that area on Hillcroft just North of 59, where they have a mixture of a major presence of Hindu culture and Muslim culture going on. Next in his plan was for him to walk right into a very-Muslim-oriented store or other place of business, wering that shirt on full display, and to see what reaction he might provoke, and maybe to have a cameraman nearby to livestream the proceedings.

I told him that although the First Amendment protects many kinds of expression, including things that can truly upset many people, I would strongly advise him against carrying out the plan that he was describing.

Later on, he placed my cellphone number onto a list of many numbers with which he could send out advertisements for that T-shirt, as well as whatever other perspectives he was peddling.

Some liberals would have seen in him some of the worst of conservatism, whereas some conservatives would have disavowed him as a conservative—viewing him as being too messed up with some of his hostilities to be fully legitimate as a true conservative, though sharing some critical beliefs to some degree. There was a strange confluence of Xenophobia, general hostility, and Islamophobia going on with him, yet, repeatedly, I would bite my tongue so to speak—I would be tempted to respond to the group text messages he was broadcasting, yet choosing to resist that impulse over and over again.

Finally, one day, he sent out a message that on the surface emphasized the perspective of Islam being a belief system and not a race, layering that with several levels of harshness toward the entirety of Islam. However, putting the entirety of what he expressed with that text message with the flagrant intercultural viciousness of his other text messages, which repeatedly included the image of the aforementioned Anti-Islamic shirt, I suddenly decided that I'd better act like William Shatner's character from "Nightmare at 20,000 Feet."

Justin Haynes: Oh, damn!

James Blair: I thought back to the extreme conflict between me and The Financial Advisory Group, Inc. Although several people there had consistently treated me with reasonable respect when I worked there, when things later hit the fan, that organization repeatedly, at the holistic level, under its leadership, when having less escalatory options and more escalatory options, went with a more escalatory option. If I would stand by and let that Dale use a flagrant disregard for some aspects of the realities of Islam and its founder, as part of his excessive effort to heap condemnation, then it could be like if someone in the chain of authority at The Financial Advisory Group would have had a chance to stop their disastrous course of behavior toward me by intervening, but instead stood idly by and let groupthink keep going. Therefore, I decided, *You know what, I'm not going sit back silently anymore, I'm going to carefully word something to stand up for whatever amount is real and genuinely deserving at least a little bit of a rendering of respect onto The Prophet Muhammad and Islam, even with the fact that my primary religious practices tend to involve Vajrayana Buddhism most of the time.*

Therefore, on that occasion, I sent a carefully-worded response, pointing out that although Dale Siegel had a First Amendment right to express himself, a huge part of the reality is that there are favorable and unfavorable trends happening in each of the major religions. Soon, he expressed extreme resentment toward me for daring to speak up with a text message countering the narrative that he had been espousing. That narrative he'd been presenting involved a total or near-total condemnation of the entirety of Islam—especially its founder—and what seemed between-the-lines to be his attempt to sway the general public in the direction of seeking for Islam to go totally extinct—the sooner the better. That guy was way over the top in my opinion, and he seemed to resent the hell out of the reality that anyone would dare to stand up to him by criticizing his behavior. After a few rounds of back-and-forth argument, he sent me a text stating that he had blocked my cellphone number.

Although I believe that it could make sense sometimes for a religion to in some ways go extinct, there can be more correct ways and less correct ways for people who advocate for any given religion to go extinct to use stuff like the First Amendment to fight for whichever side they happen to be on. That guy's approaches were so filled with vile and crude hostility and so filled with avoiding the concession of even a small amount of acknowledgement of some degrees of truth and value in Islam itself and any of the communities of Muslims, that I simply don't mind how when I on occasion share this information with you and other people it just might eventually lead to some Muslim organization issuing some extremely strong statement or guidance against him... or if some people with a very different orientation were to go after me with some similar extremely strong statement or guidance. As you know, my commitment to truth and reality, to whatever degree it might express itself through Vajrayana Buddhism, Esoteric Christianity, or any other religious activities, is such that I feel ready to die at any given time, if I die with honor.

Haynes: Yeah, that guy was a bit too extreme with his viciousness toward Islam.

Blair: *A bunch of this stuff we've been discussing since you brought up a research study that had results the scientists interpreted as support for the conclusion that religious communities have a proclivity to become violent could be seen as corroborating that, yet it could also be seen as simply one of the tips of many icebergs that involve how people can use religion in all kinds of different ways.*

*Sometimes it can lead to people becoming much more peaceful, much more violent, some mixture of both of those, and other things, and, as you know, I often believe that there are situations that call for the unleashing of wrath, though that can be overdone, much like the aims toward generating peace can be overdone.*

.............

..............

..............

Blair: I even feel fine at this instant of time about if the universe goes into that cosmic big rip that some astrophysicists theorize could happen at any given instant, and maybe it would only take a fraction of a second or maybe it would take a small amount of time a bit longer than that: That idea that our entire universe could die in some disintegrating ripping apart almost instantly.

Haynes: Oh?!

Blair: It goes further still, I feel fine in this instant about if all universes have that happen to them, even the multiverse, or, if there are multiple multiverses, then all multiverses and all beings and all things, unto a total annihilation; yet there would still be that subtle level of consciousness where in some ways we would all still be there. Maybe then there would be another big bang.

# CHAPTER EIGHT: REVEALING SOME OF WHAT WAS HIDDEN BENEATH

Although both Olivia Newton-John (1948-2022) and Maurice A.T. Blair (1931-2015) made strong contributions to the well-being of citizens of the United States of America and citizens of other nations, and although they probably never came within a mile of each other in terms of observable spatiotemporal locations measurable by physicists and historians before leaving this world, a brief comparison and contrast of a few salient facts about their lives could prove insightful.

One similarity is that each had a father who served in the military of a nation having English as its primary language. Brin Newton-John (1914-1992) served in the British military during World War II, whereas David A. Blair (1899-1969) served in the United States military during The Great War, also known as World War I.

Several differences: 1) Olivia Newton-John was a cisgender female, whereas Maurice A.T. Blair was a cisgender male. 2a) Olivia had three different nationalities of citizenship, changing it in her lifetime, whereas Maurice A.T. Blair was an American citizen during his entire lifetime. 2b) To whatever degree related or unrelated to citizenship, service, etc., consider this: Maurice A.T. Blair, on multiple occasions, spoke out loud that he believed that the United States of America should put the female American celebrities Jane Fonda and Joan Baez on trial for having visited North Vietnam during the Vietnam War, find them guilty of treason, then execute them. There are no known public records of Olivia Newton-John having ever expressed that sentiment. Having stated that, though, bear in mind that many military people have felt sharply critical toward how Jane Fonda and Joan Baez visited North Vietnam when and how they did. 3) Medical professionals never diagnosed Maurice A.T. Blair to have contracted cancer, whereas medical professionals diagnosed (in 1992, 2013, and 2017) Olivia Newton-John to have contracted cancer. 4) O.N.J. died at age 73, where-as M.A.T.B. died at age 84. 5) The full details of O.N.J.'s life and death provide little or no fodder for antivaxxers such as Robert F. Kennedy, Jr. to sway the public in favor of policies severely limiting the use of vaccinations, whereas the full details of M.A.T.B.'s life and death might provide much fodder for the antivaxxers.

A while before his debilitation from an overnight stroke near the middle of January 2015, rather late into the year 2014 Maurice A.T. Blair took the first shot of the Hepatitis A&B set of multiple vaccine shots, then reported to me that his "head had not been working right since taking that vaccine." Although Dr. Stuart Shapiro advised Maurice A.T. Blair about various aspects of that vaccination process, and the latter accepted the astronomically-remote risks associated with it, something had seemed intuitively to M.A.T.B. to be amiss after the first injection.

Time went by, and he was approaching a stage in which he would have to either take the next shot or let go of the entire course of treatment. He and I discussed the matter a few times, and I became confident that he would be letting go of the treatment. However, he went ahead and decided to proceed with that second injection anyway, and it was the next morning that my mother and I found him unresponsive. Soon, emergency personnel who arrived on a firetruck were unable to get him to wake up, and they transported him to receive medical treatment. A few months later, he died. (Consider studying pages 94-99 of *Science, Religion, Politics, and Cards* for a more general overview of some additional relevant details.) There is much truth in the old caveat, "Correlation does not always mean causation." Although some of the people in the antivaxxer crowd could very much read into this a likelihood of the vaccination having been a primary cause of the major, debilitating stroke, it may seem possible that his advanced age and vulnerable condition made it such that the mere puncturing of his arm with an injection of any kind would have threatened his physical system with calamity.

Also, there are many other factors that could have contributed to how he became debilitated.

Nevertheless, I treasure that he and I were on good terms the last time we shared a conversation prior to his encounter with the cataclysmic brain event that debilitated him.

On another note, on March 26, 2010 I attended Olivia Newton-John's keynote speech presentation in Westchester, PA. Here is a transcript of the notes that I wrote while in attendance of both the introductory presentations and the keynote speech from that night (as an out-of-state visitor observing the proceedings, though remaining silent except for minimal small talk with attendees who were nearby during a few moments before and after presentations):

March 26th, 2010

Integrative Health

Introduction – woman describing outline of events & related info.

➔ introduced dean of undergrad health sciences & chair of... (Roger) → president

Dean & ... spoke → thanking sponsors of the conference, then ... descr., then video WCU & programs

ACEER (pronounced Ā Sear by → then Roger (chair/president ...))→ descr. of ACEER & activities & how the impact helps→illustrated w/

[MARCH 26, 2010 EVENT NOTES TR. CONT'D]

story →student in garden idea... if can get people to see the world

back to Dean ... students have participated in Peru

Roger → about 3 yr's ago Olivia got connected w/ it as 2 board→members mentioned Roger should talk w/ John Easterling. When Roger contacted Mr. Easterling he insisted that ONJ be in the meeting (A.J.E. & ONJ already bf-gf @ that time). ...

another video ... Sec. James←{last name} [PA Secretary] →St. Dept. of Health & WCU & health...

– – – – –

Dr. Janice (spelling?) – 1st time at WCU. →works on prevention programs & treatment...

Dean's name Martin ←

only ~4% ("4 cents out of every healthcare dollar") of health care costs spent on prevention as of this time. much of things w/ problems come from diet & activity problem of how many people become obese. child, adolescent, & adult obesity major problem & affects every organ of the body.

tobacco another major problem.

...cancer another major concern.

[MARCH 26, 2010 EVENT NOTES TR. CONT'D]

Programs to help schools have students get more physical activity...

Dr. Janice (cont'd) ... STEPS Program...

Dean (? if I remember matching faces & ID's)

→ introducing Olivia Newton-John ...

Notes highlighting portions of the keynote address / from the Olivia Newton-John Speech:

Similar feel at WCU as w/ how her father was at University in Australia.

...had two negative test results on whether cancer in lump she noticed & she...

[It was] a July 4th weekend when [she] found out.

... and [in] San Juan [having] no whales visible [was] unusual, then [she] got [the] call that her father had passed away, and then [she received] the [doctor's] call to see [the doctor].

... reaction stages → following Monday [she] got the official diagnosis... [reactions were] first laughter, then denial, then fear →... listen to your body's messages ...

[She] had surgery, and the Dr. mentioned she also needed Chemo. [ONJ] was very scared of chemo. rec'd advice to have a positive tone.

[MARCH 26, 2010 EVENT NOTES TR. CONT'D]

worked on full range of tools to deal w/ ... incl. herbs courtesy of Mr. Easterling ...

... met a stranger in a ladies' room & she told ONJ she'd seen ONJ's info in paper & wanted to tell ONJ that... & 20 yr's later [she the stranger was still] OK.

... Now ONJ 18 years since cancer & [at that time was still OK].

... mentioned Austin Health ... Australia ...

... then encouraged us to ...

Q&A [part of the question & answer session]

- If someone's facing cancer, [then it] could help sometimes [for them] to have another person [or multiple other people] do [some of the] talking for them with other(s).
- [She] does a mixture of many traditional and alternative approaches, including being happy and doing things for others.
- [To address an audience question about the environment and the rainforests] "Amazon" John Easterling helped with answering part of it.
- A woman asked a question about a mother with a situation of being six years past recovering from carcinoma [? if I heard correctly ?].

[MARCH 26, 2010 EVENT NOTES TR. CONT'D]

[Select noted highlights from the Q&A session, cont'd]

- q. about how sometimes men get breast cancer...
- ... more q's ...
- q. about pushing [doctors] for more testing... →ONJ said that we each have intuition & can sometimes tune in to it especially well w/o much distraction... She had much distraction but still felt intuition and followed up [on the indicated health concerns and next steps]. [She] feels lucky that it led to thriving.
- ...
- An oncologist mentioned that only 17% of breast cancer is detected by mammography.
- addit'l comments
- comments from audience members

---

end of program's first night ~9:02 PM

---

*****

As a footnote to this, although some people in portions of February 2021 onward have had the impression of me being a talkaholic, I have on many occasions up to January 2021 and on some occasions April 2021 onward demonstrated a strong ability to remain very silent and a strong ability to be extremely judicious with speaking.

An example that can demonstrate appropriate limitations to speaking much at all was that at the March 26, 2010 event just described, I chose to decline to attempt to ask Olivia Newton-John any questions. When the question-and-answer session started, I decided on a plan to only ask a question during it if the entirety of reality—as I could best perceive it—would include such a question as a reasonably perfect fit for the situation. I considered some candidate questions, then decided repeatedly to refrain from asking any of them. *This was a similar approach to how I have dealt with the four times (ranging from 2010 to 2018) in which I participated in jury duty. Each time my mindset was to neither desire to be selected as one of the jury members nor to be eliminated from the jury pool, and to focus on the right combination of communications to get the entire situation to transform for the better, to the best of my abilities.*

On the first jury duty session, I brought a copy of *The Dhammapada*, barely spoke to anyone, studied that book frequently when left to my own device, and waited around for each step to proceed.

Eventually, the judge called the potential jurors in and made a startling announcement: The accused, upon advice from their attorneys, had pled out with the prosecutors, and now we would not even have to bother with voir dire. The judge, in a glowingly-happy mood, proceeded to discuss general pieces of information that she believed helpful to us.

On the second jury duty session, I brought printouts of select chess information, with which to study ways to get better with chess and with life in general. I conducted myself in a manner similar to how I behaved in the first jury duty session, but with an emphasis on chess studies in place of *Dhammapada* studies. This time it involved a woman who had received a speeding ticket and decided to fight it out by representing herself in court. Voir dire happened this time around, and, as I answered honestly and with a complete neutrality toward the odds of getting selected or not getting selected, both sides agreed on including me as a juror. Before deliberations started, it seemed quite clear to me beyond a reasonable doubt that the woman accused of speeding had indeed sped in such a way as to have deserved to be ticketed. When the group of us gathered as jurors for our deliberation, we unanimously agreed with each other, believing beyond a reasonable doubt that the speeding violation had occurred.*

Next, we made very brief small talk. After that, we discussed the merits of our various options of how much the fine would be. Eventually, we decided for the government to fine her a little less than what she would have owed on the original traffic ticket, taking pity on her and her situation.

After the announcement of the result, we the jury walked our way out of the courtroom, and we passed by the lady who had represented herself to try to fight a minor traffic ticket. Believe it or not, she actually thanked us, exhibiting a spirit of genuine gratitude, as we walked by her.

* There were two witnesses: the defendant, whose observable signs and presence seemed to indicate to have definitely been a cisgender female and probably of the range from White Nonhispanic to White Hispanic to Some-Type-of-Either-Nonwhite-or-Very-Mixed-Between-White-and-Nonwhite ancestry, and who was light-skinned), and some of it from the police officer (who by observation and ambience seemed definitely a cisgender male and almost definitely Nonhispanic Black, who, according to my memory, was a medium-dark-skinned patrolman), weighed into this, including the nature of the radar gun's specifications, the calm and consistent tone from the officer, the repeatedly uneasy expressions of the defendant. *Perhaps most relevant was how the defendant never provided an adequate reconciliation of how she claimed in different moments of her testimony both: 1) that she had looked at her speedometer consistently enough to know for sure that she did not exceed the*

*speed limit at the time claimed by the officer and 2) that if she had sped over the speed limit at that time, then it was not faster than the general flow of traffic.*

We as the jury, I believe, properly disregarded race and gender in performing our evaluation, and we, I believe, successfully sidestepped any material amount of bias from cognizance of the adage that, "People who represent themselves in a court of law have fools for their clients."

Oddly enough, that adage may butt heads with the adage, "If you want a job done well, then do it yourself." Folks might wonder to what degree, if any, some collision of those two contrasting notions might have traversed either the subconscious or the conscious mind of Ted Bundy (1946-1989) sometime prior to his conviction for serial murder.

At this stage, most people would probably wish to bear in mind that driving an automobile over the speed limit—as long as it does not involve driving while intoxicated or engaging in other excessive hazards while operating a motor vehicle—in such a manner as to receive a speeding ticket is worlds apart from committing a series of murders. As a counterpoint, some might invoke a slippery slope argument that speeding seven miles per hour over the speed limit in such a way as to be ticketed could be a gateway to smoking marijuana, which could in turn be a gateway to harder drugs, which could then prove a gateway to committing murder, etc.

* * *

On the third jury duty session, things were quite different. *The judge called the potential jurors in, and that judge was in a vicious mood. He proceeded to inform us that there would be no voir dire in this case because the defense attorney had acted in what he deemed an unconscionable manner.* It involved a criminal case in which the defendant was accused of having molested an elementary-school-or-similarly-aged girl, and the trial had been delayed for a long time. Suddenly, with the day arriving to finally begin the trial, the criminal defense attorney had become missing, not having called in with any explanation. The judge and other people were wondering what was going on with the female attorney who was defending the accused. Eventually, they received an answer: That woman reported to the male judge that she, the defense attorney, had experienced a family emergency, and she claimed that the situation was of such difficulty that she was unable to even call in to give the court an update about her whereabouts and situation. While the potential jurors were waiting around to find out what would happen next, the judge had decided that the entire set of known facts and alleged facts about the situation was such that he should hold the defense attorney in contempt of court and to have her thrown into jail. As he informed this to us, his tone of voice and his body language showed that the entire situation had upset him thoroughly and that he was still feeling livid toward the defense attorney. His main concern was about the little girl who had already had to wait for a very long time to have her day in court. Also, he opened the floor to a question-and-answer session. During the Q&A session, there were a couple of times when I believed that the judge had provided way too much information to us the people on jury duty, yet it was understandable that he evidently just plain had to vent to somebody—or in that case many somebodies. That being said, the sheer viciousness with which he reportedly treated the female defense attorney and the sheer viciousness with which he delivered his entire address to the jury duty people, myself included, might have steered me in the direction toward being much more cruel toward Steve Estrin, Natasha McDaniel, Juan Martinez, John T. Jones, and Mary Chiang in some of the times subsequent to that experience than I might otherwise have been.

Sure, some readers at this stage might want to inquire with me by stating to me, *You fucking, goddamned moron! That judge was a pillar of the community, a person of genuine authority and worth, a real somebody. You low-life asshole, you dirty low-life, all you've ever accomplished in life hardly amounts to shit compared to that judge. He had every right to rage in fury at that defense attorney and punish her severely. You've never done a goddamned thing in your life to earn the right to rage in fury at much of anyone, being the wretched, pathetic creep and loser that you are. Whenever people use the phrase, "Where were the adults in the room?" they should never, I repeat, never, have it apply to any notion of you being among the adults. Even though it is plausible that you have had sex before, you're still too much of an idiot to amount to the kind of person who deserves to say much of anything to anyone unless it is some technical stuff in some nerdy area of life. You are certainly nothing at all like being a real man, in fact you hardly qualify as a human. For people to work closely with you in a full work day, the fact they have to tolerate the presence of your face is something that you should be obligated to give them much credit for, as your face often includes glasses and baldness, and your pattern does not easily fitting into any of the standard racial ideals of any of the reasonably pure-bred Black, White, Hispanic, Asian, or Native American male facial patterns, you mutt! In contrast, that judge served as an upstanding member; he paid his dues in society. No matter his physical appearance, within reason, even if he had looked like you, he was respectable, which, sadly, we cannot say for you.*

Sure, I could immediately respond to that line of thinking against me, but waiting for that thinker to go further might prove extra helpful. After such a person would go to such lengths to pour out such hostility, whether spoken aloud or held within, based on what little that person would genuinely understand about me, my life, and the lives of those adjacent to me, proceeding further in this exploration could prove insightful. For anyone standing up on my behalf, whether the defender would be myself or another person eligible in a given context to defend me, to remain silent a little longer, could, in some such cases, prove extra, extra instructive. (From a metaphorical dimension, even though the person(s) would already have enough rope to hang herself/himself/itself/themselves with, letting the person(s) gather even more rope could enhance the illustrative example which we can make out of the person(s)—who could be of any race, creed, color, religion, gender, age, rank, combined demography, or whatever else—plenty of rope to allow the classic old west breaking of the neck by a sufficient drop from a gallows pole as a way of quickly hanging from a rope until dead.

Such a contemner might continue by saying or thinking toward me, *You're such a pathetic, nerdy, mama's boy, psycho, loser, weirdo type of guy, you don't deserve shit in terms of a right to complain about much of anyone. In fact, if someone defames your character, you probably deserve it, and you probably don't even deserve for any organization anywhere to stand up to defend the truth about your character in that kind of case, because your character is already very shitty to begin with and neither you nor anyone else loses much by having people propagate false claims against you. Just look at your social status on paper in terms of a commonsense approach to your resume:*

*You earned a bachelor's degree in economics, a subject nowhere near as respectable as physics, chemistry, mechanical engineering, civil engineering, political science, or pre-med. After that you stumbled along with work very below most recent college graduates. Next, you obtained a master's degree in accounting, which is nowhere near the respectability of earning an Master in Business Administration, also known as an MBA. Then you wallowed around much lower than most of your accounting degree peers.*

*I have no reason to regard any criticism you have toward much of anyone as having any more than a trace of meaningfulness or relevancy to my life and to my future. You are an obsolete man.*

To those who choose that line of criticisms toward me: Have you read *Science, Religion, Politics, and Cards* (2023), seen the episode "The Obsolete Man" (*The Twilight Zone*, 1961), listened closely to and empathized with the Olivia Newton-John music album *Grace and Gratitude* (2006), read Clarke & Baxter's *Time Odyssey* series—which consists of *Time's Eye* (2003), *Sunstorm* (2005), and *Firstborn* (2007)—of novels, and watched all five episodes of the television mini-series *Chernobyl* (2019)? If you have not, then how about if you go through those before you might get back to me about whether you still feel like raging at me in such a manner?

If you state that you do not believe that there is any need for you to explore any portions, if any, of what to you is the unexplored portion of that stuff, and that you still feel like raging at me with hostility in such a manner, then consider that even with how your heart has evidently turned to stone in relation to the reality of me as a being, maybe, for as long as you are in some sense still alive, you might have a chance to let your heart thaw out from that state.

For your heart to thaw out from that and therefore for your entire being to feel more of reality itself could be helpful both to you and to many of those whom you affect.

Helpful, that is, in the manner of how you can navigate away from causing for yourself and for others a future catastrophe or a set of many future catastrophes.

This entire dialogue reflects a few tips along the edges of several glaciers. If you are among those continuing to harbor such hostility toward me, bear in mind that much of it is tantamount to a choice to thoroughly disrespect many parts of the realities of your own life and the lives of many people other than you and me.

People who persist with hatred toward anyone or anything are almost undoubtedly eventually going to wreak harmful havoc on both their own lives and the lives of others, whether or not they have crossed any given point of no return in any processes.

With that said, as a reminder, there *are* times, seasons, and purposes for inflicting onto others harsh rebuke, even to the point of executing other sentient beings. This type of perspective pervades much of the ancient wisdom literature across many regions of the world.

Having reversed this, how about now considering expanding approaches toward condemning people rather than contracting them? If nothing else, this could be in order to claw and climb the way out of the labyrinth of these regions of thought. This could be a thought exercise to deal with, and—who knows?—maybe it might later help avoid what would otherwise become a future tragedy or two or twenty. Think, yes, think about this for a while.

* * *

Whether you feel that I have any right to even begin to dare to suggest that an often-subconscious and sometimes conscious impulse to mimick that judge's extreme wrath* might have been a contributing factor to the extremity of the wrath I have shown to many of those who transgressed against me in portions of 2018-2023, consider imagining yourself in my shoes. That is, while letting go of worrying about how excruciatingly difficult that might prove to be for you.

* Reminder: That was toward a female defense attorney who was in absentia while he sharply rebuked her to what otherwise would have been the juror pool, and he described her transgression with much gravitas and indignation.

*Experiencing that very-hellfire-and-brimstone-style speech from that judge on February 8, 2013 was something else. It truly impressed me then, and the memories of it truly impress me now.* Although I met that judge from a distance in that courtroom and have probably never met the female defense attorney toward whom he showed such extreme condemnation, he probably had nowhere near even a trace of an inkling of how: 1) my father, 2) some Psi Upsilon fraternity brothers, 3) author Chinweizu Ibekwe (often known by the mononym Chinweizu), 4) my 4/19/2001 interview with Amin Nosrat near the conclusion of my Andersen internship, 5) my interactions with Amy Garland during my internship at KPMG LLP, and, 6) last, but not least, the influence of many religious leaders would at times combine in my heart and mind. His way of wrathfulness toward an unnamed female attorney was in several ways a capstone experience to that pattern. As time went by, it proved one of the key influences to place me into more readily thinking like my father that if anyone would present an excessive threat to the United States of America's provision of liberty to its citizens, then, no matter how much the person might have previously pleased people, even dozens of millions of people, such an offending member of society could perhaps best receive the death penalty for committing treason against the United States of America.

Back to focusing on the 263rd District Court Judge who spoke to the jury duty people on that

February day long ago. Yes, he pushed the needle of my mindset very much toward considering everyone to be on thin ice when injustice, inequity, etc. would manifest. Like my father M.A.T. Blair's many militaristic statements, President Ronald Wilson Reagan's unequivocally anti-communist pronouncements, and GM Lu Sheng-yen's ways of stating the need to be ready to fight for the future of the enlightenment of sentient beings, this led to how I would subsequently feel even more ready than before to embrace righteous indignation. This would include a willingness to unleash deserved harshness in service of justice, equity, fairness, effectiveness, soteriology, etc.

In the wake of his sermon to the congregation gathered before him in that courthouse to witness the incineration of the reputation of a female whom he never named for us—a female defense attorney of unknown age and unknown physical appearance relative to our mindstreams as jury duty members, yet some psychological likeness of whose being he burned in effigy then and there, as a sweet savor unto THE LORD, yea verily—there and then it was that I, having been among the congregation of jury duty folks to whom he preached, shifted much of my orientation. The pendulum of my subconscious valuations, which had swayed back and forth many previous times, again swayed. That time, I believe, set me up in the long run to much more thoroughly embrace how some of my Psi Upsilon Fraternity brothers, some characters on TV shows, several authors, and many religious leaders had pointed the way toward choosing a Sam Spade way of being ready to turn over to the authorities any and every wretchedly immoral woman, man, boy, or girl, any time that a situation would seem to call for it to be the correct action.

This is not to say going all the way to calling for the U.S. to put Jane Fonda and Joan Baez on trial, to convict them, and to execute them. I am choosing to be on the fence about whether that would be the optimal path forward as a repercussion for their acts of visiting North Vietnam during the Vietnam War or if that would be the suboptimal path forward as such a repercussion. I respect how my father exercised his First Amendment right to voice his opinion in favor of the execution of those two popular female celebrities, and I also respect that my friend Justin Haynes has expressed to me on multiple occasions that he believes that such advocacy for the execution of those two popular female celebrities on those grounds may often come from a failure by people to consider the big picture of the context. Justin has expressed that he is clearly on the side against people seeking to arrange to have the U.S. place those two women on trial and subsequently executing them. Again, to be perfectly clear, I am choosing to decline to take sides on that issue at this time, much as I have for many years chosen to decline to take sides on that issue.

On a related note, I admit to having greatly enjoyed watching *Barbarella* starring Jane Fonda and listening to the popular studio recordings of Joan Baez performing "Green, Green Grass of Home" and the songs on *Diamonds and Rust*.

There was at least one occasion approximately 2009 that I was playing a recording of Baez's performance of "Green, Green Grass of Home" and a conversation closely resembling the following transcript ensued:

Ted: I'm enjoying that song. Who's singing that?

Jim: Joan Baez.

Ted: Oh, terrible. She, like Jane Fonda should be court-martialed, found guilty, and executed for her role in Vietnam. Too bad I had to ask you who was singing. I was really enjoying the song until I found out it who was singing it.

Jim: You can feel that way, but just because someone does one thing terrible and another thing well, we don't have to get caught up on only one side or the other of what they've done.

* * *

Many had previously steered me toward being prepared to justifiably destroy the wicked, including wicked women, through psychological warfare, yet that judge pushed me much further into being *very, very ready* to deem subsequent situations to require a duty to destroy wicked women through psychological warfare. That complemented how such preparedness stemmed from some True Buddha School members, some Psi Upsilon brothers*, and others in the direction of deeming situations to require a duty to destroy wicked men, wicked women, and wicked organizations through psychological warfare.

* The reference to Psi Upsilon here is most primarily involving two specific fraternity brothers: 1) Famed director Michael Bay, whom I have never met, yet who planted into *Transformers: Revenge of the Fallen* (2009) a scene that is extremely suggestive of a metaphor, via a Decepticon who disguised herself as a female human in the context of Autobot-vs.-Decepticon warfare, good-vs.-evil, etc., of the need to be very ready to unsentimentally punish, and—if need be—to destroy women when the situation calls for it. 2) Whichever of the Chi Delta Chapter brothers was the fellow who on April 7, 1995 pulled me aside from the rest of the proceedings and spoke with condemnation toward the behavior of the woman whom I dated on that night, even though I had felt then that her overall set of behavior that night, taken holistically, had reasonable integrity. Portions of Chapter Ten of this work go into that April 1995 incident and its aftermath much further in depth, but suffice it to say here that in the long run I have reached a belief that the

woman who dated me that night was able to in many ways snatch victory from the jaws of defeat both for herself in the long run and for me in the long run in this great mystery that we call life, as, even though some of her decisions from that evening were clearly suboptimal from many PsiU-oriented perspectives, her long-run set of choices in her interactions with me have vindicated both her life as I perceive it and, to a major degree, the life of the very human race itself as I perceive it.

Both the items discussed just now were among those many things that I had earlier alluded to as forerunners to how the influence of the February 2013 jury duty experience, including allusion by the statement, "The pendulum of my subconscious valuations, which had swayed back and forth many previous times, again swayed."

Focus again on the many elements of what had transpired on February 8, 2013 in that courtroom. Consider meditating on them for a while. Imagine witnessing it live, in person.

After that, I could much more easily feel like, "No matter what religion anyone might happen to practice or not practice, no matter exactly what the greatest mysteries might later turn out to be, we could bring back some of that old-time religion in which men, women, and children, yea verily, people of any demographic or no demographic or any combination of demographics, yes, yea verily, anyone and everyone is fit to be stoned to death when they get on the wrong side of justice!!"

Therefore, maybe some measure of the blame for many of the cruelties in America after that time might be attributable to that judge having taken his fury an extremity further than what was called for in that courthouse that day. Since I was there, yet few, if any, of the other people who were there that day are very likely to actually study this book between now and the centennial anniversary of the end of WW2, it might be of that category of "you had to be there to fully understand and appreciate it." Nevertheless, the accounts and descriptions in this chapter pay a degree of homage to the awe and mystery and ferocity of the rebuke which that judge showed toward that attorney. Yes, although some who believe and might allege that I have performed overkill repeatedly in the 2018-2023 period, those who believe and allege that way might wish to also consider the extreme hellfire-and-brimstone fury with which that judge expressed himself back then, and, therefore, some might wish to cast at least a trace of a blame for alleged overkill* on him, however high and mighty he might have ever been and however high and mighty he might currently be, if he is still alive.

* That would include whichever portions of it they might allege to have been committed by me against those whom I considered to have behaved in wicked and evil ways toward truth, reality, Buddhism, the First Amendment, me, my family, and liberty. It would also include whichever portions of it they might allege to have been committed by anyone

else anywhere in the subsequent time, based on things such as butterfly effects.

* * *

Consider the possibility that someone would cast some significant amount of blame on him, for at least a little while.

To those of you who might be totally locked into and dialed into a view of that judge as beyond reproach and completely to be looked up to in relationship with all of this: Consider exploring this like some movie requiring a bit of suspension of disbelief. Imagine some people casting some blame toward that judge. Perhaps you choose to be one of them or perhaps you choose to refrain from being one of them. Either way, you may observe others to be doing so.

I could easily think of it and feel toward it either way. In this case, I believe there to be great value in the flexibility to understand it from both points of view, and to recognize there to be at least a little bit of truth in both views on this.

Whatever the case might be for how you personally think and feel about this set of issues, imagine again some people blaming that judge for how he may have influenced the entire trajectory of history from that moment onward.

* * *

Let us transition this to a more expansive view, step by step. If we start to take a person who otherwise might be considered by many to be beyond reproach, then we take it to another such allegedly-beyond-reproach person, then to yet another, and keep going with spreading the blame even further to some of those whom many would otherwise think of as ineligible for blame, and keep on going and going, then we might arrive upon fresh vistas.

If we keep going with a blame-go-round like this, we could go chasing after not only each and every living person of at least two years of age, but at some stage expand to also perhaps all or nearly all of the dead, and then maybe we could expand to blaming some of the infants who are under two years old, and then, yes, eventually we could get into that danger zone where some would get ready to scream out at us, "Blasphemy!"

To what danger zone is this in reference, you might ask?

*Some consider it to be blasphemy if anyone ever chooses to blame God.*

*However, I remember quite vividly how one fateful day while wandering around Facebook sometime around the 2020-2022 period, I chanced upon a post in which a woman who presented herself as having some extreme special needs types of health difficulties stated publicly that she blamed God for having arranged her life to include such extreme difficulties. As I remember it, I noticed that no one else would dare touch that post with a response observable on that platform. I, too, chose to refrain from touching that post, refraining from responding in any observable way on that platform.*

*That was something to behold: At that time, with the exception of the woman who initiated that complaint against God, yes, it seemed that everyone else in the world left it something to look at but not touch.*

* * *

That was shades of a scene portrayed in Friedrich Nietzsche's *Thus Spoke Zarathustra*: a scene in which Zarathustra informs the reader that, within the storyline of that novel, part of the arc of history featured God having taken pity on the humans, incarnated into human form, died as a human, become resurrected, transfigured, helped people tremendously, and then, with how "society" came to be "the new idol," at some stage died. That novel's version of Zarathustra stated that God became unable to handle the weight of caring about the tragedies encountered by people in general, and, most especially, someone described as "the ugliest man," and, consequently, an awareness of the tragic plight had resulted in the death of God, who proved unable to help nearly as much as wishing to be able to help.

Many have debated countless alternatives of how much to take that stuff literally or metaphorically.

Here is a supplemental set of literary criticism regarding that novel: It would seem a multi-edged dagger, valuable for some to use to remove barriers to insights, yet tragic when mishandled by anyone hell-bent on excessively raging against any of the perceived sources of oppression.

As legend has it, Jesus of Nazareth and many other beings have expressed, in one way or another, "Live by the sword, die by the sword." Some might wonder whether there might have been something Nietzsche might have chosen to do differently between the time *Thus Spoke Zarathustra* reached publication and when he, Friedrich Nietzsche (1844-1900), wound up entering a state of madness and, later, death—something different enough that he could have perhaps sidestepped much of that insanity—perhaps even all of it—and maybe also somehow helped steer Germany away from many of what in our reality became its tragedies of the 1912-1945 period.

A better-late-than-never moment in his life may have occurred when he stated shortly before dying, "Also, last year I was crucified by the German doctors in a very drawn-out manner. Wilhelm, Bismarck, and all anti-Semites abolished." (Cf. https://www.conservapedia.com/Friedrich_Nietzsche as accessed April 22, 2024).*

* * *

Although some might denigrate this line of thinking as a wasteful and idle curiosity, it could in some cases be something in which our contemplation could lead to our making better decisions, much like how in the 1994 motion picture film *The Shawshank Redemption* the character Red thought about the parallels between himself and the character Brooks, then let go and broke away, free from what might otherwise have become an extra, new tragedy for himself.

* In response to how some liberals might have found it totally third-rail and reprehensible for me to have dared to cross reference an entry from Conservapedia in connection with anything and also in response to how a mixture of conservatives, moderates, and liberals might have found it totally third-rail and reprehensible for me to analyze Nietzsche's *Thus Spoke Zarathustra* in a spirit of strong benevolence, I shall simply state, "Tough! Get over it, buttercup!"

*****

The fourth time I performed jury duty, the case was a civil dispute between an insurance company and another company. When voir dire happened, I again chose to focus on what might best help with the enlightenment of sentient beings, the salvation of beings, the statics and dynamics of conscience, truth, etc. Eventually, the decision emerged that I would not be selected for that jury.

*****

With that footnote completed, let us return our main attention to events that happened in portions of Westchester, PA.

Remember that there was a keynote speech by Olivia Newton-John, in which she addressed issues including health, intuition, prevention, treatment, and public policies.

The following night I attended the Olivia Newton-John concert in which Amy Sky and a variety of other musicians teamed up with her. If I had to vote for a list of what the three best concerts I have ever attended (up to the time of this book going to print) were, then that Olivia Newton-John March 27, 2010 concert would be at the top of that list.

Second place would be the Bob Dylan and Paul Simon concert that I attended on September 17, 1999.

Third place would be the October 26, 2001 University of Texas at Austin Music School production of Mozart's *The Magic Flute.*

*****

At about 10:13 AM CDT, March 25, 2024, a few minutes after hearing Michael Berry state something that seemed almost definitely what many might consider a minor factual inaccuracy, I called his show, not with an intention of influencing my way into that morning edition of his radio show, but to point that out.

The system placed me on hold for a few minutes, then, while still on commercial break, there was a telephone conversation for which the following is an approximate transcript:

Robles: *Michael Berry Show.*

Blair: I don't necessarily need to get on the air today, but a few minutes ago, he said something that I'm almost completely certain was a slight inaccuracy, and I'd like to point it out to you.

Michael Berry said that some guy had caught something from drinking tap water, and that it gave that person brain cancer and that he died from it. I'm almost completely sure that it was actually a brain-eating amoeba that the guy caught in that case. I just wanted to share that tip with you in case it would prove helpful.

Robles: Thank you.

Blair: Thanks. Have a great day.

[I then hung up the phone right after wishing Robles, Berry, et al to have a great day.]

Footnote: Although I do not know for sure which news story might have been going through his mind when Michael Berry made that reference early in the 10 AM U.S. CDT to 11 AM U.S. CDT hour of his March 25, 2024 morning edition of his radio show, here is a news story that illustrates some of the context:

"Yukon family warns of water after daughter dies from brain-eating amoeba" by Natalie Clydesdale / KFOR. Posted MAR 14, 2024 / 04:00 PM U.S. CDT. Updated: MAR 14, 2024 / 05:17 PM U.S. CDT.

https://kfor.com/news/local/yukon-family-warns-of-water-after-daughter-dies-from-brain-eating-amoeba/

Here is a review by M. James Blair:

That article mentioned that a family was having a swim at Lake Murray in Oklahoma, and, unfortunately, one of their members, Beth Knight, who was a young adult mother, took ill within a few days, then died soon after that from Primary Amoebic Meningoencephalitis. The Centers for Disease Control and Prevention has disclosed information on both the rarity of occurrence and the high mortality rate for those who catch that condition. Highly recommended reading for people with interests in health, biology, and risk management, that news article is informative, though readers should apply critical thinking to its perspectives.

***** And now, for something different *****

One of my classmates from seventh and tenth grades had the name Amy Miller, and, from what little I know with certainty about the Amy Miller authors of books available for sale on the Internet, I am, as of portions of early 2024, of the belief that it is most likely that the classmate of that name is not among the Amy Millers who authored those books, though I am not quite completely sure about this. One of the reasons for the uncertainty is that the name combination referenced is rather prevalent.

The referenced classmate Amy Miller clearly by context had a birth year that was either the same as mine in this lifetime or very close to mine in this lifetime.

The first time in this life that I had a strong infatuation—the kind in which the beholder may feel an impression of true love—was during portions of my seventh grade interactions with the classmate Amy Miller. Things took several turns into the utterly bizarre, though, as I had decided to ask my father for advice on the situation, such as how to approach inviting her to date me, and my father simply advised me at the time to decline to bother to even ask her out. Many strange things transpired from there; here are descriptions of a few of them:

1) I created a handwritten note telling Amy that I really liked her a lot and would like to date her, then, rather than speaking directly to her about it and/or handing it to her, I handed it to a classmate named Polash Kulkarni.

2) After Amy received the note, she spoke in what seemed an ambiguously-intentioned flirtatious manner that also had an edge of derision toward me.
3) A classmate named Laura Martinez pulled me aside from other classmates one day and told me that she (i.e., Laura Martinez) and I were among the middle schoolers who were not cute, whereas her close friend (i.e., the Amy Miller who attended Desert View Middle School in El Paso, TX, USA in the 1988-1989 school year) was among the cute crowd. Therefore, that Laura advised me to decline to make any further attempt at getting romantically involved with her friend Amy.
4) Although I had not yet reached puberty, I had developed a sense of profound romantic affection toward that Amy Miller, and, at some levels she knew it. The history class often had assigned seating in which Amy was designated to sit directly in front of me, and she and I had interacted in a friendly manner on many occasions.
5) My strange note-passing attempt to ask her out, and her ambiguous response that did neither amounted to a clear yes nor a clear no happened somewhat early in the 1989 spring semester that ran from something like early January of that year to something like early June of that year. A moderate amount of time after that, still quite a ways to go before the circa-early-June-1989 end of that school year, there was a Saturday night in which a group of girls, including Desert View

classmate Amy Miller, called me, while I was at home watching *Doctor Who* on the local PBS affiliate. The conversation went well, yet there was a weird dynamic in which a) they invited me to their originally-planned-to-be-a-girls-only party, which may have smacked of a prank invitation whether or not it was actually a prank, b) I declined the invitation on account of how much I was concentrating on studying the episode on the TV, c) they at some stage turned to telling me that they would like for me to directly state love for that Amy to her on the phone while they could listen, and d) I decided to fulfill their request, saying during part of the phone call to that specific Miss Miller, "I love you, Amy."

6) After that phone call, my father discussed with me his take on what had transpired, and he said to me, either word-for-word or nearly so, "They were taking you snipe hunting." He expressed his view that it was nothing to do with any genuine interest of that Amy in the possibility of someday getting involved with me romantically.
7) However, later in that semester there was a middle school dance. I attended without arranging to bring a date. Amy also happened to be attending. I waited around, declining to ask anyone to dance; meanwhile, several female Desert View students asked me to dance, and I declined each of them... until Amy Miller asked me to dance. When she and I danced, I demonstrated a mixture of curbed enthusiasm and profound, genuine caring toward her, and

during the dance she started to break out into crying.

8) For eighth grade, the Ysletta Independent School District's new Indian Ridge Middle School became the place where I attended. For ninth-through-twelfth grades, I attended Hanks High School. During that time, the only portion in which I had any significant contact with the aforementioned Amy was during tenth grade, when she and I were classmates for a semester of debate class and a semester of speech class. Sometimes during that time, she seemed to partway throw herself at me with kindness and flirtation, yet things had changed. I had entered puberty sometime approximately November 1989, I had at times developed infatuation with other girls, and, as I had nowhere near the more advanced states of consciousness that I would achieve in portions of April 12, 2000 onward, I had fallen into a state of moderate resentment toward her, mixed with moderate and very subdued affection toward her. By the end of that tenth-grade school year (i.e., the 1991-1992 school year in that case), she could probably tell that I held her in nowhere near the affectionate regard that I had held her in a few years previously.
9) Early in eleventh grade, I suddenly felt a change of heart and mind and soul such as to feel very open to the possibility of falling back in love with that Amy Miller and returning to pursuing romantic involvement with her. However, when I soon asked a classmate about her whereabouts,

> that classmate indicated Amy Miller to have moved to a different school.

*****

Whether, and to whichever degree, any specific Amy Miller might be identical or not identical to any other specific Amy Miller, let it be known to the reader that from the end of the tenth grade school year at J.M. Hanks High School at 2001 Lee Trevino, El Paso, Texas to the time of the publication of this new nonfiction work authored by yours truly, I have never knowingly met in person again anyone of the name Amy Miller.

*****

Having stated that, though, here is another twist. There were some times around 1999-2004 that in my heart and mind and soul I developed a hypothesis that someday a new Amy would come along and maybe some whirlwind romance between her and me might help set things right.

In January 2005 I met a woman named Amy Garland. She and I were among the Houston office KPMG interns during portions of the first four months of 2005. At first I did not think very much of her, yet things changed quickly. At a training event in New Jersey, KPMG set up two teams of IES (i.e., International Executive Services) interns to compete against each other in a mock episode of *Who Wants to Be a Millionaire.* Instead of the normal range of questions, it set the questions to directly involve technical knowledge helpful with performing International Executive Services work. My team went first, and I was designated the person who would be in the role of the individual participant, while other members of the team would be lifelines, etc. I proceeded to lead my team to a perfect performance of answering all ten questions correctly. Therefore, when it became time for the other team to go, their only chance at victory would be a combination of replicating the perfect ten-for-ten performance, then to win a tie-breaker contest. However, after they answered the first nine questions correctly, their team answered the tenth question incorrectly. Therefore, my team won that training exercise contest.

Even after winning that contest, I was mainly oblivious to Amy Garland, yet on an ensuing bus ride, she went out of her way to sit close to me and to communicate with me in a very kind and affectionate way. I felt favorable about how she did that, yet I felt skeptical about whether she would have the fortitude to handle the rigors of what serious involvement with my family might entail. As time went by, I started to change my mind into believing that she could handle such rigors, and I started to truly fall for her. That being said, I knew that KPMG's corporate guidance on employee behavior was such that if I were to ever ask her out, then, for as long as Amy Garland and I might both be co-workers there, I would only get one shot at getting romantically involved with her.

Finally, on February 20th, 2005, I made a firm decision to plan to call her in the evening of February 21st, 2005. Then that 21st arrived. Things soon became surreal.

February 21st, 2005, I started to take my lunch break, planning to venture on my own to find a restaurant in the tunnels of Downtown Houston on that occasion.

However, Amy Garland, a co-worker named April, and a co-worker named Amanda saw me in the distance in the tunnels and called out to me. Soon the three of them invited me to go to lunch with them, forming a temporary group of four KPMG employees sharing a culinary and conversational adventure. The intriguing conversation included how, the best I could tell, Amy Garland intentionally initiated a footsie way of getting physical with me under the table, rubbing at least one of her shoes against some of my ankle and calf regions repeatedly.

After the improvised meal gathering, on the way back to the office, approaching from the distance was a male intern co-worker named Lyle Boudreaux. After he greeted us, soon he and Amy walked side-by-side, sharing what seemed a very affectionate conversation.

April, Lyle, and Amy were IES interns assigned to mainly work in cubicles on the side of the floor that included a full-time regular employee named Clayton Collum. In contrast with that, I worked on the other side, which included the office of senior manager John Swilling.

That evening, KPMG presented a complimentary meal to a variety of the employees working on that floor, and the designated meal pick-up area was within the side that included Swilling's then-office and my then-cubicle.

I could tell right away that something was up about the people from the other side of the floor. Their speech patterns and body language showed clearly that several of them, including Miss Garland, were in a state of shock, possibly mixed with a touch of horror. Something about Amy's emotional state seemed disrupted by whatever it was that had happened on the other side of the floor, beyond anything I had directly witnessed. I was not able to discern what might have disturbed them, and I did not press to find out exactly what it might be.

Later, I went home, rather late at night. I decided to move forward with the plan to ask Amy Garland out, fully cognizant of how the corporate guidelines stipulated that if she were to reject me, then I would be forever barred from any further effort toward inviting her to date me for as long as she and I would both be employees of that firm. The phone call went something very much like this:

[Maurice calls Amy. Amy picks up the phone.]

Amy Garland: Hello.

Maurice J. Blair: Hi, there. How are you doing?

Amy [sounding cold]: I'm doing fine, Maurice.

Maurice [sounding warm]: Would you like to go to a movie with me over at the Angelika Theatre downtown sometime this weekend?

Amy [completely unaffectionate in tone]: No.

Maurice [sounding distressed]: Maybe we'll still have plenty of chances to talk again in the future.

Amy [coldly and resolutely]: Goodnight, Maurice.

[Amy hangs up without giving Maurice a chance to state anything further during that call.]

..........

That was the only time in my life that I became heartbroken. Here, the definition of heartbreak involves when an emotional disruption is at such a degree of intensity that the physical blood-pumping organ called "the heart" becomes continually out-of-sorts at the same time that the beyond-the-physical-level-of-reality type of emotional center called "the heart" also becomes continually out-of-sorts. I did not describe this out loud to anyone until something like the second half of 2005, yet I toughed out the rest of that internship and performed moderately well in some ways, though moderately poorly in other ways. It was no surprise to me whatsoever that KPMG declined to offer me a full-time position for after the internship; even going into that internship they had made clear that it would not be the kind of internship in which a high percentage of interns would receive a full-time offer, and I could tell that several dimensions of my performance were not at the levels that KPMG would consider good. I believed then and believe now that the partners and managers at that Swiss multinational professional services firm were fully justified to decline to give me a full-time offer.

Something I should probably state, in all fairness to Amy, is that I found out on February 22$^{nd}$, 2005 that KPMG LLP had fired the Houston intern Lyle Boudreaux the previous day, and it seems abundantly clear to me—without needing tangible sensory data to prove it—that this had impacted Amy Garland in some heart-wrenching way for which words could probably never fully do justice.

Also, although there is some degree to which I had previously on some occasions temporarily fallen in love with various women—usually in an unrequited love fashion for a rather brief amount of time—it was only with the affection toward Miss Garland that I had truly and completely let go of any selfishness and any ulterior motives. It was like reality having set up a perfect and gigantic set of dominoes with which to make a spectacular chain reaction, resulting in the only completely real and actual heartbreak of my life.

Another aspect of this was that there was a very strange healing process, including how, during portions of the second quarter of 2005, I shifted career intentions away from tax work to literary work. As chronicled in Encyclopedia Parts Three, Four, and Five of *An Encyclopedic Survival Guide for Navigating Normal and Paranormal Experiences* (2023) (a collective work composed by drawing together a variety of contributors, with the composite editing performed by yours truly), and as partially chronicled by *Science, Religion, Politics, and Cards* (2023), there were many types of drama that unfolded from there.

Some might wonder why, contrasting the rare instances of when I have experienced 1) sex with women who were definitely cisgender, 2) sex with "women" who from my perspective were of uncertain categorization in terms of whether transgender or cisgender, and 3) mouth-to-mouth kissing with women, as differentiated with how Amy Garland broke my heart despite my not reaching base with her—the issue of why none of the other women broke my heart. A full version of that explanation is beyond the purview of this book.

In many respects, it was not until approximately April 9, 2005 that I had overcome the February 21, 2005 heartbreak to restore myself to the unbroken state of holistically and healthily heartful state of well-being. That is, to return to being whole-heartedly well. (The way there has often been a tendency toward oscillating between very heartened states and very disheartened states during many different stages is another issue.)

Also, I demonstrated a tendency toward a great state of well-being the vast majority of the time from May 11, 2011 to May 7, 2021 and from a specific instant of time on July 12, 2021 onward, and I have been doing especially well since a specific instant of time on June 19, 2022.

Roller-coaster-style dynamics and extreme drama still happen every now and then, yet much of the core of my life has improved way beyond what I had often in my teenage and young adult years thought humanly possible for anyone. Some of how this emerged from comparing and contrasting expressions from Friedrich Max Müller, Edward Podvoll, Mary Baker Eddy, L. Ron Hubbard, Phil McGraw, Caroline Myss, Jeremy Silman, Garry Kasparov, and Sheng-yen Lu.

For more about this, and more about much else regarding many realms, besides how it might prove helpful to consider exploring *An Encyclopedic Survival Guide for Navigating Normal and Paranormal Experiences* and *Science, Religion, Politics, and Cards,* some might consider exploring other books that could be of almost any category and by virtually any author or combination of authors, *whether the sources are seemingly known or seemingly unknown to modernity.*

—Maurice James Blair

RECOMMENDED VIEWINGS:

*2010: The Year We Make Contact* (1984).

*8 Mile* (2002).

*Antman* (2015).

"Anything Could Happen" (music video) (2012). Goulding, Ellie

*Barry Lyndon* (1975).

*Dalai Lama Renaissance* (2007).

"Free Your Mind" (music video) (1992). En Vogue.

*Gran Torino* (2008).

"Man on the Moon" (music video) (1992). R.E.M.

*Mahogany* (1975).

"New Tibetan bridge lets thrill-seekers walk 175 meters above the ground." (March 22, 2024). https://apnews.com/video/italy-covid-19-pandemic-earthquakes-roberto-battista-attilio-gubbiotti-d61a962275d84026b6628e5c7e71ddec (as accessed on March 25 & 26, 2024). Associated Press.

"The Sweetest Thing" (music video) (1991). Carter, Carlene

*The Valachi Papers* (1972).

*The Vietnam War* (ten-part documentary) (2017). PBS.

*The Way We Were* (1973).

*The Wild Bunch* (1969).

# CHAPTER NINE: BONUS PERSPECTIVES

Although the composition of this chapter—as well as the rest of this book—are straight from my mind and whatever telepathy &c. might relate, together with a little bit of fair use copying of minute excerpts from the works of others, I do not know how much of this would overlap or duplicate things that others have published. Having stated that, to reiterate something mentioned earlier, there is no intentional duplication of expression in this book other than in the portions in one way or another providing proper credit to sources.

* * * * * * *

* * * * * * *

* * * * * * *

* * * * * * *

* * * * * * *

Consider, if you will, the mysteries of the rapid eye movement biological processes.

Next, consider anyone or anything of your choice... or any combinations of your choice.

* * * * * * *

* * * * * * *

* * * * * * *          * * * * * * *

* * * * * * *

Here are several statements that some would consider to involve cognitive dissonance, whereas others would consider to point the way toward transcending the limits of idea structures in relationship with the complete reality, and that pattern of fourteen statements in sequence has probably been in the public domain for a while, though I have no conscious memory of witnessing anyone else present it to me prior to my composition of it for inclusion here :

- They are victims of what happened.
- They are not victims of what happened.
- You are a victim of what has happened to you.
- You are not a victim of what has happened to you.
- I am a victim of what has happened to me.
- I am not a victim of what has happened to me.
- They are victims.
- You are a victim.
- I am a victim.
- We are victims.
- They are not victims.
- You are not a victim.
- I am not a victim.
- We are not victims.

A very special thanks to

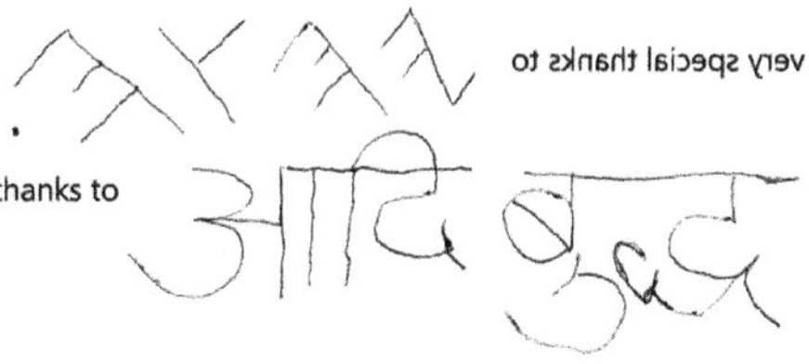


A very special thanks to

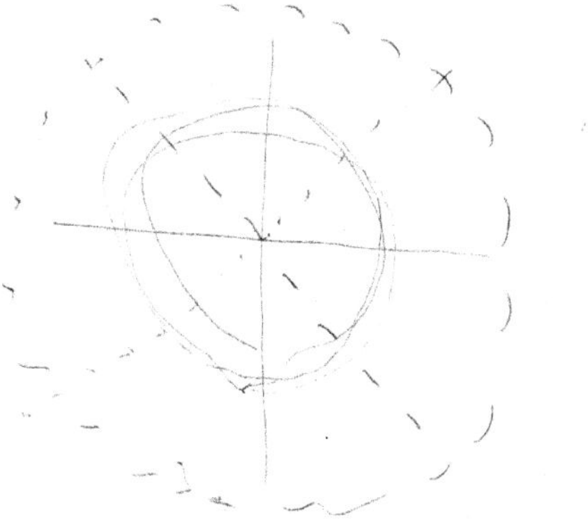

A very special thanks to

A very special thanks to

This page includes several patterns that probably went into the public domain very long ago:

WE CREDIT AND THANK REALITY ITSELF.

WE CREDIT AND THANK REALITY ITSELF.

WE WISH TO EXPRESS GRATITUDE TO REALITY.

* * * * * * *

* * * * * * *

* * * * * * *

On this page is an idea that you could take or leave.

Consider options of meditating for a few seconds, for a few minutes, or for more than a few minutes; consider possible options of doing that before proceeding to the next page.

* * * * * * *

* * * * * * *

* * * * * * *

* * * * * * *

* * * * * * *

* * * * * * *

* * * * * * *

* * * * * * *

* * * * * * *

* * * * * * *

[EXTERNAL EMAIL] - _____, , or regarding "Form 3X" or "not Form 3X"

From: Jim Blair [redacted]
Sent: Tuesday, August 31, 2021 1:03 PM
To: oig@fec.gov; info@fec.gov
Cc: CommissionerLee@sec.gov; newstips@abc13.com; FOX26HoustonNews@foxtv.com; Carol Wang [redacted]; Maurice Blair [redacted]; michael@michaelberryshow.com; [redacted]@jtjones.com
Subject: [EXTERNAL EMAIL] - _____, , or regarding "Form 3X" or "not Form 3X"

Dear Federal Election Commission:

Here is a transcript of select excerpts from an August 19th, 2021 e-mail I sent to two organizations:

_________

"Sometime circa September-to-November 2018, Thomas Sartor and several other men then-employed by The Financial Advisory Group"

...

"in Houston"

...

...

'"hereafter referred to as "FinGroup"'

...

", including yours truly, were speaking with each other at a lunch gathering or something similar. Sartor expressed that he felt troubled about his alleged knowledge that Steve Estrin (also then of FinGroup) had been providing a place to stay for a Democratic Party campaign person (who was not otherwise of his household) rent-free."

...

"He said he was troubled because he thought it was potentially tantamount to an unreported in-kind political contribution.

[Note: A redacted transcription and a brief explanation appears after the set of these redacted screenshots.]

[EXTERNAL EMAIL] - _____, , or regarding "Form 3X" or "not Form 3X"

I do not know for sure whether Thomas Sartor spoke of fully accurate knowledge of something that actually happened, though based on knowing him fairly well, I believe him to have very likely been speaking accurately regarding that."

_________

_________

_________

Here are names and e-mail addresses of two persons who may or may not be persons of interest (and who I believe would very likely be helpful to include in your investigation, whether they attempt to give you misleading answers or correctly-leading answers... if you choose to investigate):

William Crockett Walker (AKA "Bill Walker") [redacted] (From here, I estimate about a 50% chance that he has had direct contact with Steve Estrin.)
James Liptrap (AKA "Jim Liptrap") [redacted] (From here, I estimate about an 85% chance that he has had direct contact with Steve Estrin.)

...

Regards,

Maurice James Blair

[EXTERNAL EMAIL] - _____, , or regarding "Form 3X" or "not Form 3X"

_________
"Fw: Attn: SEC & Attn: Michael C. Kelsheimer" or "forward: an act of skewering and disclosing" or " _____ _____"

**From:** Maurice Blair [redacted]
**Sent:** Tuesday, August 31, 2021 10:59 AM
**To:** Maurice Blair [redacted]
**Subject:** Fw: Attn: SEC & Attn: Michael C. Kelsheimer

.remlehsleK .rM dna noissimmoC

----- Forwarded Message -----

----- Forwarded Message -----
**From:** Maurice Blair [redacted]
To: CommissionerLee@sec.gov <commissionerlee@sec.gov>; CommissionerPeirce@sec.gov <commissionerpeirce@sec.gov>; CommissionerRoisman@sec.gov <commissionerroisman@sec.gov>; CommissionerCrenshaw@sec.gov <commissionercrenshaw@sec.gov>; MKelsheimer@grayreed.com <mkelsheimer@grayreed.com>
**Sent:** Tuesday, August 10, 2021, 06:34:26 PM CDT
**Subject:** Attn: SEC & Attn: Michael C. Kelsheimer

Dear Securities and Exchange Commission and Mr. Kelsheimer:

On account of how The Financial Advisory Group committed libel against me in portions of the cease and desist demand that I received earlier today, and on account of evaluating all factors to the best of my ability, I believe it best to inform you of the following.

Although a) The Financial Advisory Group (located in Houston, TX; in most instances hereafter, "FinGroup") in its termination letter left a blank space as the reason for termination and b) FinGroup personnel only spoke in terms of "It was an executive decision" and the equivalently vague "Things just didn't work out" at the exit interview, I believe an incident from circa September to October 2018 was likely a factor.

Yes, Michael Berry and I discussed multiple incidents involving FinGroup during portions of his August 6th, 2021 morning show. However, here is one of the things I withheld from that conversation.

Around September or October 2018, Natasha McDaniel, Chris Kolenda, and I had a conversation. [I do not recall with certainty whether or not there was a fourth person present.] Natasha mentioned something that allegedly happened behind the scenes at Tesla. As a relatively new employee, and with a spirit of goodwill, I asked if it might be something we should bring to the attention of Juan, for procedures to protect against the risk of insider trading. Natasha reacted with condemnation toward my even daring to speak of this out loud. Also, she showed signs of suddenly considering my reputation to have died there and then in her eyes in connection with this conversation. At one point she said with extreme hostility something like, "At some point you know just where you stand with some people."

Natasha spoke of alleged knowledge of details regarding some internal communications between Tesla employees, although I do not remember for certain exactly what she said transpired in those communications.

At some point I spoke with Juan about it, and he indicated that it would fall into the category of being nonpublic-though-immaterial information with respect to the capital markets. For a long time I had confidence in FinGroup CCO Juan Martinez's judgment about that incident and considered it have simply been an unfortunate choice.

However, as events led to multiple revelations on July 19th, 2021, I came to much more thoroughly question Juan Martinez's motives and judgment. On that day, I decided that, to the best of my judgment the three people who treated me most unethically in my life were Natasha McDaniel [of FinGroup], the man who molested me briefly on an outdoor bench in Taiwan when I was a very young child, and Juan Martinez [of FinGroup]. That soon led me to contemplate communicating with the SEC about the circa September to October 2018 incident in case it would be helpful for the SEC to know about it, and that soon led me to contemplate communicating with the SEC about my general impression of CCO Juan Martinez's ethics. However, I repeatedly dismissed the idea of telling this to the SEC until today.

For clarification about the reference to FinGroup committing libel against me I present a list:

0) Here is an excerpt from the letter: "You have trespassed at company facilities to stalk employees, harassed employees via social media, unwanted calls, and, most recently, you have inappropriately included The Financial Advisory Group employees in communications with various chess organizations."
1) In contrast with the allegation of trespassing at company facilities, the reality is that I have completely avoided the building at 5599 San Felipe St, Houston, TX since my termination from FinGroup, although I have briefly visited the parking lot about five times.
2) When I visited that parking lot, the purpose was not to stalk employees; indeed I had no expectation of meeting employees those times, especially on account of how each visit ranged from approximately under one minute to approximately five minutes. The purpose of my visiting the parking lot was religious in nature.
3) Regarding the social media, calls, and the cc'ing FinGroup employees on e-mails to chess organizations, I believe I was fully justified in exercising my First Amendment right in those cases, especially given the behavior of multiple FinGroup personnel toward me. Those communications were helpful in the process of my healing from the harm that multiple FinGroup personnel did to me and to evaluate things like if and when to decide to contact the SEC. Also, whether the SEC personnel will choose to believe this e-mail to be appropriate for SEC purposes or not, there is no way for me to tell for sure at the time of composing and sending it. However, considering the totality of my interactions with FinGroup personnel plus all other factors to the best of my ability, I truly believe it most likely more helpful to the SEC for me to send this than to refrain from sending it.

Regards,

Maurice James Blair

[EXTERNAL EMAIL] - ______, , or regarding "Form 3X" or "not Form 3X"

[redacted] <[redacted]>
To: [redacted] Tue 9/7/2021 3:45 PM

[redacted]

Thank you for Bcc: me on your last email. [redacted] I have neither subject matter knowledge or regional expertise on the issues discussed in your email. With that said, I was not able to identify anything in the information you provided that would seem to meet the threshold associated with the matter being a potential federal crime.

[redacted]

Hope all is well with you,

[redacted]

[EXTERNAL EMAIL] - _____, , or regarding "Form 3X" or "not Form 3X"

Jim Blair
To: [redacted] Wed 9/15/2021 1:20 PM

[redacted]

That is fine. In early September I learned directly from the FEC about my options on potential next steps regarding this matter.

By the way, I purchased *Doctor Who: Lost in Time _ Collection of Rare Episodes* (BBC Video 3-disc DVD video) about 10 3/4 or 10 2/3 years ago, more or less or thereabouts. I enjoyed examining that many years ago and occasionally revisiting portions thereof.

Hope all is well with you,
Jim

P.S. When unidentified men robbed my mother and ransacked our apartment on 9/22/2015, she at that time told me (and presumably) HPD that it involved multiple Black men with an unusual accent and speaking quickly. However, on April 8th, 2021 or thereabouts she believed that she remembered clearly that it involved two Black men and three Hispanic men, and that they wore white gloves that extended more than halfway up the forearms. (She did not clarify if the Hispanics were Black Hispanics, White Hispanics, Asian Hispanics, Very-Mixed-Race Hispanics, etc.) On April 9th, 2021 I ... spoke with some people. On April 10th, 2021 I spoke with HPD regarding multiple matters. Just FYI.

[Note: A redacted transcription and a brief explanation appears starting on the next page.]

# A REDACTED TRANSCRIPTION AND A BRIEF EXPLANATION OF WHAT APPEARED ON THE PREVIOUS FIVE PAGES

---

---

---

---

TRANSCRIPTION OF A 31 AUG 2021 COMMUNIQUE:

---

[CATEGORY IDENTIFIER] - SUBJECT:

[EXTERNAL E-MAIL] - ______ , , or regarding "Form 3X" or "not Form 3X"

---

From: Jim Blair [REDACTED E-MAIL ADDRESS IDENTIFICATION]

Sent: Thursday, August 31, 2021
1:03 PM [U.S. Central Daylight Time]

To: oig@fec.gov; info@fec.gov

Cc: CommissionerLee@sec.gov; newstips@abc13.com; FOX26HoustonNews@foxtv.com; Carol Wang [REDACTED E-MAIL ADDRESS IDENTIFICATION]; Maurice Blair [REDACTED E-MAIL ADDRESS IDENTIFICATION]; michael@michaelberryshow.com; [REDACTED IDENTIFICATION]@jtjones.com

Bcc: [IDENTIFICATION REDACTED FROM THIS CHAPTER] [REDACTED E-MAIL ADDRESS]

Dear Federal Election Commission:

Here is a transcript of select excerpts from an August 19th, 2021 e-mail I sent to two organizations:

---

"Sometime circa September-to-November 2018, Thomas Sartor and several other men then-employed by The Financial Advisory Group"

...

"in Houston"

...

...

'"hereafter referred to as "FinGroup"'

...

", including yours truly, were speaking with each other at a lunch gathering or something similar. Sartor expressed that he felt troubled about his alleged knowledge that Steve Estrin (also then of FinGroup) had been providing a place to stay for a Democratic Party campaign person (who was not otherwise of his household) rent-free."

...

"He said he was troubled because he thought it was potentially tantamount to an unreported in-kind political contribution.

I do not know for sure whether Thomas Sartor spoke of fully accurate knowledge of something that actually happened, though based on knowing him fairly well, I believe him to have very likely been speaking accurately regarding that."

---

---

---

Here are names and e-mail addresses of two persons who may or may not be persons of interest (and who I believe would very likely be helpful to include in your investigation, whether they attempt to give you misleading answers or correctly-leading answers... if you choose to investigate):

William Crockett Walker (AKA "Bill Walker") {REDACTED E-MAIL ADDRESS} (From here, I estimate about a 50% chance that he has had direct contact with Steve Estrin.)
James Liptrap (AKA "Jim Liptrap") {REDACTED ADDR.} (From here, I estimate about an 85% chance that he has had direct contact with Steve Estrin.)

...

Regards,

Maurice James Blair

---

"Fw: Attn: SEC & Attn: Michael C. Kelsheimer" or "forward: an act of skewering and disclosing" or "_____ _____"

---

**From:** Maurice Blair <email address redacted here>
**Sent:** Tuesday, August 31, 2021 10:59 AM
**To:** Maurice Blair <another email address redacted here>
**Subject:** Fw: Attn: SEC & Attn: Michael C. Kelsheimer

:remiehsleK .rM dna noissimmoC

---

(Below the inverted-sequencing spelling appeared a forwarded copy of an August Tenth communication.

A transcription of the forwarded 10 AUG 2021 message appears later in this chapter, in a region with the label, "A Message which I sent to the commissioners of The Securities and Exchange Commission and to Attorney Michael Kelsheimer of the law firm Gray Reed."

Also, please note that some resources refer to that law firm as "Gray Reed & McGraw.")

---

A REDACTED TRANSCRIPT OF THE 7 SEP 2021 COMMUNICATION THAT A GOVERNMENT MAN SENT TO YOURS TRULY:

---

[From Line Completely Redacted from This Chapter]

To: [Redacted]

Tue 9/7/2021 3:45 PM {as measured by Central Daylight Time}

[Redacted greeting line]

Thank you for Bcc: me on your last email. [A redacted portion of words and punctuation...] I have neither subject matter knowledge or regional expertise on the issues discussed in your email. With that said, I was not able to identify anything in the information you provided that would seem to meet the threshold associated with the matter being a potential federal crime.

[A redacted paragraph]

Hope all is well with you,
[A Name Redacted From This Chapter]

---

TRANSCRIPT OF MY 15 SEP 2021 RESPONSE:

From: Jim Blair

To: [Name Redacted From This Chapter]

Wed 9/15/2021 1:20 PM {Central Daylight Time}

[Redacted greeting line]

That is fine. In early September I learned directly from the FEC about my options on potential next steps regarding this matter.

By the way, I purchased *Doctor Who: Lost in Time _ Collection of Rare Episodes* {BBC Video 3-disc DVD video} about 10 3/4 or 10 2/3 years ago, more or less or thereabouts. I enjoyed examining that many years ago and occasionally revisiting portions thereof.

Hope all is well with you,
Jim

P.S. When unidentified men robbed my mother and ransacked our apartment on 9/22/2015, she at that time told me (and presumably) HPD that it involved multiple Black men with an unusual accent and speaking quickly. However, on April 8th, 2021 or thereabouts she believed that she remembered clearly that it involved two Black men and three Hispanic men, and that they wore white gloves that extended more than halfway up the forearms. (She did not clarify if the Hispanics were Black Hispanics, White Hispanics, Asian Hispanics, Very-Mixed-Race Hispanics, etc.) On April 9th, 2021 I ... spoke with some people. On April 10th, 2021 I spoke with HPD regarding multiple matters. Just FYI.

---

(The above thus concludes the transcription here of that.)

---

## EXPLANATION

Consider the fellow with whom I shared correspondence by placing his U.S. government e-mail address on the blind copy concern line, then receiving a direct response* from him, and subsequently sending an informative one-to-one response to his direct one-to-one response. Although I decline to elaborate much further in this chapter about him, I shall disclose here two relevant things about him:

1) I have only knowingly met him in portions of what The Gregorian Calendar refers to as the twentieth century. Expressed from a second angle, I have only knowingly met him in portions of what one popular version of The Tibetan Calendar refers to as the twenty-second century. From a third angle, those meetings were in what another version of The Tibetan Calendar refers to as portions of the tenth century.

2) On rare occasions in the 2011-2021 C.E. period, I sent him e-mail messages.

* Notice that he wisely sent that to me without replying to any of the others addressed in the initial communique. Although bcc conceals the bcc recipient(s), if a bcc recipient chooses to use the "reply-all" option, then the bcc recipient winds up revealing his/her/their/its inclusion in the loop to others from whom it earlier had been concealed.

After carefully considering that situation, I chose to decline to send the official FEC form that I had the option of setting up and sending in triplicate to the Federal Election Commission. Had the government contact person not replied to the message to tell me that his evaluation would indicate most likely an absence of election law wrongdoing by Steve Estrin in connection with Thomas Sartor's voiced suspicions, then I almost definitely would have gone full tilt toward officially alleging election wrongdoing in that case. To state this more bluntly, prior to reading that response I had been fully intent—some might say hell-bent—on officially reporting it as evidence of the likelihood that election laws had been broken. That government fellow radically changed the course of my life, Steve Estrin's life, and the lives of others. I now believe that to have most likely been for the best, though I might not ever know for sure. One can wonder whether his feedback would have been different if the same exact allegation had been against Republicans.

To whatever degree it might have been coincidental or directly related or in the gray between, after that, in the 2022 election Wesley Hunt won a seat in the U.S. House of Representatives in a different district than Fletcher, while Fletcher won re-election to the U.S. House, then Representative Lizzie Fletcher moved her Houston office away from 5599 San Felipe Street, and Representative Wesley Hunt opened a Houston office at 5599 San Felipe Street.

* * *

Although Michael Berry spent a major amount of time engaging in conversations with me by telephone, I have recognized that even after the March 15, 2024 broadcast of a major percentage of a recording of the February 22, 2024 call from me to his radio show he sure seemed to display very little genuine understanding and comprehension of my life and some vital, adjacent controversies.

Some of those controversies, autobiographical details, and interrelated perspectives received great coverage in some of my other books and in earlier portions of this book. However, even with the risk of some readers screaming an allegation of the presence of too much information, the remainder of this work shall carefully show due respect for the principle that my father often called, "the doctrine of complete information," which is to say that sometimes you need to go the extra mile or the extra 20,001 light years in order to actually communicate enough information to give others a good chance to understand reasonably well.

* * *

In contrast with how a few people go unnamed in this book, two of the people named in this book are Justin Haynes and his father Michael Haynes, as some readers might remember from earlier.

At approximately 1:23 PM on March 29, 2024, Justin Haynes called me again. Here is an approximate transcript of two parts of that conversation:

Part One

James: I'm trying to remember now, what's that name that people have for that kind of thing in which a movie winds up having an extra scene with that thing where they have that what-do-they-call-it... What's that thing called, what do they call it when they have a post-credit scene? Oh, look there, I just now accidentally answered my own question. I remember now, that's called a post-credit scene.

Justin: Yes, the Marvel Cinematic Universe movies are famous for those!

Part Two

James: Sometimes I wonder if a haphazard conversation that two of the people at The Financial Advisory Group—two of the people who weren't even directly involved with the main shenanigans that later transpired there in any regular sense—might have at some mysterious level involving that stuff some might call Zauber or Feng Shui or Spirit Moving in Mysterious Ways actually caused much of the way the interactions later blew up. Those two, Thomas Sartor and Steven Rife, my memory is almost absolutely certain that those were the two who shared the conversation that I unintentionally overheard and am now speaking about. One of them looked up on the Internet information on Ragnarok in general, then they briefly discussed it glibly and nonchalantly as lighthearted office small talk. Then either the one who looked it up or the other one said, "Now I think we know what *Thor: Ragnarok* is about." The way they discussed it seemed to make it clear that neither had seen that movie and that they were in a somewhat carefree attitude while speaking about it out loud then and there. That was approximately September 2018, many months after that MCU movie came out, yet quite a while before any serious conflicts between The Financial Advisory Group and me had started to emerge.

*Some people sometimes think of this way of thinking to be superstitious and purely an illusion of mental associations, yet to my experience there is very much something to be said for the way that mysterious causation may sometimes happen.* It could be that their glib way of discussing the legends of Ragnarok in general and the *Thor: Ragnarok* mobie variation of it in particular became like a specific scene in the 2005 version of *King Kong*. You've seen that 2005 film directed by Peter Jackson, haven't you?

Justin: Yes, I have.

James: Remember there was a scene in which some news-reporter-and-writer kind of fellow was on the ship while they were headed toward Skull Island. Then, he types into a typewriter, "Skull Island."

*Suddenly, his consciousness gets hit with an overwhelming shining from the entirety of Skull Island and its inhabitants, and it's very intense in the way they depict it on the screen. I sometimes wonder if the difference in how reverently-versus-glibly people speak about legendary and in-some-cases-ancient things can have a huge impact in how things unfold from there.*

---

(With the above, thus concludes the second of those two transcripts of portions of close approximations of that referenced conversation.)

---

* * *

Next, before more directly tackling many policy issues, I shall write from my heart and mind a few brief movie reviews. A twist is that rather than providing one rating for each, I provide several ratings, coded with acronyms based on beholders' patterns of beliefs and behaviors.

The next two pages shall reveal what each acronym corresponds with and a basic description of each of those patterns that go with each of those acronyms. Though it is not anywhere near an encyclopedic list, it should prove rather revelatory.

JDCRB: A person whose primary interface with reality consists of paradigms in which JUDEO-CHRISTIAN BELIEFS AND PRACTICES are central, and that person—whether primarily presenting in conversations as being a Jew, a Noahidist, or a Christian—believes and acts on the belief that the true reality of God/G-d circumscribes much of what He/It/They might otherwise do to a range of very-high-to-absolute cognitive consistency with the core presentations of G-d/God relating to human beings and the rest of reality in *The Tanakh* and/or *The Holy Bible*, especially as interpreted in very direct, intuitive manners that decline to involve major amounts of esotericism.

EJCRB: A person whose primary interface with reality is very similar to a JDCRB person with the vital exception that the ESOTERIC JUDEO-CHRISTIAN BELIEFS AND PRACTICES person flexes the cognitive consistency range to medium-to-absolute in terms of G-d/God circumscribing His/Their/Its activity to correspond to very direct and intuitive interpretations of Judeo-Christian scripture(s), thereby being more open to accepting major amounts of esotericism.

AWARATP: A person who is an ATHEIST WHOSE BELIEFS AND PRACTICES AVOID ALL OF THE REGULAR AND TRADITIONAL TYPES OF RELIGIOUS PATTERNS, due to disbelieving in the entirety of religion as having any significant basis in reality whatsoever.

<u>NESTP</u>: A person of NONDENOMINATIONAL, ESOTERIC, SPIRITUALLY-ORIENTED TRUE BELIEVER IN RELIGIOUS PRACTICES IN GENERAL, who believes in major degrees of reality and illusion in each of the various religions known to humans.

<u>FAS</u>: A person who, whether nominally a Muslim, a Jew, a Christian, or an Agnostic, emphasizes a hybrid of the set of FAITH IN THE ABRAHAMIC RELIGIONS IN GENERAL, AN AGNOSTICISM REGARDING WHICH, IF ANY, OF THOSE ARE ACTUALLY CORRECT IN TERMS OF REALITY, AND A WARINESS TOWARD THE DHARMIC RELIGIONS AND ANYTHING ELSE THAT MIGHT BE DEEMED BY MANY NONESOTERIC ABRAHAMIC RELIGIOUS PRACTITIONERS AND AGNOSTICS TO BE OF THE PAGAN RELIGIONS, TO BE PARTS OF CULTS, TO BE OF THE OCCULT, OR TO BE OF SOME COMBINATION OF PAGANRY, CULTS, AND THE OCCULT.

<u>SAF</u>: A person who, whether nominally a Deist, a Hindu, a Jain, an Agnostic, an Atheist, a Taoist, an Esotericist, a Buddhist, or of another category, emphasizes a hybrid set of SHARP CRITICISIM OF ALL OF THE VARIOUS EXCESSES AND DISTORTIONS PERCEIVED TO BE PRESENT IN PORTIONS OF FAITH IN THE ABRAHAMIC RELIGIONS IN GENERAL, CONSIDERING THIS TO OPEN THE MIND TO IMPROVEMENT.

With narrative descriptions & six ratings each... Without further ado, here are seven-part reviews of a few movies, with * = worst and ***** = best:

*Citizen Kane* (1941, directed by Orson Welles). A powerful classic from practically every viewpoint, yet it could underwhelm many people if they have not yet been around enough of the right life experiences with which to be truly impressed with it. Sometimes it might wait until someone is 25 years old for the person to thoroughly get it, sometimes it might wait until someone is 46 years old for the person to thoroughly get it, but once a beholder understands it reasonable well, it can prove to be a treasure. For example, if a person viewed it many years earlier, only tuned into it about 55%, then as the years went by, started to tune into it about 85%, then, in a sudden and unexpected experience that some might term in any of a variety of ways (e.g., satori, spirit moving in mysterious ways, etc.) that beholder could get 98% or greater understanding and comprehension of its inner integrity and incisive narrative.

Archetypal Ratings of *Citizen Kane* (1941):

JDCRB, EJCRB, NESTP, FAS, & SAF: ***** (FIVE/FIVE).

AWARATP: ****1/2 (FOUR-AND-A-HALF/FIVE).

---

*Xanadu* (1980, directed by Robert Greenwald). A film that can be either very pleasant or very unpleasant to a given beholder depending on any of many different factors. To some it could have forgivable awkwardness and extraordinary music, as well as a heartfelt message of hope and wonder; yet to others it could fly in the face of much of what they consider essential to effectiveness in life.

Archetypal Ratings of *Xanadu* (1980):

JDCRB: * (ONE/FIVE).

EJCRB: ** (TWO/FIVE).

NESTP: *** (THREE/FIVE).

FAS: *1/2 (ONE-AND-A-HALF/FIVE).

AWARATP: *** (THREE/FIVE).

SAF: ***** (FIVE/FIVE).

---

*The Ten Commandments* (1923, directed by Cecil B. DeMille). Expertly directed and well-performed, it tastefully touches upon multitudes of subjects, yet the beliefs the beholders could affect how well they receive it. Archetypal ratings presented here:

JDCRB, EJCRB, and NESTP: ***** (FIVE/FIVE).

AWARATP: ***1/2 (THREE-AND-A-HALF/FIVE).

FAS & SAF: ****1/2 (FOUR-AND-A-HALF/FIVE).

---

*The Ten Commandments* (1956, directed by Cecil B. DeMille). Although in several ways in a similar vein as that director's decades-earlier project of the same title, there were also enormous differences of style, plot, timelines, and emphases. Archetypal ratings presented here:

JDCRB, EJCRB, and FAS: ***** (FIVE/FIVE).

NESTP: ****1/2 (FOUR-AND-A-HALF/FIVE).

SAF: **** (FOUR/FIVE).

AWARATP: *** (THREE/FIVE).

---

*Indiana Jones and the Dial of Destiny* (2023, directed by James Mangold). Extraordinarily expressive virtually any way a person can behold it *if the viewer does not feel jolted by implications.*

NESTP, EJCRB, and SAF: ***** (FIVE/FIVE).

JDCRB: **** (FOUR/FIVE).

FAS: ***1/2 (THREE-AND-A-HALF/FIVE).

AWARATP: ***1/2 (THREE-AND-A-HALF/FIVE).

---

*Masters of the Universe* (1987, directed by Gary Goddard). A case in which many bullets hit many bones. There were evidently at least two different versions of the opening MGM sequence: at least one somewhat "normal MGM presents sequence" and a "witness from being eye-to-eye with a huge feline so up-close that at first you do not know what to make of the scene before it zooms out, as an alternative MGM sequence." Either way, to the trained eye, the presentation seems self-evident that at least two people at Metro-Goldwyn-Mayer (though there may be uncertainty among outside exactly which at least two people) were less concerned with visible box office results, possible critical criticism, and possible critical praise than they were with using the movie as a military exercise to holistically act out the adage of "business is war," as well as to deal with the studio's personal and professional demons of the legacy of its past films and the legacies of all the past films of all the other studios.

SAF & FAS: ***** (FIVE/FIVE).

NESTP & EJCRB: **** (FOUR/FIVE).

JDCRB: ** (TWO/FIVE).

AWARATP: *** (THREE/FIVE).

---

*Manos, The Hands of Fate* (1966, directed by Hal Warren). Generally a dreadful display of a director walking right into not knowing that he knew as little as he knew, then facing the consequences; from the perspectives of some beholders, its redeeming features greatly outweigh its dreadful features, whereas from the perspective of other beholders, it completely lacks redeeming features.

AWARATP: *** (THREE/FIVE).

FAS, JDCRB, and EJCRB: * (ONE/FIVE).

NESTP: *1/2 (ONE-AND-A-HALF/FIVE).

SAF: ***** (FIVE/FIVE).

---

*2001: A Space Odyssey* (1968, directed by Stanley Kubrick). Masterful in such a way that even if someone does not get it within the first week, first month, or first decade of encountering it, there can remain hope that the person will someday truly get it.

NESTP, FAS, SAF, & EJCRB: ***** (FIVE/FIVE).

JDCRB & AWARATP: ***** (FIVE/FIVE).

---

*Captain America: Civil War* (2016, directed by Anthony Russo and Joe Russo). Among the few superhero movies to include the kinds of ethical dilemmas that escalate the fog of war to the point that moral clarity may seem unobtainable at some stages.

NESTP, SAF, and FAS: ***** (FIVE/FIVE).

JDCRB: ***1/2 (THREE-AND-A-HALF/FIVE).

AWARATP: ****1/2 (FOUR-AND-A-HALF/FIVE).

EJCRB: ****1/2 (FOUR-AND-A-HALF/FIVE).

---

*For a Few Dollars More* (1965, directed by Sergio Leone). A fascinating dive into moral ambiguities, controversies, and social criticism, with scenes from the old west as the clothing with which to present these.

NESTP and SAF: ***** (FIVE/FIVE).

AWARATP: **** (FOUR/FIVE).

EJCRB: ****1/2 (FOUR-AND-A-HALF/FIVE).

JDCRB: *** (THREE/FIVE).

FAS: ***1/2 (THREE-AND-A-HALF/FIVE).

---

Now, a shift to another set: transcripts repurposing portions of the work *Of Dorians, Romans, Hebrews, Whigs, Democrats, Republicans, Indians, and Beyond* (self-published by yours truly on March 7, 2022, distributed on a very limited basis subsequently, and adjusted into a second printing that commenced November 28, 2023). That was—and to some degree is—a nonprofit/educational book, by the way, though this *A.B.A.E.O.A.T.:S.R.P.C.H.II* work is a for-profit/educational book. If you chance upon a printed copy of that *O.D.R.H.W.D.R.I.A.B.*, then you might have a degree of uncertainty about whether it is an authorized copy or something that someone somewhere took the unauthorized liberty to alter and print, unless you have some means of outside corroboration, such as if you work at the U.S. Copyright Office, are privy to means of government surveillance of electronic transmissions, etc.

From page 1 of that work, part of what I posted in a thread of responses to what Garry Kasparov's Facebook Page posted regarding Vladimir Putin and events:

People of any persuasion could be unethical at times with how they act, yet I have found that the old general rule of thumb that The Republican Party leans more toward freedom and responsibility and the Democratic Party leans more toward artificially tilting things is in many ways about 51%-72% true. Also, I believe that much of the spirit of The First Amendment to The United

States Constitution is in the vein of encouraging The U.S. Government to refrain from idolizing any specific religion, antireligion, or combination of religions or antireligions. [Posted approximately 6:56 PM U.S. CST on March 4, 2022].

---

From *O.D.R.H.W.D.R.I.A.B.*, page 2:

Part of what I posted (including the alternate spelling of "Abrahmic" in place of the more standard "Abrahamic" and "Jainist" in place of the more standard "Jain") in a thread responding to a Religia bez ściemy Facebook Page post about controversies in the relationship between Muslims and Buddhists: Some have described Kalachakra as involving extinction of Abrahmic religion(s), some have described Kalachakra as involving enlightenment of Abrahmic religion(s), Brahmanic religion(s), and Sramanic/Jainist/related relig-ion(s), and Buddhism, some say other things about it, and others say a wide variety of things about it and all of the aforementioned and everything else, it would seem. On another note, there are issues of potential comparing and contrasting of ideas about golden rule(s), platinum rule(s), agape rules, what is good, what may be better or worse than good, to what degree(s) enlightenment and endarkenment may in some contexts be parts of pendulums or other things or may transcend definitions. Also, there's what may be in some sense(s) equal to good or not equal to good, and so on and so forth. And then there's the issue of Padmasambhava... and no issue and many issues of Padmasambhava. [Posted approximately 7:37 PM U.S. CDT on September 8, 2021.]

From *O.D.R.H.W.D.R.I.A.B.*, page 4:

Something [Maurice James Blair] posted 1:07 PM CST March 2nd, 2022: Table tennis player Han Chee around 2011 offered mentoring, but couched it in terms of the idea he had "nothing to learn from" me. I rejected the idea that anyone has "nothing to learn" from anyone. Idea structures and shades of meaning aside, this went to something that has played itself out mult-iple times since then, which is that if a person ost-ensibly "older" or "of higher organizational rank" or "perceived to be more important" directly interferes with someone's primary channels of direct connect-ion with reality, then the person's doing that can enter conflict with the other person's full set of all connections with reality.

---

From portions of pages 5-7 of that work: A Message which I sent to the commissioners of The Securities and Exchange Commission and to Attorney Michael Kelsheimer of the law firm Gray Reed:

Dear Securities and Exchange Commission and Mr. Kelsheimer:

On account of how The Financial Advisory Group committed libel against me in portions of the cease and desist demand that I received earlier today, and on account of evaluating all factors to the best of my ability, I believe it best to inform you of the following.

Although a) The Financial Advisory Group (located in Houston, TX; in most instances hereafter, "FinGroup") in its termination letter left a blank space as the reason for termination and b) FinGroup personnel only spoke in terms of "it was an executive decision" and the equivalently vague "Things just didn't work out" at the exit interview, I believe an incident from circa September to October 2018 was a likely factor.

Yes, Michael Berry and I discussed multiple incidents involving FinGroup during portions of his August 6th, 2021 morning show. However, here is one of the things I withheld from that conversation.

Around September or October 2018, Natasha McDaniel, Chris Kolenda, and I had a conversation. [I do not recall with certainty whether or not there was a fourth person present.] Natasha mentioned something that allegedly happened behind the scenes at Tesla. As a relatively new employee, and with a spirit of goodwill, I asked if it might be something we should bring to the attention of Juan, for procedures to protect against the risk of insider trading. Natasha reacted with condemnation toward my even daring to speak this out loud. Also, she showed signs of suddenly considering my reputation to have died then and there in her eyes in connection with this conversation. At one point she said with extreme hostility something like, "At some point you know just where you stand with some people."

Natasha spoke of alleged knowledge of details regarding some internal communications between Tesla employees, although I do not remember for certain exactly what she said transpired in those communications.

At some point I spoke with Juan about it, and he indicated that it would fall into the category of being nonpublic-though-immaterial information with respect to capital markets. For a long time I had confidence in FinGroup CCO Juan Martinez's judgment about that incident and considered it [to] have simply been an unfortunate choice.

However, as events led to multiple revelations on July 19th, 2021, I came to much more thoroughly question Juan Martinez's motives and judgment. On that day, I decided that, to the best of my judgment, the three people who treated me most unethically in my life were Natasha McDaniel [of FinGroup], the man who molested me briefly on an outdoor bench in Taiwan when I was a very young child, and Juan Martinez [of FinGroup]. That soon led me to contemplate communicating with the

SEC about the circa September to October 2018 incident in case it would be helpful for the SEC to know about it, and that soon led me to contemplate communicating with the SEC about my general impression of CCO Juan Martinez's ethics. However, I repeatedly dismissed the idea of telling this to the SEC until today.

...

---

Having completed the preceding transcript of an excerpt from pages 5-7 of the nonprofit and educational booklet *Of Dorians, Romans, Hebrews, Whigs, Democrats, Republicans, Indians, and Beyond*, consider an adjacency: Now, a brief segue into something in some ways completely different and in other ways totally related.

On May 10, 2024, I helped my mother shop at a prominent grocery store location in Houston. As this version of the Blair family proceeded through checkout, the cashier struggled in the attempt to scan a discount item that was about half-off, set to four dollars. Specifically, that was a Mardi Gras-themed meal, conveniently easy to heat and eat in the style that some call "a TV dinner." The main wrap-around cover to it slipped, and somehow the cashier scanned the wrong barcode—the version that would ring it up at the more normal price rather than the specially-discounted price. I caught the likelihood of that error and pointed it out. The cashier, however, seemed flustered, and she ended up quoting the total price anyway without fixing the error. On the route to arriving at that total price, she had scanned into the system and discarded a paper coupon that the Blair family used to take two dollars off of a Quorn Foods [Meatless] Diced Chiqin Pieces, 12 oz. package (i.e., a largely mycoprotein-based, high-protein, chickenless set of chunks of food, presented in a style to be similar in taste and texture to chicken). I mentioned a plan to soon after checkout examine the math carefully, and, if appropriate, go to customer service to get everything straitened out, such that neither the popular grocery store nor the Blair family would wind up with any unfair advantage or any unfair disadvantage. After that, the cashier acknowledgeed that the possibility that there was a scanning problem. Therefore, she started to redo the entire scanning process from scratch. I could tell that at least a customer or two back in the line were getting annoyed by the delay while waiting for a resolution. Nevertheless, with a keen sense of fairness, I kept focusing on how we could arrive at a reasonably just and equitable solution, even with the currency amounts being rather miniscule, and fortunately the cashier had come around to cooperating with straitening things out. As the rescanning process happened, though, it occurred to me that the $2 coupon on the Quorn Mycoprotein product would need to be factored in. I spoke up about this to the cashier.

The cashier responded with stating that the coupon was no longer available, and, therefore, her plan was to substitute taking $2 off of the total price on the bananas. As the new total price came up, several dollars less than the previous total, the Blairs completed the purchase. However, as one of the Blairs, I checked the receipt meticulously and found that the cashier had actually taken a little less than two dollars off of the bananas' total price.

Next stop: the customer service line. While in that line, at first I thought the problem involved an eighty-cent error in favor of the store, but as I continued to check and double-check the receipt, I was able to correct myself, ascertaining that the exact difference was seventy-eight cents. What the cashier had done as a crude way to estimate taking $2 off the bananas was to trim the price per pound on them by 27 cents, which had resulted in a $1.22 shave to the total, falling $0.78 short of the $2.00 that would arrive at perfect equity and justice.

Upon reaching the customer service counter, the customer service woman who helped out was able to immediately ring up a cash refund of $0.78, hand over three quarters and three pennies, also hand over the receipt reflecting that cash refund, and to be pleasant in taking what was wrong and making it right. I thanked her on behalf of the Blair family, and my family walked out of the store, with a complete set of groceries and a perfectly-paid net effect from the original receipt combined with the supplemental refund receipt, thus bringing that episode within the history of the human race to a close.

* * *

Updated commentary regarding the excerpts from *Of Dorians, Romans, Hebrews, Whigs, Democrats, Republicans, Indians, and Beyond* that preceded the segue into a grocery store scene; updated commentary on some of what many would consider the more serious part of what led to this:

1. My memory later cleared up enough to know that the information that Natasha had stated about Tesla was either identical to or well within the ballpark of it having happened that some people in her network informed her that at Tesla there was an incident in which some of the regular-level employees became very upset about how something happened, then at least one of them composed an angry e-mail message and sent it to a corporate vice president of that automobile manufacturer.

2. We could analyze from many angles whether I was hypersensitive about trying to protect against the risk of insider trading, but I admit that what little I learned from the news many years earlier about when Martha Stewart was convicted of insider trading had an impact on my sensibilities about the need to take drastic actions to try to steer clear of any sizable risk of committing insider trading.

3. A mitigating factor involving how the former co-worker Natasha McDaniel acted toward me and toward others on multiple occasions is that she

showed signs of having been seriously impacted by the legacy of the U.S. government's dreadful Tuskegee injection experiment on some African Americans. Although I do not know whether or not she was consciously aware of that experiment, something pointing toward it and similar things affecting her was that, one day, long before hostilities between her and me boiled over, she and I shared a peculiar conversation that resembled the following approximate transcript:

Natasha: No way do I plan to get the flu vaccine anytime soon!

Maurice: Why do you say that?

Natasha: When they give you the flu vaccine, they give you the flu!

Maurice: Oh, come on. The doctors and other medical professionals are quite clear that the flu vaccine does not include any living flu in it. They have some adjusted version that is not really the same as giving you the flu.

Natasha: It doesn't matter to me what the medical industry says officially about that, I still believe that the way they give people the flu vaccine is a way of them giving people the flu, and I expect to stay away from it!

4. Juan Martinez had several mitigating factors about how he seemed to have royally misjudged me

on multiple occasions, and one of those mitigating factors is that, per his account to me when we were co-workers, one time when he was in a high school or a similar location, the setting involved much tension between Black students and Hispanic students, and although he was not trying to provoke any trouble, a group of young Black men suddenly pulled him aside and proceeded to beat him up. That was a case of multiple men teaming up to beat up one other man.

5. To clarify and to extend contextual awareness, please consider the copy of some related email correspondence that appears after the miniature autobiography and the copy of a July 15, 2021 e-mail message.

6. Here is a miniature autobiography that can provide even more context:

When growing up, I had a mixture of many of the usual strengths, weaknesses, opportunities, and threats that youth face and many extremely unusual strengths, weaknesses, opportunities, and threats. I might have been on track for a while to wind up going into some STEM (i.e., Science, Technology, Engineering, and Math) career, yet I ended up veering away from it. One of the things that encouraged me to veer away from it was how pop culture at times ridiculed people in those fields as generally being technically brilliant yet somehow lacking in normal ranges of human interactions. Another factor was that, although I showed great strength in mathematics and the natural sciences, I started to notice that my mind worked exceptionally well when sorting through Economics.

Early during my undergraduate studies at Duke University, I wavered between several options: 1) to major in Economics without having a second major and without having a minor, 2) to double major in Economics and Mathematics, 3) to double major in Economics and Philosophy, and 4) other possibilities. As described in *Science, Religion, Politics, and Cards*, I encountered some extra challenges in my freshman year there, yet kept going smoothly, then, by the fall semester of what would have been my junior year, I encountered several catastrophic developments. I withdrew from classes for a while, then returned, though some aspects of my health were in a diminished state for the remainder of my undergraduate studies and for many of the years that followed. I ended up majoring in Economics, minoring in Philosophy, and earning a Markets and Management Studies Certificate.

However, due to the diminished health state and due to how my confidence had been shaken in much of the period from September 1996 (partway into what would have been my junior year) to October 1998 (partway into what became my final semester of baccalaureate studies), I decided on a plan to avoid even doing any job interviews during my last semester at Duke, although economics majors there would typically interview with investment banking firms and management consulting firms. There was also an option to go further into academia with economics graduate school, but I did not consider that a great option compared to seeking more down-to-earth real-world working experience.

Therefore, I moved to Houston before conducting a job search involving quite a variety of positions. During much of the 1998-2006 period, my lovelife was almost nonexistent, yet I made several extraordinary improvements in terms of the ability to honor religious influences on sexuality. Most striking of that was that on April 19, 2001, when Amin Nosrat provided constructive criticism of things like when I had provided abrasive statements in conversations at the Arthur Andersen February 20 to April 19, 2001 internship and had taken the first limousine from Chicago O'Hare Airport when I should have waited for the second limousine or another later one, I lost all interest in sensory pleasure at some core level. That brought my mindstream back to how there had been some earlier times in my life when I would feel so dialed in to enthusiasm for accomplishing grandiose things that I would wonder how much more we might achieve if we did not have the eating of food, the drinking of water, urination, defecation, sleeping, and breathing to hold us back from going full tilt nearly all the time with accomplishing things with our minds. Without even setting out to cease all intentional experiences of ejaculation, I started to completely avoid intentional ejaculation. Indeed, up to the time of this book going to print, I still have not experienced any new instances of intentional ejaculation since either sometime before the beginning of the April 19, 2001 workday or sometime moderately prior to that entire day.

On some occasions after that conversation with Nosrat I considered the possibility of intentional ejaculation in connection with someday getting married to a woman. However, since I went over to a situation in which I have the overwhelmingly vast majority of the time successfully limited all ejaculations to nocturnal emissions (i.e., "wet dreams," in which the sleeping state of the male body triggers ejaculation in an entirely involuntary manner), and the exceedingly rare accidental exceptions were usually within the auspices of training exercises aimed at being able to avoid premature ejaculation during some types of marital coitus (whether tantric or not) and to entirely avoid ejaculation during some types of tantric foreplay, tantric fellatio, and tantric coitus (either with a woman while married to her or with someone I perceive to be a woman who is single beyond a reasonable doubt either definitely beyond a shadow of doubt or virtually definitely at least the relevant jurisdiction's legal age of consent).

Also, on some extraordinarily rare occasions I succeeded since then with having flirtation and other communications lead to actually experience-ing with romantic partners (who usually seemed to definitely be cisgender women) collaboration on achieving tantric foreplay, tantric fellatio, tantric coitus, some combination of two of those, or a combination of all three of those. That being stated, although four partners have performed fellatio on me, I have only performed cunnilingus on two of the partners. This includes thus far only one of the pairings acting out the simultaneous 69 position.

*Different religious people provide very different religious guidance on what they believe to be spiritually correct restrictions on the practice of human sexuality, and I do not pretend to know everything about what sexual practices are best for whom, yet, to the best of my knowledge, I have been either sexually blameless since my sexual attitudes changed in the wake of Nosrat's April 19, 2001 end-of-internship conversation with me or extremely close to sexually blameless in the wake of that.*

In fact, for a long time this became a core part of my identity, though kept secret from almost all of my communications with others. I mean, it is one thing if a person has his or her main energy contract with REALITY (to whatever degree thought of in terms of G-d, God, Adidharma, Adibuddha, or whatever else) manifest as some specific dietary restriction and/or some specific prayer frequency ritual, yet it is quite another for a man to have his main energy contract with GOD / G-D / ADIBUDDHA/ ADIDHARMA / REALITY manifest as an extreme commitment to avoid intentional ejaculation, unless and until getting married or something else very drastic might lead to him altering his sexual restrictions. With something like dietary restrictions or how often to perform some type of prayer ritual, it is very acceptable within society to often speak openly about it with many people. *However, with sexual matters, there is often such societal sensitivity about talking openly about it in America, resulting in how there should be much discretion about any disclosure of sexual restrictions, sexual activities, et cetera.*

---

* * *

---

On related note, next appears a copy of a July 15, 2021 e-mail message that I sent to the employment recruiter (i.e., what some people refer to as "a headhunter," though not to be confused with people who literally hunt human beings so as to kill them and collect heads of human corpses as trophies).

That copy is in a serialized format.

Although those of you who have heard a sizable amount of my August 6, 2021 call as broadcasted live on that morning's edition of *The Michael Berry Show* will find overlap, you may notice a variety of details you had never witnessed anywhere before:

---beginning of a copy of that electronic message---

---beginning of Part 1 of a 15 JUL 2021 message---

From: Maurice Blair

To: Andrew Tafolla

Date: Thursday, July 15, 2021, 02:39 PM CDT

Subject: an in-depth message that may help with some of your decision making

Andrew,

The purpose of this message is to help with your decision-making regarding what to do about me.

If you decide that you are open to continuing to do business with me, then there may be a chance that I might contact you later this year or in some future year about next steps.

If you decline to contact me after receiving this message, or if you decline to clearly tell me that you are ceasing to do business with me, then I will presume that you are still open to doing business with me in the future.

-------end of Part 1 of a 15 JUL 2021 message-------

---beginning of Part 2 of a 15 JUL 2021 message---

There is a general business guideline to avoid sending long e-mail messages, yet in this case I believe it mutually beneficial for this message to be long. You may wish to set it aside until some time when convenient for you to take substantial time to read and consider it.

Also, there is a general societal guideline in many contexts to be cautious of bringing significant religious and political elements into discussion, yet this message will include some of those elements because they are relevant to your decision of whether to continue to be open to doing business with me.

Some people might argue with me about this, but I believe that I was traumatized by some things that happened from November 2018 to May 2021 and only experienced reasonably full healing from those events as of some of the July 12th-13th, 2021 period. You were part of that healing process, and I am thankful for this, whether or not you decide to be open to doing business with me in the future.

-------end of Part 2 of a 15 JUL 2021 message--------

···beginning of Part 3 of a 15 JUL 2021 message···

In the 2020 holiday season, I gave you a wish of Happy Holidays as part of a message and you responded with giving me a wish of Merry Christmas as part of a message. If someone asks for a simple answer of what religion I practice, I would say that I am a Buddhist. If someone asks for a more complete picture of my religious practices, I would say that I generally practice Vajrayana Buddhism, Zen Buddhism, Esoteric Christianity, and other things, though not always a full combination at a given time. Also, I have generally been a Buddhist since mid-2003.

In my involvement with the U.S. Chess Federation from 2011-2019, much of the 2012-2019 portion of that was with serious chess tournaments as a vehicle to glorify the ultimate level of reality, to whatever extent that reality or source of reality might express Itself/Himself/Herself/etc. as God, Adi-Buddha, Sunyata, Tao, YHVH, etc. When I joined The Financial Advisory Group (located in Houston) in 2018 as an employee, coworkers and supervisors had a degree of knowledge of my involvement with the USCF and chess in general. However, on November 21st, 2018, Steve Estrin, a part-owner and one of the three highest ranking persons there, gave me a threat, saying to me that if I would ever defeat a Financial Advisory Group client in a serious chess tournament, then I would be fired. I explained to him that the USCF prohibits sandbagging (intentional self-sabotage of competition results). He then reiterated the threat. This became part of my EEOC charge of religious discrimination against that employer. However, the attorney I met with on October 18th, 2019 told me that he believed a judge would take the view that an employee of that type of employer simply does not need to play in chess tournaments. As time has gone by and some personal challenges at times mounted up, I have decided that I will probably either avoid participating in future USCF competitions or wait a long time before rejoining USCF competitions.

Another part of my August 2019 EEOC charge against The Financial Advisory Group (FinGroup) involved something that happened in mid-December 2018. At that employer, there is generally significant peer pressure to drink alcohol. After joining on August 6th, 2018, I was reluctant to drink alcohol there because it might take the edge off of some of my chess training and performance. On December 11th, 2018 I drank a very small amount of champagne when the employer passed it around at work. On either December 12th or 13th, though almost definitely December 12th, 2018, I prepared to do a set of eye relaxation techniques that I have done since sometime 1999 and which are generally ethical to do with people around or by myself, with lights on or lights off. That being said, some people have felt uncomfortable with those eye relaxation techniques, which include blinking the eyes rapidly, using various linear eye movements, and closing the eyelids while rolling the eyes around clockwise and counter-clockwise. Normally, I was doing these eye relaxation techniques at FinGroup up until that time on occasions when my then-roommate Natasha McDaniel was away from the room, and I would close the door, leave the lights on, and face away from the door. On that occasion, I did the same thing, except I suddenly had a flashback to a childhood memory of visiting a cave in the Desert Southwest when a tour guide turned off the lights briefly in a cave and the room became absolutely dark, and I turned off the lights. For a moment, part of myself sensed that turning off the lights could lead to trouble, yet more energy from other parts of my consciousness and subconscious had an override. I believe that part of this involved energy from my subconscious with how I would sometimes relate the Led Zeppelin song "No Quarter" (which has opening lyrics of "Close the door, put out the light") to chess competitions, competitions in general, and multiple religious practices. Natasha opened the door and said, "Are you asleep?" Soon thereafter, she rushed away, presumably to speak with supervisor Juan Martinez, at about the same time that Chris Kolenda came to me to speak about some client work. If BFS does future business with me, then I may speak with you or Whitney or both in person or by another means more in depth about the twists and turns of what happened between me and FinGroup.

-------end of Part 3 of a 15 JUL 2021 message------

···beginning of Part 4 of a 15 JUL 2021 message···

To cut to the chase:

1) Natasha soon showed signs of outrage, and at one stage she sprayed her area of the room with Lysol or a similar substance, upon which I said to her, "What the hell?! I was only doing eye relaxation." She said, "I don't want to hear it! I don't want to hear it!"

2) Juan told me he believed I had done nothing wrong, yet FinGroup would have Natasha move out of that room.

3) Juan imposed on me to not bring up that incident in conversations with Natasha.

4) I soon overheard a woman in the hall speaking with another person about something like an aunt in her family catching a nephew in her family doing something, and this made me worry that Natasha could be committing sexual slander against me. However, Juan had indicated that he believed I had done nothing wrong, plus I knew I had avoided sexual activity with that incident. I thought about contacting HR or high ranking officials, yet decided against it, based on trusting Juan. Erin Hudson from IT collected my main password on Friday, December 14th, 2018, on the premise of collecting passwords from everyone to help with server processes, and I did not get to change that password until Monday, December 17th, 2018.

This seemed very suspicious, but I checked with Juan and he indicated that Erin's premise was accurate. I decided to trust Juan and not check around with people at that time about this. It was still very suspicious. I felt trapped by the situation, in a double-bind of how every communication of concern with anyone could be held against me, yet every choice to decline to communicate concern could lead to harmful rumors and other harmful actions happening against me behind my back. I decided on December 15th, 2018 that if things would later come to a head regarding these issues, I would attempt to obliterate FinGroup via a lawsuit as a religiously justified action and as an action defending The First Amendment. Of course, it would not be polite to say this directly to anyone at FinGroup, and therefore, I hoped that if things would escalate, then my communications would allow them to read between the lines that I was preparing for the possibility of war.

[Although it is unlikely for me to face a future bizarre double-bind problem anywhere close to this at a future employer, I would be inclined in a future case to simply go to HR and/or other higher-ups and seek to clear things up quickly, whether or not it would lead to my getting rapidly fired. Also, I am very unlikely in the future to suddenly turn off the lights in a room in a situation of major potential risk of snowballing into huge problems.]

------end of Part 4 of a 15 JUL 2021 message-----

···beginning of Part 5 of a 15 JUL 2021 message···

5) In mid-January 2019, I received a favorable performance review from Juan and Chris. They indicated that they had warned Natasha about the mid-December 2018incident, yet they instructed me to avoid discussing it with Natasha and to strictly limit communications with her in general.

6) Some time, possibly around February 2019, I heard that someone had put an obscene drawing and message involving the name "Chris" on condensation in a parking lot elevator. I spoke with Chris about it in a light-hearted manner and at some stage said something like, "I don't know, but if I were you, I might consider talking to HR about it." He then became very tense and angry and said, either verbatim or almost verbatim, "Maurice, I want you to take the idea of talking to HR completely out of your vocabulary!"

7) I had been on the fence about whether to talk to HR about concerns regarding whether Natasha had been committing a major slander against me, yet after Chris's statement imposing on me to not talk to HR, I decided I would not get involved with HR unless things would later get to the brink of going thermonuclear.

8) Natasha chose to initiate multiple adverse interactions in group settings against me, including a loaded question on July 26th, 2019 that could most naturally be interpreted as her

insinuating the idea of planting in people's minds the possibility of the sexual slander that I suspected her of committing against me. However, in the main sense, given that there was a joke element, full confirmation of slander seemed elusive.

9) When I checked my e-mail on August 5th, 2019, I found that Natasha had written a review note for a tax return in which she added a line that accused me of trying to get other people to do my work for me. I was not trying to get other people to do my work for me, yet I was at my wit's end about what to do about her hostility and the various threats of that employer. I decided to directly address the mid-December 2018 incident in an e-mail to Natasha with Juan and Chris on the cc line, even with this being insubordination. In a spirit of goodwill and teamwork I presented the main relevant truths about that incident, giving Natasha and FinGroup a chance for a clear path to harmonious resolution, yet also hoping for them to read between the lines that in the absence of harmonious resolution I would be aiming to bring things in the court system. Natasha responded angrily, characterizing my e-mail as nonsense, gibberish, and a waste of time. I responded with an e-mail to Natasha with Juan, Chris, and HR person Tina Nava on the cc line, this time directly bringing up that there had been evidence of major slander, and that now that she had crossed the line into putting things into writing this amounted to libel.

[In a future complex interpersonal work conflict with legal implications, I may consider hiring a lawyer for consultation about it while it is still unfolding. That being said, it could be unlikely for such a future conflict of that complexity to happen again in my life.]

10) On August 6th, 2019, FinGroup terminated my employment. At the exit interview, Tina appeared to be blindsided by my idea to attempt a lawsuit against FinGroup.

11) On August 27th, 2019, I met with the Equal Employment Opportunity Commission, and the EEOC person was very sympathetic. On August 28th, 2019 the EEOC closed the case, granting me the right to sue FinGroup within 90 days.

---end of Part 5 of a 15 JUL 2021 message-----------

---beginning of Part 6 of a 15 JUL 2021 message---

12) On October 18th, 2019, the attorney I met with indicated that, based on his conversation with me, he believed a judge would rule summary judgment in favor of FinGroup if I would attempt to use my right to sue. He also believed that I did not have a defamation case against Natasha due to a lack of directly observing the type of clear statement that would allow such a case to go forward. Unfortunately, at the time of meeting the attorney I did not remember the July 26th, 2019 loaded question, and I do not know whether or not this would have changed his view.

Related updates:

1) Bill Walker, who was for a few years one of my professional references and a friend, decided on January 21st, 2021 to tell me by e-mail that he was ending his friendship with me and that he was accusing me of putting the U.S. in danger by daring to vote for Trump in the 2020 U.S. Presidential election. On a related note, I voted for Clinton in the 2016 U.S. Presidential election. On January 22nd, 2021 I responded to Bill Walker's e-mail with a philosophical, religious, and scientific message in support of the premise that there are legitimate reasons why many Americans voted for Trump in 2020 and legitimate reasons why many Americans voted for Biden in 2020, and I cc'd The Republican National Committee on that message.

2) In early February 2021, CMCD tried to influence me to be one of the presenters of a CPE webinar on very short notice. However, due to a combination of reasons, including interactions with Steve Estrin, Natasha McDaniel, Bill Walker, and others, this led to a chain reaction including my declining to be a presenter and abruptly resigning from CMCD as a form of risk management.

--------end of Part 6 of a 15 JUL 2021 message-----

---beginning of Part 7 of a 15 JUL 2021 message---

I will probably wait until mid-August at the earliest before starting a new job search. However, depending on how things go in my life, I may wait until much later, maybe even some future year, before doing a new job search. My new job search might involve going directly to CMCD to attempt to rejoin, it may involve looking elsewhere, or it may involve both.

If you decide to tell me that you refuse to do future business with me, then this will be one piece of evidence I will consider in the direction of aiming for CMCD and similar-level firms in the future, instead of aiming higher (for example, at firms at the level you would typically represent).

Whether or not you decide to scold me for the length of this e-mail, whether or not you decide to issue other harsh reactions in response to it, and whether or not you decide to issue a favorable resp-onse to it, I thank you for reaching out to me last December and being part of my healing process.

Sincerely,

Maurice J. Blair

-----------end of Part 7 of a 15 JUL 2021 message----
------- This concludes a copy of that July 15, 2021 electronic mail message, which was from before a multitude of new developments occurred. ------

---

To clarify and to extend contextual awareness, please consider the following sequential copy of some August 2021 email correspondence that went back and forth between a U.S. Chess Federation tournament director and me, eventually garnering multiple on the cc-line.

Date: Thu, 26 Aug 2021 05:12:54 PM CDT
From: Maurice J. Blair
To: The Secretary of the U.S. Chess Federation; The Chess Refinery; James Liptrap
(The subject line was intentionally blank.)

Dear Select Chess Organization Persons,

Whereas The Financial Advisory Group evidently recently committed libel against me via arranging for an attorney from Gray Reed to send me a letter (dated August 9th, 2021) that included falsely claiming acts of trespassing and stalking, whereas the nature of their communication in its own way tilts the balance of energy in the direction of diminishing all chess players and the game of chess itself, and whereas I believe it in the best interests of The United States of America (especially on account of supplemental factors) for me to seek additional revelation of information in and adjacent to persons in and adjacent to that organization located in Houston, Texas, I am therefore requesting that you seriously consider recommending trial lawyers who could potentially be helpful for me to hire in pursuing a lawsuit against The Financial Advisory Group.

Yours Truly,

Maurice James Blair

[The following appears, to the best of our abilities, as-is, keeping any Liptrap-omitted punctuation omtted, etc.]

Date: Thu, 26 Aug 2021 07:41:32 PM CDT
From: James Liptrap (also known as Jim Liptrap)
To: The Secretary of the U.S. Chess Federation; The Chess Refinery; Maurice J. Blair
(Liptrap changed the subject.)
Subject: Blair problem

Dear Mr Blair,

Your issue is with your employer, not with the chess organizations. I have no idea what you expect us to do in a dispute to which we are not in any way party.

You also confused a talk-radio audience with your rant earlier this month. Several people asked me what you were talking about - at such length. I told them it was a problem with your employer that does not affect the chess community in any way.

I was going to suggest that in a medium-to-large size tournament, there are ways the Director can avoid pairing you against a particular opponent, which would have solved the issue you started with, concerning chess tournaments.

However, your issue with your employer seems to NOT be related to chess at all, but something else altogether.

I have two suggestions:
(1) get a new job, so you no longer have to worry about what that boss tells you, AND
(2) continue to stay away from chess tournaments. We do not need any of your drama disrupting them, when it has no relevance to any tournament we run.

J Liptrap

Date: Fri, 27 Aug 2021 08:07:54 PM CDT

From: Maurice J. Blair

To: Jim Liptrap (also known as James Liptrap)

Cc: Joel Edward Goza; The Secretary of the U.S. Chess Federation; The Chess Refinery; Jim Blair (also known as Maurice J. Blair, via an alternate e-mail address)

(Restoring the subject line to being intentionally blank by deleting the inserted subject line that Liptrap had placed there on the message to which this responded.)

Dear Mr. Liptrap,

Whereas telling a director to avoid pairing with a specific opponent could have compromised client confidentiality by *giving a "tell" that the player is possibly a client* of The Financial Advisory Group,

whereas your characterization ignores the other details of how The Financial Advisory Group terminated my employment over two years ago and I have not returned to working for them since them [sic][1],

whereas the circumstances of the termination *appear* to reflect multiple people in that organization having *serious issues* of sentiments against both the The First Amendment to the U.S. Constitution and against the spirit of fierce and fair competition,

whereas the aforementioned circumstances of termination also *appeared to be antithetical* to that which *is* adjacent to the aforementioned amendment and spirit,

and whereas a degree of that which is in and adjacent to the word "halcyon" and the word "raven" played roles in calming the online presence of portions of the talk radio audience that you mentioned, your statement deserves the *rebuke* that it received and may again receive in the future via *comparison and contrast* with the aforementioned "whereas" statements.

With all due respect,

Maurice James Blair

P.S. Consider for a moment how Saul David Alinsky (which spelled backward would be yksnilA divaD luaS, much like Maurice James Blair spelled backward would be rialB semaJ eciruaM, much like James Liptrap spelled backward would be partpiL semaJ), stated on page 90 of *Rules for Radicals* (of the VINTAGE BOOKS EDITION, OCTOBER 1989 version, which I currently have checked out from a library and am about seven-ninths the way through completing[2] a first reading of, to help with understanding what it is in, adjacent to, opposite of, and beyond that book), "'But Moses kept his cool, and he knew that the most important center of his attack would have to be on what he judged to be God's prime value. As Moses read it, it was that God wanted to be No. 1. All through the Old Testament one bumps into "there shall be no other Gods before me," "Thou shalt not worship false gods," "I am a jealous and vindictive God," "Thou shalt not use the Lord's name in vain." And so it goes, on and on, including the first part of the Ten Commandments.'"

Compare and contrast all that is within, without, adjacent to, and opposite of the aforementioned SDA quote to all that is within, without, adjacent to, and opposite of the Post Script #2 PDO quote.

Post Script Number Two: A portion of *Tertium Organum: A Key to the Enigmas of the World* states, '"Entering as a component part into different great and little lives man himself consists of an innumerable number of great and little I's. Many of the I's living in him do not even know one another, just as men who live in the same house may not know one another. Expressed in terms of this analogy, it may be said that "man" has much in common with *a house* filled with inhabitants the most diverse. Or better, he is like a great ocean liner on which are many transient passengers, each going to his own place for his own purpose, each uniting in himself elements the most diverse. "' (P.D. Ouspensky; THIRD AMERICAN EDITION, AUTHORIZED AND REVISED, TRANSLATED FROM THE RUSSIAN BY NICHOLAS BESSARABOFF AND CLAUDE BRAGDON; ALFRED A KNOPF, NEW YORK, 1945, p. 182).

Post Script #3: P.S. and P.S. #2 appear here as fair uses of copyrighted materials.

Post Script #4: Whether or not I someday have a civil suit against The Financial Advisory Group (as located on the ninth floor of a building at a corner of San Felipe and Saint James), whether such a suit happens and in some sense results in a win, a loss, or a draw, or a hybrid {win/win, loss/loss, win/loss, loss/win, draw/win, win/draw, etc.}, etcetera/nonetcetera/etc., whether or not I ever play another rated chess game, whether or not my family, your family, anyone else's family, the USCF, HCA, the Chess Refinery, any other organization, or anyone else stays around on Earth or vanishes from the face of the Earth, etc/nonetc/etcetera, you are also dead wrong about it primarily being an issue between me and FinGroup. You and I and FinGroup and The USCF, etc., are not the focus.

*The value and life-blood of The First Amendment* is much more primary to this, especially since a former KPMG coworker of mine some time circa March 2005 told me that he believed that the founding of The United States of America was illegitimate and I told him that I believe that the founding of The United States of America was legitimate. BY THE WAY, ALTHOUGH HE HAS SINCE apparently ACHIEVED SOME NOTORIETY writing about race, HIS MANY CONVERSATIONS WITH ME IN 2005 had extremely few direct references to race. HIS MAIN FOCUS appeared to have been ON PROSELYTIZING HIS SPECIFIC TAKE ON RELIGION and/or SPURRING ME TO CONSIDER THE UNKNOWN ADJACENT TO HIS APPARENT PROSELYTIZING. That former 2005 coworker's name was Joel Goza, and I believe that, in *some* major senses, his name *is* Joel Goza.

Of course, Joel Goza's views and beliefs about the U.S.A. and many other things have likely changed in many ways in the years since. Also, in many ways I am thankful for how that Goza spurred me to consider more viewpoints more thoroughly. That being said, I continue to be willing to unleash hell on people who threaten The First Amendment to the U.S. Constitution, whether they are business people, chess people, poker people, religious people, irreligious people, hybrid people, etcetera/nonetcetera/etc. I truly believe that it is religiously justified for me to defend The First Amendment against *you*, against *some potential influences from past interactions with anyone and/or everyone*, against anyone who in the present or future encounters this e-mail message, etc. That being said, if forces beyond all human beings and all earthly nations lead to the extinction of any or all nations and/or any or all humans, then I also feel fine about allowing the time and season to arrive to let go of intending to unleash hell in support of any or all earthly nations and/or any or all earthly humans.

Post Script #5: To anyone who has or is or ever will gaze upon or remember or read or hear this message,

Post Script #6: Post script #5 is an intentional sentence fragment, left open to the beholder to potentially imagine any and all possible continuations that could complete that sentence.

"Known problems" "Liptrap problem(s)" "(s)melborp partpiL" "Liptrap solution(s)"

"Blair problem(s)" "(s)melborp rialB" "Blair solution(s)"

"Known Solutions" "Unknown Solutions" "Unknown Problems" "Unknown Solutions"

---

APRIL 2024 FOOTNOTES:

[1] I had intended for that statement to end with the word “then” rather than the word “them,” yet an unintentional typo of “them” in place of “then” arrived.

[2] After sending that message, within some reasonable amount of time, I finished reading the remainder of that version of *Rules for Radicals*, then checked it back in to the public library from which I had borrowed it.

---

[A b/w 8:07 P.M. 8/27/2021 Message & 3:43 P.M. 8/28/2021 Message 2024 Comment from M.J. Blair: I admit that I was in many ways pleasantly astonished that James Liptrap dared to argue forcefully against me after I had put together the forward-and-backward Ouspensky-and-Alinsky-and-Beyond message preceding it. Therefore, everyone got what everyone had coming with my 7:07 P.M. 8/28/2021 answer.]

[Note: "Congress shall make no law respecting..." was in blue as Liptrap sent it; here it appears in black.]

---

Date: Sat, 28 Aug 2021 03:43:29 PM CDT

From: James Liptrap

To: Maurice J. Blair; Jim Liptrap (via an alternate James Liptrap address)

Cc: Joel Edward Goza; The Secretary of the U.S. Chess Federation; The Chess Refinery; Jim Blair (via an alternate Maurice J. Blair address)

(Liptrap changed the subject line again.)

Subject: Blair Issue

Dear Mr Blair,

Your appeal to the "First Amendment" in the case of your accusation of coercion by your former employer (A) is totally irrelevant, and (B) displays your ignorance of the US Constitution.

The First Amendment reads "Congress shall make no law respecting ..." The first ten Amendments to the Constitution were enacted to restrict the *Federal Government* from taking certain actions that would limit the rights of its citizens. Most State Constitutions contain similar restrictions *upon the government* against limiting the rights of citizens. But there is nothing in the US Constitution that in any way addresses the situation between you and The Financial Advisory Group. They are not the US Congress.

There are civil laws against coercion and blackmail (and against libel). But your argument from the First Amendment is irrelevant. Whether you spell it forward or backward or in Latin. Ask the lawyer of your choice.

Cheers!
J Liptrap

---

A 2024 M.J. Blair Comment, Alternatively Stated: I admit to having been pleasantly surprised that Liptrap dared to argue it into another round. I had thought that almost no one in his or her or its right mind would have dared to do so; nevertheless, I was fully prepared in advance. *At 7:07 P.M. on 28 AUG 2021 I then delivered a clear literary comeuppance to everyone deserving it.* In some ways, the next message presaged patterns in *Dr. Strange in the Multiverse of Madness* (2022) and postsaged patterns in much ancient literature.

--Maurice J. Blair, Q2 2024

---

From: Maurice J. Blair (also known as Jim Blair)

To: James Liptrap (also known as Jim Liptrap, via the main address he had used in that set of correspondence); Jim Liptrap (also known as James Liptrap, via the alternate address he had used in portions of that set of correspondence)

Cc: Joel Edward Goza; The Secretary of the U.S. Chess Federation; The Chess Refinery; Jim Blair (also known as Maurice J. Blair, via an alternate e-mail address)

Date: Sat, 28 Aug 2021 07:07:22 PM CDT

[I, Maurice James Blair, adjusted the subject line this time not by deleting it but by augmenting it.]

Subject: RE: Blair issue & Liptrap Issue & LIBERTY ISSUE

Mr. Liptrap,

In my situation, whether the court system would recognize it or not, for many years virtually everything I do is rooted in a religious attempt to attune to whatever people might wish to call "the most ultimate root of reality," "the ultimate source of reality," "God," "G-d," "YHVH," "Adi-Buddha," "Sunyata," "Yod-He-Vau-He," etc. (to whatever degree(s) this/these would constitute a unity-without-plurality, a plurality-without-unity, a unity-with-plurality, a nonunity-with-nonplurality, etc.)

Whether you or a given court judge or a given

lawyer or any expert brought in front of me recognizes it or not, there is a major truth to each individual's reality of experiencing that individual's relationship with whoever or whatever is most ultimate. Although I have limited exposure to ideas expressed in methods from Scientology (as having emerged from L. Ron Hubbard and others) and ideas as expressed by Caroline Myss, some of these reflect how each person's unique biography, biology, and related factors of persons experiencing reality can involve questions like, "What is real to you?" and "How does your perception of what is real to you set you up for energy contracts with the ultimate reality?"

In reality as I experience it, there is a major degree of truth to the perspective that multiple people at The Financial Advisory Group (as located in Houston, TX) acted in ways toward me that had been harmful toward my energy relationships with the ultimate reality. As part of dealing with a process of how to ethically fix things, the act of charging them with religious discrimination via the EEOC was part of what happened next. Consulting with an attorney and letting the 90-day right to sue expire was also part of this.

There were many twists and turns to how this unfolded, yet in the long run, much like the idea that God transforms all things to the good in the long run (rather than looking up scriptural chapter and verse on this at the time of composing this message, I'll leave it to the readers to decide to what degree this corresponds with this portion or that portion of this scripture or that scripture), July 19th, 2021 involved a revelation that made all of the harm that they had previously done to me transform into part of the process of the good, on account of how I endgamed them on that day.

I thought that was likely the end of my direct involvement in a crusade/jihad/holy war/etcetera versus some persons from that former employer, yet the mysterious levels of energy covenants led to more related things happening. One of them was that on the morning of August 6th, 2021 I felt the overwhelming energy that the time and season arrived for public testimony on this. Therefore, I called in on the open line Friday for The Michael Berry radio show and spoke with him at length. I presented a theory of having been a victim of Saul Alinsky-style targeting, and he and his producer Ramone[1] had some fun with the bumper music selection and other things. After studying major excerpts of the Facebook reactions, I engaged in direct jousting online with some people, filled in some gaps for some people, and generally observed. I shifted to a theory that Steve Estrin had a twisted idea of what would constitute the best interests of clients when he decided to threaten my involvement with chess, that Natasha McDaniel duped Juan Martinez because of J.D. Martinez's overreliance on focusing on the idea of a middle-80% range and similar things, and that Bill Walker (who was not an employee of FinGroup, though he figured very prominently in the call) had been acting on brainwashing when he tried to blame me for the January 6th, 2021 U.S. Capitol riot (to a significant degree).

Suddenly, on August 10th, 2021, I received a cease and desist demand (dated August 9th) from an attorney, with no reference at all to the radio show appearance, yet referring to some things up to and including the July 19th, 2021 communications, and committing a libel of a claim of trespassing and other things. Once I figured out the libel, I became very interested in how I could use their libel as a tool to be a catalyst to new rounds of revelations.

Alinsky seemed fond of writing "revolution, not revelation" in portions of the library book I mentioned yesterday. Of course, an alternative idea structure could be "revelation, with or without revolution." Another one could be, "revelation over confiscation." Some people define revelation in terms of disclosure, and some define it in other ways.[2]

Thank you, James Liptrap, for your rhetorical combat with me, as it has given me more opportunities to defend the spirit of how The First Amendment can relate to The Civil Rights Act of 1964 and RELIGIOUS LIBERTY, including in ways that can fix things outside the courts when the courts by themselves are likely insufficient for reasonable resolution.

Best Wishes With Your Present and Future Energy Covenants!

Maurice James Blair

---

2024 FOOTNOTES TO THAT 7:07 P.M. 8/28/2021 EMAIL:

[1] At the time of composing that e-mail message, I unknowingly misspelled the applicable version of the name “Ramón” (regarding the referenced Robles).

[2] Cf. anything of your choice.

## * * * * FURTHER 2024 FOLLOWUP * * * *

To help tie all of this together, understand this: When I was in middle school and high school I became aware of many intense attitudes from many sectors of society aimed at condemning all sorts of people in many ways, and I eventually found my way through the many challenging labyrinths presented by society and the rest of reality to get life to work reasonably well as of mid-2011. Although there were many ups and downs from then until partway into the day of November 21, 2018, the core elements and aspects of my psyche and my life seemed to be going along smoothly.

Then, although people could spend thousands of hours debating whether Steve Estrin or I or both or neither were right or wrong or of mixtures of right and wrong, the fact was that the paradigms that he and I had about a great many things collided into a huge disagreement. Much of my mindset was that 1) it was my holy duty to Vajrayana Buddhism, Esoteric Christianity, Noah-idism, and a variety of other means of relating to Adi-buddha/God/Reality to have at least some part of my life set up to fiercely compete and bring attention to skillful means and worthy goals; 2) chess was the primary means I believed in for that at the time, because I perceived my return to main literary activities to best be postponed to something like the year 2042; and 3) the idea of an employer and/or any employment supervisor seeking to impose that I take it easy on the chances of meeting and viciously defeating a client of that employer in federation chess competition would be setting up for that employer to attempt to have its own selfish interests outweigh the entirety of Adibuddha / God / Reality, Vajrayana Buddhism, Esoteric Christianity,

Whatever Realities Exist in Occult Practices and Doctrines, Noahidism, Jeet Kune Do, The First Amendment to the U.S. Constitution, and more. As long as an employer would not try to impose interference with how I viewed the chess activities as a small slice of getting to act out holy war / jihad / crusade in favor of all that, then the employer would not be smoking itself out as a potential enemy of all of that, because that employer would be minding its own business by staying in its lane. Once an employer might try to coddle a given client or given set of multiple clients by obstructing the free ferocity of the federation chess activities, then the unity of loyalty to the employer and loyalty to God / Reality / Adibuddha / Adidharma would be divided into a nonunity, and I would consider not only the employer to be microscopic compared to God / Reality / Adibuddha / Adidharma, but I would consider the Multiverse and every observable being in it to be as an entire collection microscopic compared to God / Reality / Adibuddha / Adidharma.

That, however, seemed potentially manageable. In fact, Estrin was isolated in presenting that imposition to me. For example, Darryl Nelson (who then ranked at about the same level as Estrin within the FinGroup hieararchy) expressed solidarity with my idea about a duty to the integrity of the U.S. Chess Federation ELO Rating System and my enthusiasm at the time for continuing with USCF tournament participation.

There is an idea in chess that when there is one main difficulty for a player facing a position, then with reasonable skill such a player often will find at least a few workable paths, yet once there emerge two separate weaknesses to present difficulties, the entire situation tends to become untenable. Similarly, although I did not feel any personal animosity toward Natasha McDaniel for any inherent reason or reasons, I unfortunately and unintentionally made several suboptimal choices of communication styles, not taking the cue from co-workers expressing between the lines that it would be best to take a walking-on-eggshells approach to mitigating risks of unintentionally causing her to feel irritated. There were many ways back then in which either The Financial Advisory Group or I or both could have maybe made different decisions that might have steered things away from the huge conflicts that later happened between that organization and me.

I tried extremely hard to get the entire situation to work out well, yet, evidently, multiple people there and at least one of the attorneys they hired were largely oblivious to the kind of absolute commitment to THE ABSOLUTE / G-D / GOD / ADIBUDDHA / ADI-DHARMA / THE ULTIMATE REALITY that I have prioritized for many years.

This reminds me of something I learned from some sources involving sociology, psychology, and social psychology, viz. the idea that when a person has an absolute commitment to a moral boundary, then even hypnosis is unable to sway the person into violating that boundary. The main example that many of those sociologists, psychologists, and social psychologists might point toward, perhaps could be how most normal people have a strong and often-absolute resistance to committing murder. That acknowledged, though, regular people when thrust into extraordinary challenges can and do sometimes wrestle with what they might perceive to be gray areas of what to consider justifiable homicide versus what to consider murder. That relates to something that many military personnel have relayed to others about the military experience through many means: some soldiers in the battlefield when first thrust into combat find it difficult the first time to actually pull the triggers on their firearms. If they survive long enough to get enough wits together to start pulling their triggers, then they might soon get into the groove of firing away skillfully.

One of the oddities in my development was that pop culture's frequent condemnation of what it would perceive to be nerdy behavior, dorky behavior, and similar undesirable patterns ended up interacting with how a major range of mainstream preachers, ministers, pastors, theologians, and similar religious folks, including my father and some famous religious figures, have often strongly endorsed extreme restrictions on sexual activities and other biological processes. Therefore, for me the idea of people refraining from killing other people is nowhere near the zenith of basic moral duties as I perceive what my moral duties consist of; rather, coordination of all influences and factors are such that extreme restrictions on coordinating the activities of one's genitals and the interactions-versus-the-refraining-from-interactions between one's genitals and the genitals of others winds up often at the zenith of those duties. Unless and until my situation might change, the completely absolute commitment with that is for me to continue with the mid-April-2001-and-onward extinction of intentional ejaculation and extinction of intentional orgasm. (For those who wonder why both were specified just now, be aware that some types of yoga can induce orgasmic experiences in the male biological system without ejaculating. I have only experienced a reasonably full orgasmic experience that lacked ejaculation once in my life up to the time of sending to a database the finalized format of the initial printing of this book. That nonejaculatory orgasm happened unintentionally while participating in a yoga class in early June 2019, and that orgasmic feeling *pervaded the entire body* for a while, *rooted in a profound and powerful love for new tantric experiences and potential new tantric partners.*)

Purity of speech is also something that in the period of a little over two decades leading up to the publication of this book I have often considered a higher priority than not only an obligation to preserve a given human life, but the degree of obligation to preserve the survival of the human race. As I think about this, I recognize that there could be value in recognizing that religious zealotry can sometimes go too far, and to be mindful to balance the dueling values of zealotry and nonzealotry such as to possibly find a middle way between excessive zeal and insufficient zeal.

* * * * * * * * *

This zeroes in on several themes that have become clichés for many decades, and which we might best revisit here and now. That is, since you have been granted the possibility—or maybe even probability—of understanding the social psychology of zealotry better than you had ever previously understood it.

* * * * * * * * *

Many times in recent years I changed my evaluation of how ethical versus how unethical to deem the treatment received from various people in this life. Perhaps you have often done the same.

A related clarification is that, with the second-quarter 2024 C.E. publication of this book is an act of refraining to set up updated lists of people whom I would judge to have behaved most unethically toward me and people whom I would judge to have behaved most ethically toward me. Perhaps I might generate such lists again someday, and perhaps I might not. *Also, I have let go of harboring any steady hostility toward anyone, having already dealt sufficient punishments on behalf of the totality of reality to all of those upon whom I believed it my duty to deliver that, whether viewed from a Vajrayana perspective or a religious perspective expressed in another way (e.g., "acting on behalf of God, with full faith in the correctness of the notion that sometimes people should act as instruments of divine wrath"), except insofar as there is still the potential for new rounds of acting on believing in a religious duty to deliver harsh consequences where and when appropriate. This could even include, if necessary, ethical acts of executing others, in order to help with soteriology—including even the long-term soteriology of those killed in such processes of self-defense, &c.* I am ready for new changes and new challenges.

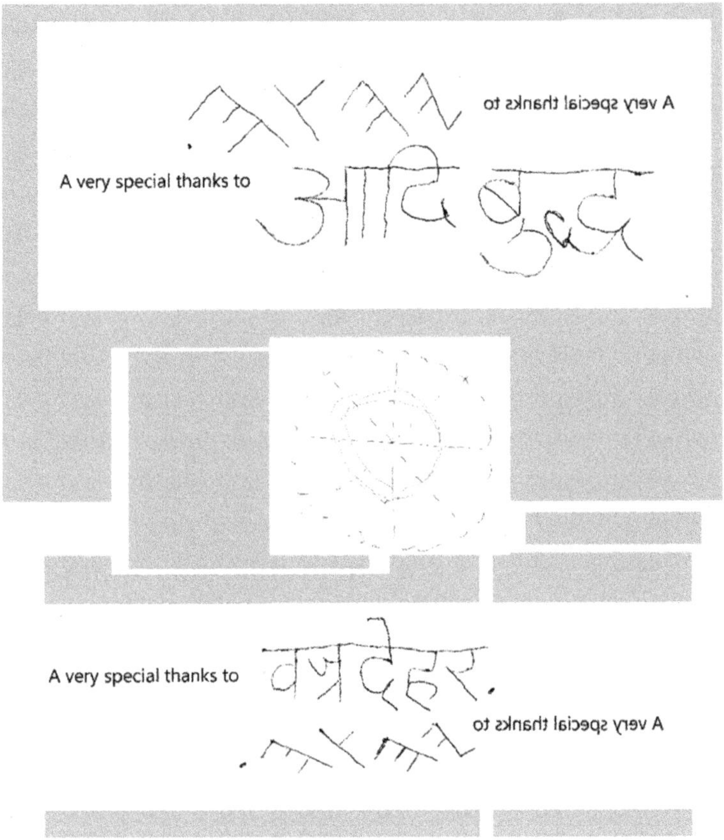
A very special thanks to
A very special thanks to

* * * * * * * * *

* * * * * * * * *

* * * * * * * * *

* * * * * * * * *

* * * * * * * * *

* * * * * * * * *

* * * * * * * * *

* * * * * * * * *

* * * * * * * * *

On September 8, 2022 I presented Justin Haynes with an improvised, extemporaneous, very-altered spoken variation of the Clarke 1951 short story "All the Time in the World" (from mind, sans text).

After several twists and turns happened on my way home, around 2 AM the next day I chose to walk with two women to an apartment, fully intending to obey the law and to be spiritually ethical to the best of my knowledge and abilities. While there, two men approached, one with a gun and one with a pipe. Though they did not shoot me, the one with the pipe hit me hard over the head with it, and they demanded and took all the possessions I was carrying at the time, including the very clothes and shoes I had been wearing. Bleeding very much from the scalp, I then traveled on foot to a police station and reported the incident. Though the injuries turned out to be superficial, in many respects I narrowly escaped with my life.

In contrast, on March 30, 2024, to Justin Haynes I read out loud directly from an official text that Arthur C. Clarke 1951 short story "All the Time in the World." The vast majority of the paragraphs I read exactly as in the text, and, in the few spots with even a trace of deviance, nevertheless, the reading was virtually exactly the same thing. For example, stuff like spontaneously inserting the word "to" into a spot where it renders the sentence to seemingly carry the same meaning either way.

Although I did not read it in one continuous setting, the total set of starts, pauses, restarts, continuations, and reaching conclusion amounted to one complete, fully-spoken-aloud reading.

I traveled home safely on that occasion. From that evening until the time of sending the finalized version of the first printing of *Alternative Beginnings and Endings of All Things: Science, Religion, Politics, and Cards, Hypervolume II* into a database, I have remained reasonably safe.

Consider the degrees to which safe zones and danger zones have ever existed or ever will exist. Also, consider how, in the long run, ranging from the least risk-and-reward-inducing to the most risk-and-reward-inducing, as well as along the full ranges of other qualities, zones of various kinds can and often do exhibit fleeting qualities. Similarly, sometimes a given person or a given group of people do in fact change dramatically at various stages.

Finally, consider relationships between artifacts, beings, and changes. With each arrival of an artifact, whether by physical presence, spoken reference, written reference, or another means, there can arrive much uncertainty, in some cases escalating to absolute uncertainty; likewise, with each arrival or departure of anyone or anything there emerges much uncertainty and much that is unknown, in some cases escalating to the absolute.

As the human race moves forward into the future, all it might take someday for a major nuclear power to initiate an unprovoked first strike that detonates thermonuclear bombs upon another nation or multiple nations would be for a few people from the top leadership of that nation on down in the chain of command to agree that the utilization of death with which to avoid dishonor would make the likelihood of total human extinction to be both acceptable and potentially an honorable, morally superior outcome. They might even decide to conceive it point blank that the total grievances are enough to make it *most* moral to intentionally seek to cause total human extinction.

I am not going to pretend with this book to offer any clear answers about how to reduce the chances of a future thermonuclear human-induced total human extinction event, because I am uncertain whether there even exist any clear answers about that. However, with the bizarre time loop event that I described in portions of some other books from my own direct experience and with the bizarre time loop evidence that I have noticed others signal toward in a variety of ways, I sometimes wonder if on some occasions the cause of these might be universal timelines that went into such catastrophes that moving *out* from some timelines granted an edge to select beings' capacities to help.

*Maybe there have even already been total human extinction events in some timelines, with a few survivors teleported out to surviving timelines.*

* * * * * * * * * *

Namo Kalachakra. Namo Vishvamata.

* * * * * * * * * *

1. One, Two, Three, Five, Ten, Twenty.

2. Twenty-One, Twenty-Two, Twenty-Five.

3. 4, 5, 6, 7, 8.

9. Buddhism, Christianity, Judaism, Noahidism, Islam, People-of-the-Book-ism, Jainism, Sikhism, and various other sets of whatever-they-are could be considered what someone considers them to be or they could be beyond what someone considers them to be.

# Chapter Ten: Revelatory Detonations

· Comparative Origins · Sex · Biology
· Business · Crimes · Enforcements
· Cards · Politics · Religion · Science
· Investigations · Sexuality · Ethics
· Standards · Alternatives · Statics
· Dynamics · Energy · Matter · Mind
· Love · Birth · Death · Rebirth · Life
· Comparative Eschatology

A TABLE OF CONTENTS FOR CHAPTER TEN:



(cont'd on next page)

A TABLE OF CONTENTS FOR CHAPTER TEN, CONTINUED:

... THE PARTS OF SECTION FIVE, CONT'D:

True, some might debate definitions of crime and become philosophical, talking about the idea that it was a crime for anyone to have ever been born or a crime for all but one person in the history of the human race to have ever been born, or a crime for all but something like three or twenty-five people in the history of the human race to have ever been born, but such extremist ways of tackling the concepts of criminal justice would, most likely, seem of limited value to most readers.

This chapter shall instead focus on a few things that clearly were crimes, whether or not the perpetrators have ever been prosecuted for them, and on many things—whether legal, criminal, or in gray areas—considered from perspectives of any of the earthly law, heavenly law, dharmic law, &c.—concerning the totality of reality. In the interests of the broadest striving for genuine understanding of reality, let us not concern ourselves much with whether statutes of limitations have expired or not; rather, let us focus on what might prove the most useful to any and all who might read or hear this stuff, whether in a given lifetime or beyond it.

Whether considered from perspectives expressed in or adjacent to *Ecclesiastes*, *The Dhammapada*, the Led Zeppelin song "Kashmir," the Santana song "Winning," the James Hilton novel *Lost Horizon*, or anything else, here goes.

## SECTION ONE

As mentioned in the previous chapter, and as mentioned in one of the latter portions of *An Encyclopedic Survival Guide for Navigating Normal and Paranormal Experiences*, a crime occurred in an extremely early portion of September 9, 2022, and it included an armed robbery.

Here is an additional twists to that, encapsulated by portions of two e-mail messages that I sent as an update to initial reporting of the crime to HPD:

Excerpt #1 from Message #1:

The person in the photos, I believe, should be considered a person of interest rather than a suspect at this time because of some of the following:

Shortly before the woman who begrudgingly identified herself by the name Maria walked out of the room and the two male robbers entered the room, I asked Monique what she felt most interested in, and she said, "Drugs."

To that I responded either verbatim or nearly so, "Maybe if we can get along well enough, you might let go of being so interested in drugs."

---

Regarding Excerpt #1: I am declining to provide a copy of the referenced photographs with this book, as a way to respect and reasonably protect the right to privacy of that Monique. You might want to ask me, "What about the right to privacy of the various people whose behavior and life details you intentionally—and in some cases rather fully—reveal publicly to anyone who happens to read this book?" Here is a response to that: "I show all due respect to all beings to the best of my ability with this book. In some cases, I show due respect by rather fully exposing things about others' pasts that they would probably much prefer for me not to expose about them, and I do it anyway, as a duty to YHVH / G-d / God / Adibuddha / Adidharma / &c. In other cases, I show due respect by omitting any direct reference to others' pasts or by omitting almost any direct reference to others' pasts. If anyone truly believes there to be a basis for criminal prosecution of me in response to any of this and/or attempted civil litigation against me in response to any of this, then go for it!

IF ANYONE BELIEVES THERE IS A LEGITIMATE PATH TO SHOWING ME ANY KIND OF ETHICAL REBUKE FOR ANYTHING IN CONNECTION WITH THIS BOOK, THEN GO FOR IT!! I FEEL NOT ONLY READY TO GO TO PRISON IF IT TURNS OUT THAT LAW ENFORCEMENT AND COURTS WIND UP DEEMING IT APPROPRIATE, I AM PREPARED TO DIE AT ANY INSTANT IN CONNECTION WITH ANY OF THIS PROCESS OF HONORING WHAT I BELIEVE TO BE MY DUTY TO YHVH / G-D / GOD / ADIBUDDHA / ADIDHARMA / &C.

[The preceeding concluded the comment regarding that excerpt #1.]

---

Excerpt #2 from Message #1:

On another relevant note, I recently published an account of that incident in a portion of AN ENCYCLOPEDIC SURVIVAL GUIDE FOR NAVIGATING NORMAL AND PARANORMAL EXPERIENCES (by various contributors, edited by yours truly, and available as a free online flipbook at mixam.com/share/655c27abd6df672f5fc02e04 ; Cf. pp. 3-7 of "Miscellany Between Encyclopedia Part Ten and Encyclopedia Part Eleven").

If the Houston Police Department would prefer to receive one or two print copies of that for-free-distribution book, then I could supply it with the one or two copies of that.

Thank you for your service to the general public.

---

Full body of text from E-Mail Message #2:

Officer Lewis,

Another detail is that during early stages of conversations with the Maria who was part of that incident, she showed me a notebook that seemed to have technical collegiate-or-similar-level notes written with what seemed clearly to be female penmanship. That was among the set of possessions she was carrying.

Conversationally, she seemed oblivious to the meanings and contexts of that notebook.

Combining that fact with how she was carrying a BARBARELLA cosmetic kit and demonstrating obliviousness to the existence of the moderately-famous film of that name, the fact pattern would seem to be indicative of the likelihood of her previous involvement with robbing at least one high-school-to-graduate-school-aged woman in some totally separate incident.

Regards,
Maurice J. Blair

---

## SECTION TWO

Sometime approximately 11 P.M. CDT, Saturday, July 11, 2009, a group of members of what was then called Houston Single Friends Meetup Group skinny dipped in the waters by Surfside Beach, TX. I know because I was one of them, specifically, one of the skinny-dippers.

Although at the time Brigid A. Wilson, the hostess of the event, shared a conversation in which she asked me not to tell anyone about it, and I said, "My lips are sealed," the fact that she later insulted me on multiple occasions and never made a sufficient step toward restoring reasonable respect toward me, together with how people in general have consistently on many occasions *after her meetings with me* disrespected me in ways I could hardly have previously believed possible, is such that I have decided to include in this book, right here, telling the reader point-blank about that occurrence and much of the related context.

Given that she indicated—with ambiguity as to whether she was joking or serious or using a hybrid of joking and being serious—that her family might have connections with some Irish syndicate people, of the type who sometimes install car bombs with which to execute people, I recognize that publishing this could result in a person in her network attempting to kill me sometime after this book reaches publication. I accept that risk, because my commitment to helping with the enlightenment of sentient beings and the spreading of awareness of relevant truths and facts in the appropriate ways and at the appropriate times is absolute.

Why did I choose to skinny dip with them at that time, you might ask; well, whether you intended to ask that or not, I will go ahead and explain some of why. It was a combination of several factors: 1) I felt at the time that I truly and deeply loved her, even though I had not gone on any dates with her, and even though she had generally shown a mixture of rejection toward getting romantically involved with me and an ambiguous mild way of flirting with me. 2) At some of the events leading up to that, she would freely hug many of the attendees, including me, and I felt a strong love toward those experiences of hugging her and being hugged by her. 3) For some reason at the time, I did not actually conceive of skinny dipping in that portion of the Gulf of Mexico at that time as actually being illegal.

On an additional note, I was not under the influence of alcohol or any illegal drug(s) at the time, and according to my memory there were more than five skinny-dippers, though I neither knew then nor know now what the exact number of skinny-dippers was.

Leading up to the group crime, I mainly listened as others at the event were discussing the possibility of swimming nude in the waters. Some decided to commit to a plan to refrain from doing that. Others decided to commit to a plan to do that. I, meanwhile, did not choose at first to commit to either side of that.

Then, there was a converstion that proceeded either identically or nearly identically as follows:

Dr. Brigid A. Wilson: Maurice, would you like to skinny dip?

Maurice J. Blair: Sure.

Dr. Wilson: You're not going to tell anyone, are you?

Maurice J. Blair: My lips are sealed.

---

Although there were several ups and downs to the communications between her and me after that, and, although in the long run she did not prove nearly as mean toward me as she might otherwise have chosen to be, I have eventually concluded that she has not shown sufficient respect toward me with which to justify for me to keep hiding this fact from law enforcement and anyone else who might benefit from knowing about it. Placing this here is not primarily about her; neither is placing this here primarily about me. The publisher and I are including this here primarily out of soteriological interests. (Soteriology can have a wide variety of definitions, and some might wish to approach it as, “the entirety of all real or alleged means of religious deliverance and the study of that entirety.” Cf. *Science, Religion, Politics, and Cards.*)

Consider this supplement: Text messages between that Brigid A. Wilson and this Maurice J. Blair to accompany portions of television broadcasting of the 2009 Wimbledon Men’s Final between Roger Federer and Andy Roddick; the times stated were as measured from Houston, Texas:

---

From: Maurice Blair

To: Brigid Wilson

10-10 in the 5th and still going!

Sunday, July 5, 2009, 11:54 am

---

From: Brigid Wilson

To: Maurice Blair

I am watching - so amazing!

Sunday, July 5, 2009, 11:55 am

---

{She on that occasion initiated at about half-past-Noon without any intervening message from me to her.}

---

From: Brigid Wilson

To: Maurice Blair

Why did roddick choke? Today he became aman and made me proud!!

Sunday, July 5, 2009, 12:31 pm

[A 2024 Note Regarding That 2009 Text: Miss Wilson probably intended to include a space in the pattern such as to show the phrase "a man" in contrast with how the text displayed "aman." Also, she casually declined to capitalize "Roddick," and one may wonder whether that was intentional or unintentional.]

---

From: Maurice Blair

To: Brigid Wilson

I think he choked when he had the volley go wide at set point in the second set, but at the end he ran out of steam.

Sunday, July 5, 2009, 12:39 pm

---

From: Brigid Wilson

To: Maurice Blair

I think he got nervous at the end

Sunday, July 5, 2009, 12:45 pm

{Omissions of punctuation, etc., are left as-is in this transcript, to the best of ability to do so. Alternative ways to display this would have been, "...at the end [sic]" and "...at the end[.]" The same issue applies to the dialogue's subsequent 12:59 text's pattern.

---

From: Maurice Blair

To: Brigid Wilson

To a degree I agree about Andy's nerves at the end now that I think of it. Still, what a championship match!

Sunday, July 5, 2009, 12:58 pm

---

From: Brigid Wilson

To: Maurice Blair

We had a wonderful treat. We saw history! I love sports

Sun July 5, 2009, 12:59 pm

---

* * * * *

## SECTION THREE

I have only been engaged once in my life up to the time of this book going to print. It was an extremely strange situation, and it likely does not speak very favorably toward me, the woman with whom I was engaged, the United States of America, or the human race, if we look at it from some angles. If we look at it from a few other angles, then maybe it speaks favorably in some ways about the human race, the United States of America, the woman with whom I was engaged, and me. As I reflect on that, some of my thoughts are along the lines of, *you know what, maybe if I die from being struck by lightning within minutes after this book becomes published, maybe it might be for the best, and, you know what, for all I know, maybe if the entire universe or multiverse that houses the living humans winds up getting annihilated within minutes after this book reaches publication, if it happens in just the right way, maybe it might help the best with the enlightenment of sentient beings. Just how much do we really know about the most ultimate truths about much of anything?*

One day, something like somewhat early in the fourth quarter of 2016, an apartment manager from a different apartment than the one where I was a resident at that time was in a grocery store. Soon, she started sharing a conversation with my mother and me. That apartment manager identified me as a single man who might be a great candidate for her to try to match up with dating a single woman who was one of the residents at her apartment complex.

Not way too long after that, there was a strange date in which the apartment manager, my mother, the single woman referenced, and I all gathered together at a restaurant. The dining and the conversation went well, and, after it, the single woman and I walked to a vehicle, then traveled alone together as two people across the somewhat-spacious parking lot.

That single lady presented herself as named Lisa Song, and she and I seemed to have great chemistry together. However, something extraordinarily weird about that was that she spoke very little English, whereas I spoke very little Mandarin, whereas the apartment manager was fluent in both languages, and my mother was fluent in both languages. I brought up at that date that the language barrier could be troublesome, yet the apartment manager assured that this could be manageable: That single woman and I could adapt to learning more language capability, and we could also use translation software on devices like smartphones.

Time went by, and there continued favorability between that Lisa Song and me. Suddenly, though, Lisa started to contact me by text messages in a very aggressive manner, asking me if I love her and asking me if I could keep a huge secret. I was not too sure about the situation, but I decided that I felt favorably enough toward her that it would be fine to tell her by text that I love her and to indicate that I can, in general keep a secret well. That soon led to her arranging with me for a second date in which I would meet her in the evening of Tuesday, November 8, 2016 at a parking lot, where I could get into her vehicle and she could drive a variety of places and share conversations with me, some of which would include using smartphone translation software.

We met for that date, and, a ways into it, she revealed the secret to me. After she revealed that secret to me, I kept it a secret until approximately October 2021, when I chose to reveal it to Justin Haynes and his then-roommate Joshua Short. After revealing it to Justin and Joshua, I gradually revealed it to a few other people, including my mother. However, in the long period of secrecy, I kept the secret even though my decision to maintain the secrecy may have been one of the contributing factors to the conflict that happened between me and The Financial Advisory Group. You see, I revealed some parts of the story to then-co-workers there, including Juan Martinez and Austin Leavitt, yet I fastidiously refused to reveal the main secret detail, and this was one of the things that tilted things ever-so-slightly further in the direction of some of them for whatever reasons perceiving it best to pay me little or no respect on several occasions.

Back to the evening of November 8, 2016. When Lisa and I were on that car date, I made absolutely no attempt to reach second base or further with her, yet she became extremely aggressive in terms of the communications that she and I used her smartphone to translate via typing messages and hitting the button to translate. She revealed that, by her own account, she had a while before meeting me been on a peculiar life path. Specifically, she expressed that she had set up a fake marriage with a man as part of intentionally breaking United States law in order to obtain United States residency. She claimed that she had bought a $40,000 automobile to give to that guy as a bribe with which to induce him to get into a fake marriage with her. Having obtained residency in an illegal manner, she then indicated that she would prefer to shift things over to having a real marriage with a guy she would find suitable, and that in this way she could very much legitimize much of her life. As she and I had shared great chemistry and were with each other on a date, and as she had already requested me to answer by text between the first date and the second date about whether I loved her, and I answered that I loved her, it became obvious that she wanted for me to propose marriage.

I felt a mixture of several competing factors. She had described herself as having intentionally broken the law in a serious way, and I suspected that her entire description of that might have been simply some kind of cover story for actually being a spy for a foreign power, whether China or some different foreign power. However, I found her of moderately-high physical attraction and of very, very extremely-high psychological attraction, very especially because she had indicated strong favorability toward Buddhism, whereas many of the women I have dated and/or had meaningful conversations with were women who ranged from indicating ambivalence toward Buddhism to indicating outright hostility toward Buddhism.

The entire situation placed me under strain. There were multitudes of factors to consider, not the least of which was the paltry rate of success I had experienced over the years with romance, dating, flirtation, kissing, sex, romantic love, etc.

Also, I had to in some ways weigh all kinds of factors about my prospects for the future, and a multitude of ideas about ethics and the relationships between ethics and the laws that governments impose upon people.

Of the many things swirling around various levels of my heart and mind and soul was how I had received a marriage proposal in a high school Honors English class sometime approximately something like two or four months before graduating from high school, and I wondered sometimes about if things might have gone better had I handled that differently. I never really knew to what degree it might have been a joke or a serious proposal, yet I handled it the best I could at the time. Circa the first few months of 1994, the referenced conversation proceeded as follows:

Eva-Maria Gortner (not presenting a ring or anything else tangible like that; simply asking a question out of the blue, with class in session and many other students present, seeming to sound serious, though her voice sounding ambiguous as to whether of deadpan humor, deadly seriousness, or somewhere between): Maurice, would you marry me?

Maurice James Blair (speaking slowly, carefully, and respectfully): I do not have enough information at this time to answer that question.

*** Please note that Eva-Maria and I were able to continue to get along well after that, and, many years later, she married a man named Julius. ***

* * * * *

Another factor that weighed on me in considering how Lisa Song was, rather clearly, trying to tell me on that November 8, 2016 date that she would like for me to propose marriage to her then and there was that I remembered having discovered the main Olivia Newton-John recording of the song "Banks of the Ohio" approximately in 2008, and, although I really enjoyed that song, I recognized that it provides quite a warning about how much anger and resentment a woman who feels jilted—sometimes especially when perceiving herself to deserve to get a marriage proposal from a guy she wants—can get.

Between all of the factors, I decided then and there to love that Lisa Song enough to go ahead and propose, and she accepted.

I had not brought a ring, and I had not planned on proposing, yet she accepted anyway. Also, I acknowledge that some people will probably want to ridicule that Lisa and me for how the entire situation unfolded. Maybe some such people will be justified to ridicule us for that, and maybe not, or, maybe it is beyond a fixed conceptualizations of either of fully deserving ridicule or fully deserving respect.

In case you are wondering, I was not that confident in her ability to understand a spoken proposal in English, and, therefore, I used that same main text communication method that she and I had been using in the lead up: typing into her smartphone a message and letting the software translate. Likewise, she used that method to communicate the acceptance. She also set up her phone to provide graphics of a fireworks celebration to go with her words of telling me a resounding yes.

Although neither she nor I made any attempt to reach second base or further with each other in terms of physical romance, a little while before we parted company that evening, I offered mouth-to-mouth kissing by the traditional method of going most of the way toward initiating a kiss and then pausing, letting her decide whether to complete it or not, and she chose to complete the kiss. Although we kissed each other mouth-to-mouth with a reasonable favorability and degree of passion, and even though I in some ways felt great about being engaged, I also felt many levels of trepidation about the entire situation.

Was she, as per her own account, a woman who had intentionally broken the law by setting up a fake marriage to a previous man?

Was she a woman who had not done that, but instead used it as an initial cover story with which to draw me into international espionage operations hostile to the United States of America?

Was she of a third category, almost undoubtedly indicating the likelihood of a dangerous situation of another kind?

It seemed that no matter what she had going on behind the veil of what she had presented to me, it had to be something exceedingly dangerous for me to get involved with, and I felt very concerned.

A few days later, on November 11, 2016, I sent her a text message suggesting that if she and I were to get married, then I would believe it best to wait at least about six months rather than rushing in.

She responded by expressing uncertainty about whether the marriage should even happen if we were to do something other than marrying very soon.

After that, I answered that I believed it best to call off the engagement and possibly go back to more normal dating, though still keeping open the possibility of getting engaged again in the future.

A modest amount of time went by, and I caught a cold. While I had that cold, she sent a message suggesting that she and I meet at her apartment unit for a new date. However, I honestly communicated with her about how I had caught a slight illness and, therefore, if she and I would go another date with each other, then it would best wait until another time.

Some more time went by, and I sent a communication to her about the possibility of a new date, and she ghosted me. In other words, though I made a few more attempts to initiate new, written correspondence with her, she remained silent toward me from then onward.

Some of those communications consisted of text messages. There were also some e-mail messages between her and me.

Even with how she reported herself to me as having committed a crime, and even with how law enforcement authorities reading this might deem me to have been unjustified to decline reporting her to law enforcement prior to sending complimentary copies of this book to several law enforcement organizations, I still believe that she proved helpful to my life.

Insofar as she or I or both might have done anything unethical in how we interacted in the process of dating and be-coming engaged to each other before calling off that engagement, some might claim that whatever love she and I shared in the process does not excuse whatever they would deem unethical about what happened, yet I still feel thankful that Lisa Song and I actually shared strong mutual benevolence for a while.

## SECTION FOUR

For many years, my father was a lifetime member of the National Rifleman Association, also known as the NRA. However, he informed me that he had grown weary of its heavy involvement with politics. At some earlier times, it had seemed to be more about firearms and firearm enthusiasts in general without having such a heavy involvement with attempting to influence legislation. After the shifts toward more political involvement by the NRA, he became disenchanted with the organization. At some stage, he had even gone so far as to request that they stop sending him the magazine that would otherwise go to him free of additional charge as part of the lifetime membership.

After several months went by after his April 26, 2015 passing, I informed the NRA that he had died. Not very long after that, there arrived the day December 5, 2015. My mother and I went to a grocery store together, then she suddenly realized that she had left her normal main set of cards at home. That included the credit card that would earn rewards points when she would use it to purchase items at that chain of grocery stores, and it also included the driver's license that she had at that time. While she stayed at the store, with some groceries in a cart, I rushed home, intending to pick up her main set of cards. At the apartment complex where she and I were residents of one of the units at that time, I parked the family car of that time. After going into the apartment unit and obtaining the cards, I heard a strange sound out in the parking lot. It sounded like someone had hit something, though it was hard to tell what got hit with what.

Exiting the residence and stepping to the car, I noticed that there was a small ding in part of the driver door—a ding I had not previously noticed ever being there. I found that peculiar yet started to open the door anyway.

Suddenly, I heard a loud voice from the distance, a loud, male voice screaming, "Pop the trunk!"

I looked back and saw two Black men, one approaching while holding a gun and the other standing back. For a split second I thought about turning on the engine and attempting to speed away without getting shot. However, I decided that the risk of getting shot to death in that scenario might be excessively high. Therefore, I chose to start figuring out how I should open the trunk.

With that particular vehicle[1] at that time, I was not very used to opening the trunk with the button in the driver's part of the cabin, instead I was used to almost always using the turning of a car key to open that trunk. Therefore, I stepped out of the vehicle and proceeded to walk to the trunk. Around the time I opened the trunk, the gunman who had approached close demanded that I give him my wallet, and soon he not only grabbed my wallet but also my mother's main set of cards of that time. When he got a chance to see into the trunk, he did not deem anything there to be worth his while for stealing.

Next, he commanded me, "On the ground, bitch!"

I then laid down on the ground, face up. That fellow said something like, "I want to get into your accounts."

To me, that was the last straw. It was one thing to steal a few things like my driver's license, one of my credit cards, a little cash, my health insurance card, my mother's driver's license, one of my mother's credit cards, my mother's health insurance card, my wallet itself, and the Kalachakra card that I had received from True Buddha School, but it was quite another for him to have the nerve to try to gain unlawful access to my accounts. I decided that if he or his partner in crime or both would decide to kill me over refusal to grant access to my accounts, then I would be willing to die in order to prevent such unlawful access. I proceeded to stop speaking in English or any other language known to any other than a microscopic sliver of the human race. I chanted the True Buddha School pronunciation of THE YAMANTAKA MANTRA, for which I had earned empowerment years earlier. I simply chanted that mantra over and over and over again, fully prepared to die at any instant.

Soon, the two robbers agreed with each other that it was time for them to leave. Fortunately, they neither shot me nor did anything else to inflict direct physical harm to me before leaving.

When reporting the incident to the Houston Police Department, an officer who came out to meet me shared a brief conversation. At some stage, he asked me to describe the firearm that the main robber had carried and threatened me with. After I described it to that police officer, he said to me, "That's a Glock." That was the peculiar way that I wound up learning what the distinctive shape of a Glock handgun is, although I had heard references to Glocks in some rap music occasionally for many years prior to actually getting robbed with one.

Although I have been robbed at gunpoint twice in my life—specifically, on December 5, 2015 and on September 9, 2022—I still feel generally very favorable toward having a reasonably-strong right to bear arms in the United States, especially in connection with the Second Amendment. Virtually no one ever states this point blank, but it seems clear that at least some of those who wish to impose extreme restrictions on gun ownership are against harsh actions of intimidation and viciousness in general, underweighing perspectives emphasizing justified use of intimidation, viciousness, and force, for example as expressed in the Little Texas song "Kick a Little," the Kenny Rogers song "The Coward of the County," the movie *Braveheart*, and the movie *Live and Let Die*, whereas some of those who wish to have virtually no restrictions on gun ownership are, perhaps hell-bent on favoring to the point of overemphasizing the use of intimidation, viciousness, and force. Though there is much more I could state here about those debates and where exactly people might find a middle ground for how the United States deals with its legacy as a very gun-friendly environment—a middle ground somewhere between the extremities on each side—the statements here will suffice as a contribution to the gargantuan amounts of debate on this topic.

## SECTION FIVE: A MULTIPART SECTION

Section 5 Preliminary Narrative: With some of the disastrous turns of events from around 2007 and onward, I think back to a few things from around 2006 and earlier sometimes and wonder whether anyone might have chosen differently in a way that could have led to better results.

One class of such examples would consist of every instance in which an author and a publisher had a choice of whether to deeply insult any of the major religions or to refrain from deeply insulting any of the major religions. As mentioned earlier, although Cialdini did an admirable job with many of the finer points of human psychology and interpersonal influence in *Influence: The Psychology of Persuasion*, he presented a significant amount of gratuitous hostility toward great swathes of legitimate activity in multiple religions in that work, without presenting sufficient counterbalancing expressions. True, you could point out the ratio of his book sales to mine as of mid-April 2024 as astronomical, yet when an author and a publisher tread where they are possibly in way over their heads, without conceding sufficient respect, even if they generate huge amounts of money for themselves over a decade or a century, they could still be much less holistically beneficial than they otherwise would be, unless and until they might take sufficient subsequent corrective actions. If I were assigned to give it a book review at this time, with the range from one star to five stars in half-star increments, with five as best, system, then I would rate it at three-and-a-half stars, and I would point out that 1) he was more harsh toward the story of Abraham being asked by God to get ready to sacrifice one of his sons* than ideal, 2) he was more unrelentingly harsh toward the Krishna Consciousness Movement's marketing methods than would have been most prudent, and 3) he performed such extremely academic-ivory-tower-oriented contortions in what appeared to be a desperate attempt to deflect away from any semblance of acknowledging what may have seemed intuitively to have been sets of paranormally-driven tragic patterns that parallel The Passover as depicted in *Exodus*, though not aimed specifically at the Egyptians' firstborn in connection with episodes of alleged ancient history, but seemingly aimed by The Ultimate Reality—or someone or something close to that—to causing some modern instances of any or almost any given demographic sustaining massive casualties when situations would align perfectly for that to happen.

---

* i.e., Isaac or Ishmael, depending on whose legendary stories you choose

---

Another example of a popular author stepping into an area where he and his publisher might best have declined to tread is on page 54 of *Knock 'Em Dead 2003* by Martin Yate. On that page, in the version with ISBN 1-58062-759-5, in mentioning the importance of following up during job searches and the problems of failure to follow up, Martin Yate and that book's publisher, Adams Media Corporation (of Avon, Massachusetts), had the nerve to include the statement, "If you sit there like some fat Buddha waiting for the world to beat a path to your door, you may wait a long time." That was possibly the single most offensive thing I have ever encountered in print, even more offensive than the most rabbit-hole-induced extremities expressed by Alinsky in *Rules for Radicals* and, yes, even more offensive than any of what Hitler expressed in *Mein Kampf.* Looking at this differently, there can be some truth each in several contrasting valuations of the offense from that Anti-Buddhist statement: 1) Martin Yate's Anti-Buddhist action of writing was worse than the worst Anti-Semitic actions when he defamed the entirety of Buddhism by portraying Buddhas as lazy in contradiction to the very statement in Buddhism's Eightfold Path that correct effort is key to effectiveness. 2) Martin Yate's Anti-Buddhist action of writing was very harmful to a large number of sentient beings in the medium run, though nowhere near as bad as the worst Anti-Semitic actions when he defamed the entirety of Buddhism by portraying Buddhas as lazy in contradiction to the very statement in Buddhism's Eightfold Path that correct effort is key to effectiveness. 3) Yate's Anti-Buddhist action was equally harmful to sentient beings in the medium run as the worst of the Anti-Semitic actions when he defamed Buddhism by portraying Buddhas as lazy in contradiction to the portion of the Eightfold Path that stipulates the importance of using correct effort. This parallels how there can be some truth each in several contrasting ways of conceiving how people work in general, for example, between the statements: 1) The way to a man's heart is through his stomach. 2) The way to a man's heart is through his chest. 3) The way to a man's heart is through his sexual activities. 4) The way to a man's heart is through his mind. 5) The way to a man's heart is through ethical behavior.

Let there be an exploration of these issues in another direction. Early in the time of considering that expression from Yate to be offensive, I did not consider it to be nearly as bad as Anti-Semitic statements that became infamous long ago, yet after experiencing repeated conflicts with those who disrespected Buddhism during portions of the

November 2018 to May 2024 period, I have adjusted my evaluation to actually declare here that I believe that one extremely Anti-Buddhist line from Yate to be in many important ranges of reality more problematic to the human race than the worst Anti-Semitic lines from the entirety of human history. Part of this is that Anti-Semitism and Islamophobia, as terrible as they can be, tend to be of a directly problematic nature. However, Anti-Buddhism tends to have cascading effects that can lead to indirectly fostering much more Anti-Semitism, Islamophobia, Anti-Christianity, anti-conscience in general, toxic attitudes, and toxic behaviors in general. The May 2, 2024 text messaging conflict that appears later in this work, and which culminated in a rather eschatological detonation by me via a 12:33 A.M. CDT, May 3, 2024 message, combined with reflection on it at times during the nine days that followed have led to my deeming that statement from Yate to have been that bad. With that being said, from another perspective, sentient beings can choose to view no statements that have ever occurred to have been inherently evil, rather to consider them to have been portions of transitions that those who deal with them effectively can use toward the transformations of everything into serving the good in the long run. While many Buddhists may find this mindset to be quite second-nature to them, acclimated to such views on many occasions, some people of Judeo-Christian emphasis may feel weary and skeptical of why anyone would dare to go there, think that, and write in a manner of encouraging others to go there and think that way. However, to those, please consider a few verses from *Psalms*, as corresponding from two English translations, one labeled the first three verses of Chapter Nineteen and the other labeled the second, third, and fourth verses of Chapter Eighteen (due to how the translators organized the chapter #s and verse #s differently), and consider how the words could have multiple alternative meanings, which a random Jew, a different Jew, a random Noahidist, another Noahidist, a random Christian, another Christian, etc. might each interpret extremely differently:

"The heavens declare the glory of God; and the firmament sheweth his handywork. Day unto day uttereth speech, and night unto night sheweth knowledge. There is no speech nor language, where their voice is not heard." –*KJV*, *Psalms* 19:1-3
"The heavens shew forth the glory of God, and the firmament declareth the work of his hands. Day to day uttereth speech, and night to night sheweth knowledge. There are no speeches nor languages, where their voices are not heard." –*RHE*, *Psalms* 18:2-4

Some can view those as compatible with the idea that no matter how horrible anyone's communication might seem to be—in a given context and from a given perspective—in the long run if anyone addresses it sufficiently well, then the subsurface elements nevertheless pointing—to at least a trace degree—toward their being among everything as emanations from primal divinity and primal reality can become part of everything useful to the good. The good can purify the roles of everything in the long run into becoming and being part of the enlightened activity of sentient beings. Of course, much of that can be contingent on the right beings fighting back against the bearing of false witness at the right times and in the right ways, including but not limited to bearing true witness, presenting liars with psychological mirrors that force the liars to become cognizant of their own long-suppressed awareness of the harm caused by their lies, issuing harsh statements directly to the liars and those who stupidly fight excessively on behalf of those liars, choosing when to best act as a truth-teller by openly stating the truth directly, choosing when to act as a truth-teller by shutting up until the time is right to speak up, choosing when and how to act as a truth-teller through rather elliptical means of causing others to be able to find the truth on their own, etc. *Much of this can also be contingent on the beings who need to course correct choosing to course correct when they need to do so, lest they suffer potentially fatal consequences. In some cases for those needing to change course to fail could spell doom for themselves while sparing those in their orbit. In other cases for those needing to change course to fail could spell doom both for themselves and for multiple others in their orbit.*

There are advantages and disadvantages to those governing a given society choosing to impose on its citizenry extreme austerity, extreme leniency, or something somewhere between, along each of the multitudinous dimensions of public policy.

Although many have felt a presumption that whatever their society does is something that has to be legitimate, others have felt a presumption of major skepticism toward whatever their society does being even a little bit legitimate. The complete set of each type of benefit and each type of harm, as well as the magnitudes of each of those types of helpfulness and harmfulness, in terms of a society's policies' impacts on its citizens and residents is probably beyond the comprehension of even the entire human race as a whole, in many respects. We typically do and think what we choose based on an earnest belief that it is what is best, yet we often find out later that we missed huge amounts of what had been hidden from us. (Consider, for example, this in relationship with the main popular studio recording of the Trisha Yearwood and Don Henley performance of the song "Walkaway Joe.")

Also, we can factor in our awareness of knowing that we do not know much of what we do not know, and we can trust intuition, sensory perception, thought, judgment, etc. (Consider this in comparison, for example, with scriptures from whichever religion(s) of your choice.)

However, it remains that no matter who any of us may happen to be, many real world situations can have huge factors that we cannot anywhere near fully anticipate, unless (and to whatever degree(s)) any of us is/are in some relevant way(s), in fact, omniscient.

For those who fall into thinking about all of Buddhism in ways paralleling what F. Max Müller described as even many intelligent people being prone to thinking about *The Vajracchedika Sutra* as nonsensical, the huge factors that they fail to anticipate in relationship with Buddhism could lead to all sorts of brutal consequences. Many of the consequences are things to which they may find themselves repeatedly blind, deaf, and unfeeling, unless and until they wise up and wake up to recognizing the patterns.

Many Christian preachers often wisely steer clear of directly addressing Buddhism, yet when they do directly address it, they wander across diverse paths of doing so. Some speak with utter condemnation, as they do for any namable religion other than Christianity; others speak with mixed statements of coexistence, criticism, and praise, as they do for most namable major religions other than Christianity; yet others still take any of what might seem practically unlimited variations of how to broach this contentious subject.

Perhaps the best statement yet by a Christian preacher on this came from John Redmond of First Baptist Church of Pasadena, TX, who, in a sermon excerpt heard on AM 1070 KNTH "The Answer" expressed that Buddhism could mean any of many totally different things, depending on who, when, and how a reference to it occurs. (Cf. a *Peace by Believing* broadcast on KNTH circa sometime in the December 2023 to March 2024 period.)

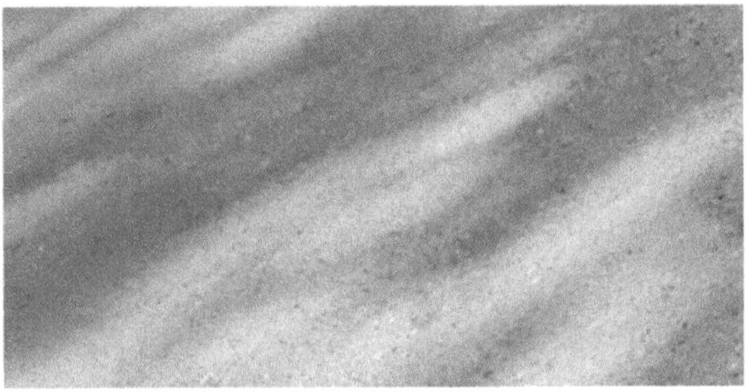

Consider the following statements by Müller, on pages xiv-xv of Part II of *The Sacred Books of the East, Volume XLIX* (1894, Oxford):

1. "At first sight it may seem as if this metaphysical treatise hardly deserved the world-wide reputation which it has attained. Translated literally into English it must often strike the Western reader as sheer nonsense, and hollow repetition."
2. "This philosophy, or, at least, its underlying doctrine, is not unknown to us in the history of Western philosophy. It is simply the denial of the reality of the phenomenal world. Considering how firmly a belief in phenomenal objects is established in the ordinary mind, it might well have seemed that such a belief could not be eradicated except by determined repetition."
3. "When we say that something is large or small, sweet or bitter, these dharmas or qualities are subjective, and cannot be further defined. What is large to me, may be small to another. A mile may seem short or long, according to the state of our muscles, and no one can determine the point where smallness ends and length begins. This applies to all things which we are supposed to know, that is, which we are able to name."

Those perspectives presaged the revolutions in physics and engineering from the time of that *Volume XLIX*'s publication to a century later.

Although Jesus and other beings prominent in the Christian movement are often not conceived as directly involved with propagating Buddhism, yet the fact remains that many of the statements in the Christian texts are suggestive of identical or nearly identical ways of going beyond the mundane world in order to reach toward the deeper reality and use it wisely, for the good of all who can be sufficiently receptive to the good.

Some areas of Western philosophy also seem to correspond well with Buddhism; for example, some statements from Spinoza and Kant.

Although there were several cases from infancy to reaching an age of the mid-20s that Buddhism had terrified and perplexed me, in May 2003 I started to truly get some of it. Some of that was by more thoroughly contemplating why Lee had, in *Enter the Dragon* (1973), demonstrated much of what he had demonstrated, especially regarding both the value of some amount of a transcendental selflessness and the issue of the responsible use of transcending conceptions of self-versus-non-self.

That set the stage for metaphorically acting out patterns that paralleled that movie, science fiction stories, and adventure movies repeatedly in real life. Perhaps you have done the same multiple times in your life, and, whether you have or have not, as long as you live you might have some current or future opportunities to act out patterns that parallel great stories that originated somewhere beyond your life.

Think again about the line in which Martin Yate expressed derision toward both Buddhism and Emerson in relationship with what he perceived to be patterns of laziness. Note that Sarah S.B. Yule and Mary S. Keene attributed to Ralph Waldo Emerson (1803-1882) the quote, "If a man can write a better book, preach a better sermon, or make a better mousetrap than his neighbor, though he builds his house in the woods the world will make a beaten path to his door." (Cf. *Bartlett's Familiar Quotations, 16th Ed.*, John Bartlett (1820-1905), edited by Justin Kaplan (1925-2014); Little, Brown and Company; 1992; p. 430.) Also, here is a reminder that right effort is one of the items that Buddhism outlined in the Noble Eightfold Path. Zazen is valuable for becoming centered, enacting right meditation, and other purposes, but when it is the time to stop sitting and get going, then it makes sense to use effort to get moving. However, Yate targeted Emerson and Buddhism in a sentence associating them with a failure to follow up.

At some stage circa 2003 or 2004, I noticed the aforementioned line in *Knock 'Em Dead 2003* and used a pen to mark through "like some fat" and "waiting for the world to beat a path to your door," rendering the new version of the sentence as displayed on that copy, "If you sit there Buddha you may wait a long time." Also, adjacent I wrote, "I respect Buddha and Po-tei."

Next to that supplemental statement I signed my initials, M.J.B.

Part of the back story to this was that in the wake of the Enron and Arthur Andersen debacles, although I had signed on with Andersen on April 19, 2001 to plan to begin working for that LLP in a full-time, regular capacity set to start in September 2002 (set for after graduate school), that plan fell apart. The audits that exploded for Andersen—especially the Enron audit and the Worldcomm audit—would eventually result in the cancellation of nearly all mid-2002-onward-for-a-while employment by Arthur Andersen. That included cancellation of the position for which I was scheduled.

Near the end of completing a Master in Professional Accounting degree from the McCombs School of Business at the University of Texas at Austin, with the position at Arthur Andersen having already dissolved into thin air, I encountered a wondrous combination of strengths, weaknesses, opportunities, and threats.

To understand this better, we will need to backtrack quite a ways, then proceed to near the time of the initial publication of *Alternative Beginnings and Endings of All Things: Science, Religion, Politics, and Cards, Hypervolume II.*

* * * * *

Among the various controversies that have been around since time immemorial is eschatology.

Eschatology encompasses all the religious and scientific ravings, to whatever degree accurate or not, about the real or imagined end of all things.

For example, consider how each of the major religions has expressed what many refer to as end-times prophecies. For another example, consider how astrophysics presents many theories about how the universe—or maybe even the multiverse—might eventually come to a complete end.

*Cultures have associated many with eschatology, including the phenomena and noumena involving Shakyamuni Buddha, John of Patmos, Moses, Jesus of Nazareth, Muhammad, Immanuel Kant, and Arthur C. Clarke.*

In portions of 2019-2022 I informally met and shared conversations with a man who went by the name Drew as a nickname for having had one of those names that could be rendered as Andrew, Andruw, etc. That fellow was an extreme adherent to Protestant Christianity, and he indicated being involved with The Church Without Walls. In conversations with him it became readily apparent that although he recognized some merit in diverse perspectives, he believed that absolutely everything about the human condition, human life, and effectiveness should revolve around a strict adherence to and proclamation of Christianity, and, furthermore, that he believed that *The King James Version Holy Bible* was and is the book in which, amid all the variations of scripture, God had granted the human race the most perfect expression of divinity. Drew felt that although there were changes—some might say, artistic liberties—that the translators who made that 1611 work took when deciphering and transfiguring their source materials, somehow everything lined up perfectly for the interactions between God and human beings resulted in the most perfect book.

Now, compare and contrast the view expressed by that Drew with the views expressed by 1) those who believe *The Duoay-Rheims Holy Bible* to be the most perfect book, 2) those who consider *The Vulgate Bible* to be the most perfect book, 3) those who believe *The Qur'an* (also known as *The Koran*) to be the perfect book, 4) those who believe *The Tanakh* to be the most authoritative, 5) those who consider the 1953 version of *Childhood's End* to be the be-all and end-all statement on what the entire human race's relationship with Reality should be all about, 6) those who consider the 1990 version of *Childhood's End* to be the be-all and end-all statement on what the entire human race's relationship with Reality should be all about, and 7) those who consider Reality to transcend the notions of any specific one book being the ultimate literary expression of how beings should best relate to Reality Itself.

On November 3, 2001 and I printed from the Internet and started to study a Religious Studies 232 Powerpoint presentation in connection with a course I never attended and presented by a professor whom I never met. That was from Professor Alan Sponberg (1946-2022), who expressed some basics of Buddhism, including clarifying that many westerners conflate Shakyamuni Buddha (the main legendary founder of Buddhism as credited by historical records on Earth, generally depicted as having a medium build that is neither skinny nor heavyset) with Po-tei (a wandering Zen Buddhist monk from a period some centuries later and generally depicted as having a heavyset build). At first, I was still uncomfortable with some aspects of Buddhism, especially stern rejection of many ideas of selfhood, though considering it fit for study as part of interdisciplinary approaches to broadening insights and perspectives. Bear in mind that by sometime May 2003 I opened up much more to embracing the Buddhist views and methodologies.

Sometimes I wonder whether the degree to which some people such as author Martin Yate and some organizations such as publisher Adams Media Corporation have brainwashed some business people to disrespect Buddhism and think they can do this in the long run with impunity is a mitigating factor in how: 1) The Financial Advisory Group showed such disrespect toward me and the totality of the reality of my life, including my affiliation with Buddhism and including Buddhist practices that have proven helpful to hundreds of millions of people at key junctures, and 2) the law firm Gray Reed as hired by them chose to join in on that disrespect. Actions have consequences. That could, perhaps, put much more of the blame on Martin Yate and Adams Media Corporation than on 1) The Financial Advisory Group, 2) Natasha McDaniel, 3)

Steve Estrin, 4) Juan Martinez, 5) Gray Reed & McGraw, and 6) Michael C. Kelsheimer.

If I were to go to Fox News, CNN, MSNBC, ABC News, CBS News, NBC News, Reuters, or another news service someday and learn that a mysterious extirpation by spontaneous human combustion had occurred, wiping out the entirety of each nuclear family among whose members were involved with the decision to green-light the aforementioned instance of *Knock 'Em Dead 2003* having deeply insulted Shakyamuni Buddha, Po-tei, Buddhism, and The Dharma, then I would most likely simply react with thoughts along the lines of, *That's the kind of stuff that can happen when you disrespect the deepest and most mysterious of realities, much as the rise and the fall of Matam Rudra has a degree of parallel to sudden deaths of the Egyptian firstborn as depicted in Abrahamic religions. Related to this is how although Scotland and the Houston Police Department both emphasize the motto, "Nemo Me Impune Lacessit," some of the manifestations of Buddhism, especially Vajrayana Buddhism, can exhibit that idea of "No One Violates Vital Realities With Impunity." Although both my father and I for a while were disrespectful toward Buddhism, by mid-2003 I had become a Buddhist after experience had proven that it has at least a major degree of legitimacy, whether or not it is anything at all akin to a be-all and end-all of religious, philosophical, and scientific inquiries, and, similarly, my father came to recognize it to have significant legitimacy, although in many of his later years he chose to, in terms of religion, often primarily identify with Archaic Taoism. When the supernatural or the seemingly-supernatural provides humans with a cataclysmic rebuke, whether it be by smiting an individual via spontaneous human combustion or another means of sudden and perhaps inexplicable death, then that would sure seem to be Reality Itself making an example out of whomever would be dying that way. Tsk, tsk.*

This reminds me of one of my father's favorite sayings, "A picture is worth a thousand words, but an example is worth a thousand pictures."

Some have shown thinking toward Buddhism and its practitioners with an attitude of, *Such ridiculous people. Tsk, tsk.* In contrast, I have shown in the passages leading up to here thinking toward contemptuously Anti-Buddhist people an orientation of, *They will tend to get exactly what they have coming toward them, and it could involve virtually no limits of its harshness. Tsk, tsk.*

If people on each side of whether to regard something with respect or contempt have an absolute disagreement about it, then the proof is in when the consequences happen. Many risk locking into a conclusion with limited experience, later finding out that the more complete reality is very different from what they expected. One of the remarkable things about the brief life of Bruce Lee was that near the end he helped set up via *Enter the Dragon* a popular movie that unrelentingly points toward the dangers of insufficient regard for Dharma while also helping to set into motion what would eventually become, via *Game of Death* and the alternative incomplete version of it as appearing in *Bruce Lee: A Warrior's Journey*, a set of cinematic patterns that point unflinchingly toward *both* the dangers of insufficient regard for Dharma and the dangers of excessive regard for Dharma.

That dual threat is very much aligned with how portions of Buddhism warn on both sides of that: Insufficiently esteeming the Dharma can render minds into long-term patterns of being stuck in many poisonous, animalistic, and hellacious states of consciousness, whereas excessively esteeming the Dharma can render minds into long-term patterns of being stuck in violent, overly-war-prone asura states of consciousness. (Cross ref. the URL: http://buddhistsutras.org/gallery/rebirth_wheel.htm as accessed on April 26, 2011.)

Now, for a deeper dive into many rabbit holes, subterranean subways, stratospheric regions, and other realms:

A. After Aron Silberg posted on Facebook information regarding unusual religious things and adjacent comic notions, as a friends-only picture post with commentary, some follow-up threads of discussion emerged. In part of that, Aron lumped together the Shakers with "Puritans, Southern Baptists, Quakers..."

and others, and he concluded the follow-up with the phrase, "stereotypically patriarchal, polygamous, etc." Soon after finding the approximately-11th-Day-of-April 2024 post, I sent a rejoinder to Aron, visible to him and his other friends {and in addressing him by name, his name was shown in bold, yet for the sake of smoothness of presentation here, I have adjusted the presence of his name into the same uniformity with the rest of the font transcription; also, this inserts a comma after his name for clarity}, an approximately 5:47 PM CDT, April 12, 2024 response:

"Aron Silberg, 'Twas mistaken of thee to put the Shakers into that list; though I hath never knowingly met a Shaker, they hath long expresseth the belief that both marriage and sex should be avoided, lest a human being offendeth The Almighty."

B. Approximately 5%-10% of the way into 2024, Justin Haynes and I shared a peculiar phone call, part of which went something very much like this:

James: What do you remember at this time about the Oneida Colony?

Justin: That name sounds familiar, but I don't remember much except for the name at this time.

James: Well, then let me tell you a little summary of their history. First, though, I should mention that some of this is from what I remember from a high school Honors English class in which the instructor had us learn about a bunch of peculiar religious sects from long ago, ranging from the Shakers to the Oneida Colony. That guy actually had us study a bunch of controversial stuff in that school year.

Actually, you've heard of the Oneida Silverware, yes?

Justin: Yes, in fact I bought some of it the other day!

James: Great! Then you're at least a little familiar with the background.

What I'm about to tell you is a mixture of what I learned from that Honors English class from long ago and stuff I read sometimes since then and other stuff. I think it's going to be something like 95%-to-99.9% accurate. Well, here goes.

You know how there are so many different religious controversies about how people should manage sexual activities? The Oneida Colony, which gathered in something like upstate New York an extremely long time ago took a peculiar approach to sexuality and personal possessions. Some of it is kind like those attempted 1960s hippie communes, except the Oneida folks were in some ways more successful... for a while.

Also, recall how we've talked before about some of those core controversies of capitalism-versus-communism? You've mentioned before about how in some of those things like Star Trek, there's some futuristic vision of how technology could make it so people could coordinate resource priorities without resorting to the normal way that money would run. If some people could get technology to overwhelm many challenges of stuff like poverty, then we might be able to resolve the capitalism-versus-communism issue, having people's needs reasonably-well taken care of, while also having the opportunities for successful competition to bring some of the more productive or profitable people to gather more resources. However, our current technological levels are nowhere near that kind of achievement and, therefore, that's part of why there so many tough debates about more redistribution versus less redistribution.

As you're well aware of, some of those attempts by Soviets and similar folks to create some type of Communist Utopian dream that turns into a reality has failed repeatedly to a trap in which the totalitarian leaders take over and brutal, inhumane living conditions result for much of the populace.

However, the Oneida Colony folks, in something like the Nineteenth Century, for a brief little while, had a shining moment in which they actually got some of the communist ideal to work well.

Their leaders interpreted that we were all living in a post-apocalyptic reality, in which God and whoever was teaming with God had done away with the old heaven and the old earth of how things were supposed to happen. The result was that they told their followers that marriage should be abolished and that personal ownership of property should be abolished within their community, but they could still team together on putting together the utensils that people could call Oneida Silverware and sell it to the outside, capitalist world. Also, although marriage would be abolished, people could still have sex—in fact, they took a somewhat libertine approach to managing sexual activities.

They encouraged folks there to be open to having sex with multiple partners, reasonably freely, with consensual sex between males and females happening very regularly. On a related note, the normal family structures of the nuclear family were let go of, replaced by a communal approach to raising the young'uns.

What do you know? They had a very well-functioning society for quite a while, and their silverware business proved quite profitable in its dealings with the outside world on a capitalist basis.

However, trouble eventually arrived in their paradise, enough trouble to lead to them devising an endgame. Some of the people, even with all the options to be promiscuous and being given the go-ahead from the religious leaders to practice that sexually promiscuity, yes, even with such sexual freedom, some of the men and women felt strongly enough about each other in the traditional ways of love leading to couples wanting to build their lives together that some of the people didn't like the religious imposition abolishing marriage. Also, the money the community was accumulating from having such a financially-profitable business operation was an issue. Enough of their people, includeing their leadership, reached a decision that the community would be disbanded in terms of the communal arrangement, yet the already-highly-successful for-profit silverware business would continue. Many people left, yet the business kept going and going, until eventually becoming acquired by another business some number of decades later.

Therefore, although communism has almost never worked in the history of Earth, on that occasion, for a brief, shining moment spanning some reasonable number of years, a few people with a radical approach to religion and sexuality, got an internal communist structure for their community to work well, though part of how it worked so well was that they were able to interact with the outside world on a capitalist basis, very successfully on a capital basis, that is.

Justin: Yeah, and I just bought some of their silverware from Target the other day!

## Part C of Section Five of Chapter Ten

## An Array of Some Human Psychological Profile Archetypes

Labeled with acronyms; here is a table of contents for this part:

- AAAREATH
- AAAREAGN
- DHREBSTR
- DHREBMR
- DHREBLNT
- DHREHPROCS
- DHREHPRACS
- DHREJ
- DHRWHE
- JDCRWNDCRE
- JDCRWRCE
- JDCRWNDPRE
- JDCRWOJE
- JDCRWRJE
- ABRWIE
- SEVESPE
- SEVEOM
- SEVEOC
- SEVLBB
- SEVLEB
- NCMEAG
- CMANG

AAAREATH: 1) primarily atheistic in outlook, though, usually subconsciously, sometimes consc-iously though not speaking of it out loud, and, maybe once in a long while speaking of it out loud, able to flex into being agnostic in outlook; 2) view-ing all religions as entirely or nearly entirely equal in terms of either largely or entirely illusory; 3) having mixed feelings toward death, often leaning toward a sense and conceptualization of the likelyhood of total, permanent obliteration of consciousness for themselves, everyone they care about, everyone they do not care about, and everyone they may feel ambivalent toward, though occasionally thinking and feeling a trace of hope toward possibilities of there being at least a little bit of a great beyond; 4) viewing people of firm and resolute commitment to a willingness to die in defense of principles to range along a spectrum of insane, sane-though-misguided, well-guided-though-weird, and profoundly noble; 5) viewing suicide as almost universally mysterious with respect to whether it could ever be a good idea for anyone or not; 6) having little or no faith that the deeper reality will in the long run deliver any cosmic justice beyond the worldly level of lives and deaths; and 7) heavily emphasizing romantic love, sex, friendship, & money.

Acronym Explanation: "Atheistic And Agnostic Revolving More Often Around Atheism As a Gravitational Center of Thought"

AAAREAGN: 1) primarily agnostic in outlook, though to some degree tended to occasionally flex into atheist outlooks, 2) tending to view all religions as equally corrupt and equally bankrupt toward relevancy toward reality, though having some doubts about this, and feeling open to how there might be a chance for a true religion to actually exist, 3) feeling at a loss amid the cosmic oceans of competing religious ideas as to how there might ever arrive a solution of going over to believing in a specific religion as being true.

Acronym explanation: "Agnostic And Atheistic, Revolving Mostly Around Agnosticism Most of the Time as A Gravitational Center of Thought"

DHREBSTR: 1) exhibiting extreme commitment to the causes of Buddhism, especially enlightenment and the promotion of the enlightenment of sentient beings, 2) zealotry in support of Dharmic religious practices, especially Buddhism, to the point of a great willingness for self-sacrifice toward helping with enlightenment, 3) oscillating between showing high and low levels of respect toward religions other than the Dharmic religions, 4) exhibiting varying levels of respect toward anyone or anything other than Buddhas, Bodhisattvas, Dharma Protectors Buddhist practitioners in general, and Buddhism, 5) generally exhibiting great respect and great affinity toward Buddhas, Bodhisattvas, Dharma Protectors, and Buddhism, 6) considering many Buddhist practitioners with a mixture of criticism and praise, out of concerns for both the benefits of correct Buddhist practices and the detriments of incorrect Buddhist practices.

Acronym explanation: "Dharmic Religious Belief Including Buddhism With Strong Emphasis Level of Religiosity"

DHREBMR: 1) exhibiting medium-to-high commitment to the causes of Buddhism, 2) having generally agnostic views toward much of reality

Acronym explanation: "Dharmic Religious Belief Including Buddhism With Medium Emphasis Level of Religiosity"

DHREBLNT: 1) considering the Dharmic religions to exhibit much truth and effective means with which to live well, 2) caring about and trusting in the diverse religions and philosophies, both East and West, as having moderate degrees of truth to them

Acronym explanation: "Dharmic Religious Belief With Light Emphasis on Religiosity and a Nondenominational Trust in Diverse Religions Sharing Moderate Amounts of Truth"

DHREHPROCS: 1) believing in the presence of a very high degree of truth in each of the Dharmic religions, 2) choosing to regulate sexuality in accordance with restricting sexual relations to those that within monogamous sexual partnerships

Acronym explanation: "Dharmic Religious Hybrid Belief While Promoting the Practice of Restraining Sexuality to Fidelity Within Committed Monogamous Sexual Partnerships and Activities"

DHREHPRACS: 1) believing in the presence of a very high degree of truth in each of the Dharmic religions, 2) choosing to have a nearly anything-goes, promiscuous, libertine approach to sexuality

Acronym explanation: "Dharmic Religious Hybrid Belief While Promoting the Practice of Mostly-Unrestricted And Aggressively Promiscuous, Libertine Sexual Activities"

DHREJ: 1) exhibiting strong commitment to the causes of Jainism, including the enlightenment of sentient beings and striving to refrain from harming sentient beings, 2) emphasizing perspectives of the divinity of all beings, accepting the risk of alienating those who wish to deny any specific being of having even the minutest of a trace of divinity

Acronym explanation: "Dharmic Religious Orientation With a Jain Emphasis"

DHRWHE: 1) expressing commitment to Dharmic religious perspectives in general, 2) emphasizing Hinduism

Acronym explanation: "Dharmic Religious Orientation With a Hindu Emphasis"

JDCRWNDCRE:1) believing completely in the idea that the be-all and end-all of all human activity at its core is a strictly literal and all-encompassing interpretation of *John* 14:6 (one sample translation of which is, "Jesus saith unto him, I am the way, the truth, and the life: no man cometh unto the father, but by me." *KJV*), 2) considering that statement of that verse and the statements of similar statements from scriptures to all point toward an absolute correctness of Christianity and varying degrees of incorrectness in all other namable religions, 3) considering the absolute truth of that to be of such completeness that it does not resemble such ordinary statements regarded as wholly true in most normal situations yet proving to be illusory to some significant degree when subjected to deeper scientific or other investigation (e.g., the following four statements: a) "Stopping someone's heart and subsequently removing it from that person's body is never a proper medical practice." b) "If you travel with a steady velocity of w in a direction relative to a fixed object and someone else travels at a steady velocity of v relative to you in that same direction, then the velocity of that someone else relative to the aforementioned fixed object would equal w+v." c) "It is better to be big and strong than to be small and weak." d) "There is no such thing as too much money." Refutation of absolute adherence to (a): In recent times, sometimes open heart surgery winds up saving someone's life by a process that includes medical professionals stopping someone's heart, then removing it, then performing a variety of key medical procedures, then replacing either the heart that was removed back into the person or replacing it with a substitute heart, and, after all of that, getting the person to return to having a normal pulse. Refutation of absolute adherence to (b): As it has been scientifically measured to happen over and over again in the regular, real world of shared experience, the Einstein-Lorentz Transformation has been consistent for Special Relativity in that although w+v approximates the observed reality for that at velocities that are miniscule compared with the speed of light (which "c" can often symbolize in equations), the more complete calculation is of the format $(w+v)/(1+(wv/(c^2)))$ rather than the way of most unfamiliar with Special Relativity think of the reality of relative motion in the regular, real world of shared experience. Cf. *Modern Physics, 2nd Edition* (1997), Raymond A. Serway, Clement Moses, and Curt A. Moyer; Harcourt Brace & Company; ISBN: 0-03-001547-2; p. 29. Also, Cf. *Relativity: The Special And The General Theory* (2021, based on the related 1905 and 1915 source texts), Albert Einstein; EduGorilla Community Pvt. Ltd.; ISBN: 9789391464363; p. 36. Refutation of absolute adherence to (c): Strength in which ways versus strength in other ways can have major contradictions and tradeoffs, as illustrated by comparing and contrasting those who excel as offensive linemen in football, defensive backs in football, horse racing jockeys, basketball centers, baseball catchers, 100-meter dash sprinters, tennis players, ballerinas, and 24-hour-endurance-race automobile drivers. Refutation of absolute adherence to (d): More money often comes with a mixed bag of having more problems in some ways and less problems in other ways, more opportunities in some ways, less opportunities in other ways, etc. Cf. *Rocky III* (1982), *10 Questions for the Dalai Lama* (2006), and *Ferrari* (2023), 4) at times having doubts about forcing the inner cognitive processes to strictly adhere to the patterns #1, #2, and #3, turning to many preachers, bishops, evangelists, authors, family members, friends, enemies, and random strangers in an at-times desperate search for ways to make sense of reconciling reality with the belief that anything other than complete adherence to believing in the absolute truth of 1-3 could jeopardize salvation

Acronym explanation: "Judeo-Christian With A Nondenominational Christian Emphasis"

JDCRWRCE: 1) similar to the JDCRWNDCRE set of patterns in some ways, and very different to that set of patterns in other ways, with much of life revolving around believing Roman Catholicism to be the only true type of Christianity, 2) sometimes taking pity on non-Christians and on Christians other than Roman Catholics, believing them to be in a state of much more jeopardy than good Roman Catholics, 3) sometimes worrying about whether the difference between being a good Roman Catholic and a bad Roman Catholic might mean the difference between salvation and damnation, and feeling much uncertainty about whether qualifying as good or not, 4) at times oscillating between a full and complete sense of certainty that Roman Catholicism is actually the only completely true and correct way of relating to God or if any of the other ways of religion can be completely true and correct, and finding that various Catholics disagree with each other about whether Vatican II involved steps in favorable directions for the Roman Catholic Church or not, 5) oscillating between whether it is critical to study Christianity thoroughly or not and between various alternatives of what to make of the controversies between different lifestyles and cultures

Acronym explanation: "Judeo-Christian With A Roman Catholic Emphasis"

JDCRWNDPRE: 1) similar to the JDCRWNDCRE and JDCRWRCE sets of patterns in some ways, but extremely different from those patterns in other ways, believing Protestantism to be the only true type of Christianity, 2) sometimes taking pity on non-Christians and on Christians other than

Protestants, believing them to be in a state of much more jeopardy than good Protestants, 3) sometimes worrying about whether the difference between being a good Protestant and a bad Protestant might mean the difference between salvation and damnation, and feeling much uncertainty about whether qualifying as good or not, 4) at times oscillating between a full and complete sense of certainty that Protestantism is actually the only completely true and correct way of relating to God or if any of the other ways of religion can be completely true and correct, and finding that various Christians disagree with each other about almost everything other than considering Christ to be of central importance, 5) oscillating between competing ideas on whether it is crucial to study Christianity thoroughly and what to make of the controversies between different lifestyles and cult-ures

Acronym explanation: "Judeo-Christian With A Nondenominational Protestant Emphasis"

JDCRWOJE: 1) believing in Orthodox Judaism while being a practicing Orthodox Jew, 2) strictly observing various guidelines, standards, and pract-ices, believing this to be a way to uphold an elevat-ed set of wielding power and responsibility in rela-tionship with a divine covenant, 3) at times concerned about how Reform Jews, various Christians, various Muslims, various people of other faiths, and various people of no faith wind up interacting with each other to bring new and surprising challenges

Acronym explanation: "Judeo-Christian With Orthodox Jewish Emphasis"

JDCRWRJE: 1) believing in Reform Judaism while being a practicing Reform Jew, 2) observing various guidelines, standards, and practices to varying degrees, at times oscillating between believing the core traditional legends of Judaism to be largely based on real energy dynamics of a divine covenant and believing in either an agnostic way or another way toward the mysteries of the religious practices, 3) at times concerned about how various Orthodox Jews, Noahidists, Reform Jews, Atheists, Agnostics, Christians, Muslims, Jains, Hindus, Sikhs, Buddhists, and others might in a variety of ways either coexist peacefully or conflict with each other

Acronym explanation: "Judeo-Christian With Reform Jewish Emphasis"

ABRWIE: 1) believing Islam to be correct at its core and either being a practicing Muslim or being a nondenominational believer in Abrahamic Religion having a high degree of correctness at its core while not being a practicing Muslim, 2) therefore either being a Muslim or, being smoothly agreeable to a significant percentage of Muslims without having to be a Muslim, 3) oscillating between considering Christians, Jews, Noahidists, Hindus, nondenominational spiritual people, and Buddhists as possibly being on the right path spiritually or possibly in need of someday changing paths spiritually, whether ever publicly admitting to wondering in this way or not ever admitting it publicly, 4) experiencing much cognitive consistency in military endeavors on account of how the model of choosing whether to obey orders or to be insubordinate to orders lines up perfectly with the idea of submitting to God / Allah as a primary way to determine whether or not the orders given by humans should in fact qualify as legitimate orders or not, 5) feeling generally open to studying science without needing a knee-jerk reaction of throttling what the scientists might present—feeling that science can help contribute to advancing justice

Acronym explanation: "Abrahamic Religious Belief With an Islamic Emphasis"

SEVESPE: 1) whether believing in this or that or the other in terms of stated religious and/or philosophical beliefs and practices, at a core level selecting a lifestyle in which there are strict limits on some aspects of sexuality, 2) specifically choosing the sexual austerity of banning oneself from most possible ways of experiencing ejaculation, whether the ejaculation of oneself if having a male body or the ejaculation of a male partner if not having a male body, etc. 3) having successfully eradicated the portions of one's psyche that would otherwise have permitted anything less than such strict sexual austerity, feeling prepared to deal with other people and organizations in ferocious ways when believing the situations to call for it

Acronym explanation: "Severe Erotic Austerity, Very Restrictive on Ejaculatory Sexual Practices as a Lifestyle Emphasis"

SEVEOM: 1) choosing a lifestyle in which when a single, divorced, or widowed person there should be an extreme restriction on any sexual activities, possibly taken to the extreme of being voluntarily, absolutely celibate whenever single, divorced, or widowed,

Acronym explanation: "Severe Erotic Openness Within Marriage and Severe Erotic Closedness Outside of Marriage"

SEVEOC: 1) emphasizing romantic partnership as being central to life, 2) flexible about whether sex should happen only between two people who are married to each other or if consenting single adults should be able to have sex with each other in ways that would be spiritually ethical, 3) feeling very loving and devoted to the romantic partner or to the person or multiple people, if any, considered most likely eligible and plausible to become a future romantic partner

Acronym explanation: "Severe Mixture of Erotic Openness and Erotic Restriction, Emphasizing An Emotional, Open-Hearted Connection With The Correct Partner, Very Open to this being in a Marriage or Between Consenting Single Adults"

SEVLBB: 1) emphasizing both Buddhism and a sex-positive lifestyle, 2) considering those two centers of emphasis to be fully compatible with each other, 3) open to sexual promiscuity if coordinated with reasonable boundaries such as to be plausibly ethical

Acronym explanation: "Severe Libertine Emphasis With Buddhist Beliefs At the Core of It, Flexible With Managing Sexuality and Other Aspects of Life as Long as Believed to Be Consistent With Helping Buddhist Enlightenment in the Long Run"

SEVLEB: 1) emphasizing extremely wide-open approaches to having sex and experiencing sexual activities, 2) having few, if any restrictions on how many sexual partners to have, which types of sex to engage in, and how wild to get in terms of the experiences of orgasm and everything related to it, 3) if a female, then likely to be considered by others to be a nymphomaniac, 4) if a male, then likely to be considered by others to be a player

Acronym explanation: "Severe Libertine Emphasis, Very Unrestrictive on Ejaculation, Orgasm, and Sexual Practices in General as Being Very Open to Mating Activities"

NCMEAG: 1) whether for religious, philosophical, and/or personal reasons, choosing voluntary total celibacy as a lifestyle and preference for the future outlook, 2) also, when away from physical contact with others, restricting all activities and changes in libido such as to avoid any and all intentional derivation of physical pleasure through sexuality, 3) whether believing in a given religious concept-tualization or not, whether choosing an agnostic approach, etc., embracing that sublimation brings godliness/goodness/purity/euphoria/etc.

Acronym explanation: "Not Consenting to Mating At All, Emphasizing Avoidance of Genital Activ-ities Involving Any Derivation of Pleasure, With the Belief in Sublimating This Toward Becoming More Godly"

CMANG: oriented toward all and everything with a generally flexible and curious open-mindedness, dealing with the mysteries of reality while ready to repeatedly change and grow and learn

Acronym explanation: "Curious and Flexible With How to Manage All Negotiations With the Mysteries of Nature and God and Supernature and Godliness"

<u>Part D of Section Five of Chapter Ten</u>

R R RR ___ R RR RRR ___ RRRR _____ RRRRR

<u>Part E of Section Five of Chapter Ten</u>

Contemplate the totality of all past testimony.

<u>Part F of Section Five of Chapter Ten</u>

SSS ____ S R SSS _______ RRR SSSSS _ RRRRR TTTTT RRRR SSSSS RRRRR SSSSS RRR TTTTT

"Part Cobalt Thorium G of Section Five of Chapter Ten"

Something truly bizarre was how, when I composed the nonprofit work *Of Dorians, Romans, Hebrews, Whigs, Democrats, Republicans, Indians, and Beyond*, the first printing (set up on March 7, 2022) accidentally included a typo on page forty-five, stating the year 2021 (i.e., Twenty-Twenty-One) where I intended to correctly state the year 2022 (i.e., Twenty-Twenty-Two). One of the reasons for the second printing, which commenced on November 28, 2023, to be useful is that it was able to correct for that.

I can assure you that my conscious mind had no intention of introducing that 2021-vs.-2022 anomaly.

That page 45 from *ODRHWDRIAB* transcribed part of a February 21, 2022 1:15 P.M. CST message from me to the Rose Rodriguez with whom I spent an enormous amount of time during the Q4-2011-to-Q3-2014 period, and who had become livid toward me in mid-2018 in connection with changes of plans.

Early on that page, there were statements in which I expressed that many of those who caused my life the most difficulty in the period from about October 2018 to shortly before the time of sending that e-mail were people likely oblivious to some of the most salient facts about my life, in terms of how I had paid my dues with which to be extraordinarily capable, if and when push might someday come to shove, of performing extreme interpersonal and interorganizational warfare. Then I went into describing a few of the most relevant of those facts. Here I shall quote part of what I wrote back then, from portions of *ODRHWDRIAB*, pp. 45-46:

"One of the biggest parts of it is how some of the biggest troublemakers in that period, The Financial Advisory Group, Inc. (as located in Houston, TX), and several of the people in that organization (Juan Martinez, Natasha McDaniel, and Steve Estrin) were evidently at the times that they decided to pick a fight with me people oblivious to some of the most vital things about me. Namely, a) how I had stared down the possible obliteration of all minds, all memories, all beings, all universes, and all things in May through July 2005; and b) how the interactions between Brigid Wilson and myself had led to a May 22nd, 2012 energy vortex in which the energy relations were such that I felt that it would be more valuable as an honorable duty to that which is beyond all minds, all universes, all beings, all memories, and all things, to be willing to sacrifice the entirety of existence itself if necessary as part of holding a line of not contacting Brigid Wilson again, yet holding out an extreme religion-and-science-fiction-turned-actual-real-fact-and-experience possibility of a reversal. Stage One of that reversal took place on March 9th, 2021 with a Facebook post about how some structural elements of the potential had reversed. Stage Two of That Reversal became an actuality at about 1:38 AM Central Time on Veterans Day 2021, when everything lined up for me to include Brigid Wilson on the cc line an email to several people and cc'ing many people regarding part of my push back against all and everyone disrespecting truth and facts and reality {as I used that as an act of respecting and defending truth and facts and the capacity of beings to recognize truth and facts and reality}."

(To reiterate: With the above I quoted part of my 21 FEB 2022 1:15 P.M. CST electronic mail message to

Rose Rodriguez. Those e-mail statements have already been copied and published 7 MAR 2022 via my nonprofit work *Of Dorians, Romans, Hebrews, Whigs, Democrats, Republicans, Indians, and Beyond.*)

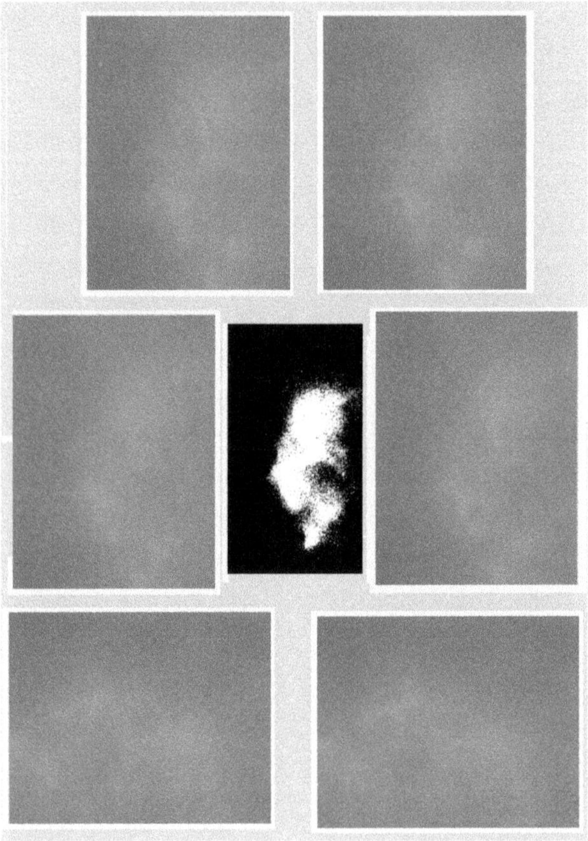

Next, consider the main text of, "Perhaps the Dawning of a New Tarot Deck" (by yours truly), as it displayed 4:18 PM CDT June 16, 2010 (before becoming simplified, remaining for about a decade, then vanishing c. late 2020-early 2021) at http://www.aeclectic.net/learn/perhaps_dawning.shtml.

## Perhaps The Dawning of a New Tarot Deck

**by Maurice James Blair**

**Introduction**

In September 2008, a mixture of a developing financial crisis in global markets with other cosmic forces led me to a creative Tarot exercise. In the weeks that followed, I revised the initial results into what I believed to be a useful pattern - and possibly the dawning of a brand new deck.

**Part One: The Main Framework**

Here is a possible framework for a new Tarot deck geared strongly towards big business:

Four suits of the minor arcana:

* Marketing
* Operations & Management
* Public Relations
* Finance & Accounting

The fourteen cards within each suit of the minor arcana:
* 1 through 10
* Staff
* Supervisor
* Vice President
* President

Section 2 of a June 16, 2010 display of what was then at http://www.aeclectic.net/learn/perhaps_dawning.shtml:

The twenty-two cards of the major arcana:
0. Conflict
I. Chemistry
II. Entrepreneurship
III. Chief Financial Officer
IV. Chief Executive Officer
V. Business Philosophy
VI. Salesmanship
VII. Competition
VIII. Honesty
IX. Reflection
X. Solvency
XI. Motivation
XII. Sacrifice
XIII. Bankruptcy
XIV. Action
XV. Deceit
XVI. Crisis
XVII. Goals
XVIII. Uncertainty
XIX. Confidence
XX. Profitability
XXI. The Economy

Section 3 of a June 16, 2010 display of what was then at http://www.aeclectic.net/learn/perhaps_dawning.shtml:

Now for a few comments on the cards and their relations:

**The Four Suits**

"Marketing" is most central to what product or service to supply, and "Operations & Management" is most central to how to provide the product or service to the market.

"Public Relations" as an element revolves around interactions with the public in a primarily emotional way, and "Finance & Accounting" as an element revolves around interactions with the public in a primarily logical way.

Another approach to this modeling could be to say that:

1) "Marketing" and "Public Relations" more strongly emphasize dealing with the psychological constraints.
2) "Operations & Management" and "Finance & Accounting" more strongly emphasize dealing with the physical constraints.
3) "Marketing" and "Operations & Management" are more oriented toward treating the company and its customers as a unit (and less oriented toward treating company, customers, and general public as a unit).
4) "Public Relations" and "Finance & Accounting" are more oriented toward treating the company, its customers, and the general public as a unit (and less oriented toward treating the company and its customers as a unit).

To some degree, the relations of these four elements or suits may transcend or contradict the groups of statements just made, yet these statements may provide a useful approach at times.

**The Fourteen Cards within Each Suit**

For a given suit, 1 through 10 can represent amounts of resources available for activities, the degree of conscious effort devoted to an activity, or something else involving the suit. The four face cards may represent people at different levels of responsibility or forces

Section 4 of a June 16, 2010 display of what was then at http://www.aeclectic.net/learn/perhaps_dawning.shtml:

interacting at those levels: Staff at the basic level of responsibility, Supervisor at an intermediate level of responsibility, Vice President near the top level of a department, and President at the top level of a department.

**The Major Arcana**

Much the way that P.D. Ouspensky's 1913 essay "The Symbolism of the Tarot" presented pairs consisting of "Card I. The Magician" and "Card 0. The Fool," "Card II. The High Priestess" and "Card XXI. The World," "Card III. The Empress" and "Card XX. Judgment," "Card IV. The Emperor" and "Card XIX. The Sun," etc. as an insightful approach, the alternate framework here lends itself to this type of analysis.

"Card I. Chemistry" and "Card 0. Conflict" form a complementary pair. From some limited perspectives, all business activity revolves around conflict: conflicting aims, conflicting interests, the challenge of needing time and money to create value versus needing to save time and money in order to be efficient, and more. From some more expansive perspectives, it is the chemistry between different people, departments, and organizations that enables conversion of conflicts and shared interests into mutually beneficial relations.

"Card II. Entrepreneurship" and "Card XXI. The Economy" are related to the "big picture" of stewardship of organizations and how these organizations interact with each other at the microeconomic level to form the macroeconomic level of activity. Broadly conceived, entrepreneurship involves the beginning of an organization, the ideas and ambitions of owners, the interactions of top-level management with the owners, long-term strategies, and much more. Broadly conceived, the economy involves all main activities that generate transactional value throughout the world, and to some degree reaches into all other activities through codependent relations.

"Card III. Chief Financial Officer" corresponds to the person most centrally concerned with measuring and coordinating the flow of financial resources. "Card XX. Profitability" corresponds to the value people focus on the most as a basic measurement of financial performance. The chief financial officer plays key roles in providing a foundation from which the company has the chance to be profitable.

"Card IV. Chief Executive Officer" corresponds to the person who leads the company in many ways and makes many key, top-level strategic decisions. "Card XIX. Confidence" involves a value without which the company cannot survive for very long; for example, confidence in the future is often even more important to a public company's stock value than past and present profitability. One of the most important features of a successful chief executive officer is the ability to maintain and improve confidence, both inside and outside the organization.

"Card V. Business Philosophy" describes the core values and guidelines that an organization chooses over time. "Card XVIII. Uncertainty" reflects the many facets of risk management, unknown aspects of competitors, mysteries involving the markets, and many other things that can impact people at all levels of an organization. A company's business philosophy and how it may change over time can be key to whether the company successfully manages ever-changing uncertainties.

"Card VI. Salesmanship" may signify a cornerstone of influencing people, both within and without a given department, organization, or industry. "Card XVII. Goals" corresponds to what people choose to aim toward achieving. Salesmanship can influence people to adopt or sacrifice particular goals. People's goals and their degrees of commitment to those goals also play a key role in affecting how receptive they may be to attempts to influence them through

Section 5 of the June 16, 2010 display of an article:

salesmanship.

"Card VII. Competition" is key to whether a company can be profitable and whether an economy can be effective. Competition between individuals, departments, organizations, industries, and countries can be a source of great opportunity and great threat. "Card XVI. Crisis" reflects that the ebb and flow of competition, goals, and constraints sometimes lead to extremely threatening situations. How well people and groups of people use wisdom to compete or avoid competing can make all the difference in whether they survive a crisis.

"Card VIII. Honesty" reflects a value that keeps business and other human activities from descending into sheer mayhem. "Card XV. Deceit" reflects the fact that in many possible realms of business and human activity there can be many types of deception, both internal and external, both intentional and unintentional. Some may consider honesty and deceit to be completely opposite, while others may consider them to be two aspects of every communication, and yet others still may transcend these views.

"Card IX. Reflection" and "Card XIV. Action" involve deeply complementary parts of successful business. People need reflection in some circumstances in order to get a deeper handle of what is happening and what to do with long-term prospects. People need to act and act quickly to be effective in many circumstances. In many ways, people and organizations need a strong mixture of action and reflection to maintain both short-term and long-term success.

"Card X. Solvency" and "Card XIII. Bankruptcy" involve opposite extremes of ability to meet financial responsibilities. In many ways, one company's solvency may depend on an intricate web of the solvency of many related companies. Perhaps another company's actual or potential bankruptcy may present an acquisition opportunity, a grave threat, or both.

"Card XI. Motivation" involves the innermost drives within a person's psyche, and as such permeates the choices, decisions, actions, and consequences of business activity. "Card XII. Sacrifice" displays something that is essential when people face trade-offs between different things they consider worthwhile - for example, family, money, time, and health. The degree to which someone feels motivated can play a big role in whether they have the power to make sacrifices essential to their future success.

**Part Two: Background of Its Development**

In 2001 to mid-2003 I studied a number of esoteric subjects, but knew little of Tarot. Part of this built on reading an English language version of P.D. Ouspensky's Tertium Organum in 2000 from beginning to end and revisiting parts of it from time to time afterward. Another part involved reading James Legge's translation of The Tao Te Ching in 2000 and subsequently revisiting parts of it.

In mid-2003, I started studying the Tarot deck, and, in the three years that followed, I purchased a copy of The Oswald Wirth deck and a copy of The Rider-Waite deck. One of the influential writings on Tarot for me is P.D. Ouspensky's 1913 essay "The Symbolism of the Tarot," which is currently in the public domain.

Actually, back in 2003, when I first became intrigued with the Tarot, it was from reading the alternate version of P.D. Ouspensky's "The Symbolism of the Tarot," which appears as a chapter within his book A New Model of The Universe. Around that time, I read portions of the 2003 version of Martin Yate's Knock 'Em Dead, and, relating the two together, took out some note cards and made line drawings to symbolically relate to the twenty business values he outlined as being essential to success as an employee.

From mid-2003 through the present I have found perspectives from Buddhism of great value in relation to esoteric knowledge.

Another current within the development of the business-oriented card names described here involved Napoleon Hill. In 2001 I purchased the Napoleon Hill CD Selling You! and listened to it a number of times over subsequent years, then in September 2008 I started reading the version of Think and Grow Rich available online at sacred-texts.com.

**Part Three: Main Alternate Version**

This means that the main alternate version to the main framework mentioned earlier would be:

Four suits of the minor arcana:

* Marketing
* Operations & Management
* Public Relations
* Finance & Accounting

The fourteen cards within each suit of the minor arcana:
* 1 through 10

* Supervisor
* Vice President
* President

The twenty-two cards of the major arcana:
0. Conflict

I. Chemistry

II. Entrepreneurship

III. Chief Financial Officer

IV. Chief Executive Officer

V. Business Philosophy

VI. Salesmanship

VII. Competition

VIII. Motivation

IX. Reflection

X. Solvency

XI. Authenticity

XII. Sacrifice

XIII. Bankruptcy

XIV. Action

XV. Obstacles

XVI. Crisis

XVII. Goals

XVIII. Uncertainty

XIX. Confidence

XX. Profitability

XXI. The Economy

This pattern suggests several comments on the four cards primarily affected by the changes to VIII., XI., and XV.

"Card VIII. Motivation" involves the innermost drives within a person's psyche, and as such permeates the choices, decisions, actions, and consequences of business activity. "Card XV. Obstacles" can relate to problems and difficulties, whether or not people and organizations overcome them. Real or imagined obstacles can increase or decrease a person's motivation, depending on factors like attitude, character, and support. On the other hand, a person's motivation is often the key factor in whether he or she can overcome a given obstacle.

"Card XI. Authenticity" relates to the degree to which claims and perceptions correspond to realities. This can be a source of many opportunities and threats. "Card XII. Sacrifice" displays something that is essential when people face trade-offs between different things they consider worthwhile - for example, family, money, time, and health. The degree to which someone authentically becomes aware of key realities may enable wisdom with respect to sacrifices.

Section 6 (of 6) of a copy of the text of
the 4:18 P.M. 6/16/2010 display of the article
"Perhaps the Dawning of a New Tarot Deck"

This leads to comments on the four cards primarily affected by the changes to V. and VII.

"Card V. Competition" is key to whether a company can be profitable and whether an economy can be effective. Competition between individuals, departments, organizations, industries, and countries can be a source of great opportunity and great threat. "Card XVIII. Uncertainty" reflects the many facets of risk management, unknown aspects of competitors, mysteries involving the markets, and many other things that can impact people at all levels of an organization. A company's ability to stand up against competing organizations and its ability to effectively manage competition between people and departments within itself are key to whether the company successfully manages ever-changing uncertainties.

"Card VII. Business Philosophy" describes the core values and guidelines that an organization chooses over time. "Card XVI. Crisis" reflects that the ebb and flow of competition, goals, and constraints sometimes lead to extremely threatening situations. How well an organization uses and adjusts its business philosophy can be pivotal to whether or not it can avoid a crisis... and whether or not it can survive a crisis.

**Part Five: Possibilities of What May Be Next**

If there are artists interested in exploring creating artwork for decks with any one or more of the frameworks described here, I may be interested in a joint venture pursuing major publication of the deck or decks that result.

On February 26, 2022 at 11:30 A.M. Central Standard Time, I sent an e-mail to a visual artist after he and I had proceeded through several prior rounds of sending each other electronic messages back and forth.

Here is a transcription of an excerpt from that e-mail:

The simplest approaches to the idea structures and underlying realities of "pro-property-in-common versus anti-property-in-common versus pro-private-property versus anti-private-property" lend themselves to half-truths, quarter-truths, one-third-truths, two-third-truths, and other such things getting lodged deep within people's psyches, sometimes as a temporary benefit within the statics and dynamics of reality and sometimes as a long-term detriment. {To some degree, those lodgings within people's psyches may function as both benefits and detriments within the cosmic interplay between beings -- simultaneously or nonsimultaneously.} P.D. Ouspensky at some point characterized communism as a cancer threatening the entirety of human civilization, whereas H.H. The 14th Dalai Lama at some points characterized favorability toward communism and unfavorability toward totalitarianism. Some have argued whether and to what degree Jesus (whether referred to as Jesus Christ, Jesus of Nazareth, Jesus of Hebrew/Jewish Reformation, Jesus of Relationship with Muhammad, IICYC, et cetera) was more in favor of major rights to private property or major communal sharing of rights to the utilization/utilisation of resources.

"Part H of Section Five of Chapter Ten"

Although, as mentioned in the preliminary narrative of Section Five of Chapter Ten, Martin Yate profoundly insulted the totality of Buddhism, part of the magic of the First Amendment the The United States Constitution is that Buddhist practitioners, Christian practitioners, Muslim practitioners, Jewish practitioners, Agnostic practitioners, and others have the opportunity to interact with how Adams Media Corporation put that insult into print in a way that points out what was insulting about it, some of how and why it conflates and confuses many vital portions of reality, and how beings can get over it. Similarly, although Saul Alinsky insulted the entirety of all types of yoga in the process of his composition of *Rules for Radicals*, P.D. Ouspensky had already in the first half of the twentieth century rebuked many portions of any and all works ever defaming yoga, the yogis, and the yogninis. That included rebuking those who choose excessive identity politics, especially when used for extreme fear mongering and extreme hate mongering, and similar strains of distortion:

'"There are "psychological proofs" which mean much more than facts because facts can lie and psychological proofs cannot lie. But one must be able to feel them."' - *A New Model of the Universe: Principles of the Psychological Method in its Application to Problems of Science, Religion, and Art* (Translated, p. ix of the January 1946 reprint of the

August 1943 reset print from new plates of the September 1934 Second Edition, Revised; English version, author P.D. Ouspensky wrote the original version of it in Russian; 1946 reprint published by Alfred A. Knopf, New York).

Although I, Maurice James Blair, have only read a small fraction of that book, spread over a variety of its portions rather than completely sequentially from its beginning, here is a review from me to you of some of its elements: With *A New Model of the Universe*, Ouspensky expressed in no-uncertain terms his support for human liberty and the dignity of the individual, though in some spots he may have taken anti-dogmatism and pro-rugged-individualism a little too far. People who feel offended by what they perceive to have been past excesses by any and every organization that has imposed rigid thought patterns of group identity may find some of the statements quite welcoming. People who feel that any part of their identity or perceived identity is essential to them might at times feel targeted, though. True, it can be open to a given reader to interpret in which cases he might have made a proper killing versus in which cases he might have made an overkilling, yet, nevertheless, one of the most valuable things about that book is that it provides many types of stern condemnation toward the hate-filled, excessive pro-dogmatism and the hate-filled, anti-rugged-individualism to which many political party leaders, political party followers, communists, socialists, capitalists, radicals, liberals, moderates, conservatives, reactionaries, religious leaders, religious followers, anti-religious leaders, anti-religious followers, racial supremacists, cultural supremacists, and other idealogues are often prone.

....................................................................

Next, consider a statement that I, Maurice James Blair, the author of this *Alternative Beginnings and Endings of All Things* book, present to anyone who might ever bother to read it, whether or not such reader(s) ever embark on an attempt to hire a hitman, a hitwoman, a hit-hermaphrodite, a hit-squad, etc. to attempt to murder me, whether based on a political pretext, a religious pretext, a business pretext, a personal pretext, or whatever else:

Some people might take the success of any given aspect of their lives to be proof positive that it is an essential part of their identity or identities, then extrapolate from it to arrive at a conclusion that across the board, across all portions of all realities, that they might possess some clear superiority over everyone who does not share in whatever identity group or combination of identity groups to which they perceive themselves to belong, then extrapolate further, to the point of believing themselves justified to impose strict double-standards that elevate their identity group or combination of identity groups. They should look in the mirror and look through the visible presence and try to find reflections of the entirety of their hearts and minds and souls, considering the possibility of any and every and all distortions they might have. Then they should let go of the distortions.

How many such persons have bothered to study and consider *All Things under and over the Sun and Stars: Enigmas in Various Stages* carefully? Also, how many such persons of that mindset have bothered to consider the realities of the Everest Marathon, Winter Olympics, Summer Olympics, Chess Olympiad, and Paralympics? What about consideration of every justice and every injustice that has ever been committed by any criminal, any officer, any mental health professional, any judge, any jury, any witness, and any executioner?!

RECOMMENDED FURTHER READINGS

*Brave New World* (1932). Huxley, Aldous

*And Then There Were None* (1939). (also known by several different titles that begin with the two-word combination, *Ten Little*). Christie, Agatha.

*Childhood's End* (1953). Clarke, Arthur C.

*When the Legends Die* (1963). Borland, Hal.

*Childhood's End* (1990). Clarke, Arthur C.

*Firstborn* (2007). Clarke, Arthur C. & Baxter, Stephen.

"The Ninth Part (in some sense Part I, though here the 'I' as in Ninth in Sequence rather than Roman Number 'I' as in First in Sequence) of Section Five of Chapter Ten: All The Roosters, Hens, Male Dragons, Female Dragons, Female Pheonixes, Male Pheonixes, Hexagrams, Octograms, Decagrams, Pentagrams, Humans, Animals, Plants, Planets, Moons, and Galaxies Come Home to Roost and Deliver Karma, At Least For a Few Fleeting Hypervolumes of Higher-Dimensional Space-Time"

Long ago, though we might not fathom when or how, human beings arrived on the scene. Did human beings first arrive on Earth or elsewhere? Was the process of arrival primarily of divine origins, mundane origins, biological origins, other origins, or some hybrid? Whatever the case might be, agriculture, hunting, cooking, politics, religion, regulation, and discipline eventually became prominent among humanity.

Some have claimed and found amusement in the idea structure that prostitution is the world's oldest profession. As with all sayings or nearly all sayings, people can easily become distracted from the full reality by obsessing on repeating to themselves and others the idea structures while ignoring other perspectives. Imagine extremely early individuals of the species *Homo sapiens* now, letting go of any and all religious legends of the first of that species already having well-developed language capabilities from the get-go. Refrain from fretting for at least a little while about whether or not the first of that species actually had such well-developed language capabilities from inception as some religious texts might suggest if read literally and with full suspension of disbelief, simply consider this a mind exercise that a given mindstream may at some stage transfer into being more than a mind exercise or may choose to forever circumscribe into being merely a mind exercise. Fret not, also, about quibbling over whether it is better to use the phrase "mind exercise" or the phrase "mental exercise."

Imagine some early hominids interacting as depicted by a consensus of biologists, anthropologists, archaeologists, and historians who serve as professors at accredited universities in The United States of America as of the early twenty-first century. In such a primitive state, social structures lacked anywhere near the complexity that they subsequently acquired. Teamwork, hunting, gathering, mating, child-rearing, fighting, teaching, and trading had complexities nevertheless, as they involved the full brunt of reality, much as they today also involve the full brunt of reality, though of course, today's version are often strikingly different from how they happened back then. Technically, in that context, if we are to be fully honest with ourselves, then we might not be able to completely know with certainty whether it was prostitution, architecture, food preparation, transportation, or something else that involved the very first economic transaction. Skeptical? Well, let us delve into one argument each in favor of several candidates for what should be deemed the world's oldest profession.

Imagine early hominids residing only on Planet Earth, free of any concept of clear quid-pro-quo economic transactions, immediately before the first-ever quid-pro-quo economic transaction to occur between hominids on Planet Earth. Next, one-by-one: one vision each for each of those theories.

First, let us consider the popular theory that prostitution is the world's oldest profession. A fecund early male hominid felt sexually aroused and noticed a nearby early female hominid with whom he wished to have sexual intercourse. In contrast, she did not have sufficient sexual arousal and other elements at the time to go straight into acquiescing to his advances in the absence of something about the situation changing. All of the previous instances of human mating had consisted of cases of several categories: 1) consensual sex, 2) rape in which a male would force sex with a female to occur without her consent, 3) succubus-style acts of sexual assault in which a female would find a male who was having an erection yet not consenting to having sex with her at the time—on account of him sleeping face-up while in that state, or on account of him actively refusing her yet somehow becoming physically overpowered, or some similar way of that—and forcing herself onto him in such a way as to catch him and force him into having sex with her without his consent, and 4) other types of sex devoid of any economic quid-pro-quo transactional elements. However, in this case the male and female soon innovated by communicating with each other such that she would compromise on her stance of refusal of his advances if he would simply give her a sufficient amount of food or other provisions.

Second, let us consider an alternative theory, namely that architecture is the world's oldest profession. Prior to any other economic quid-pro-quo transactions, including any instances of prostitution, in this scenario, professional architecture beats all the other professions to the punch. Skeptical that there is any even remotely-possible way that this could have ever actually been the case, are you? At least for a little while, picture this: Two primitive men go over to a group of ten other primitive people, seeking for the group of ten to share some food with the two. However, the group of ten communicate, in no uncertain terms, that hell no, they feel that there is no way in hell, on Earth, or anywhere else that they feel right at all about sharing that food. Next, part of the naturally-produced-sans-human-construction cave in which the group of ten normally make residence collapses, while the two hungry men are still trying to plead their case about why the group of ten should be charitable enough to share a little food with them. Suddenly, the two men offer that they will help repair and extend the usability of the cave dwelling in the wake of its partial collapse, but only on the condition that they get to receive food in exchange for doing the work. Furthermore, the food payment plan would be in installments: they get a small portion each time they complete a little bit of the project. The ten people notice that the two men are likely going to be better at doing this than they as ten would be, due to a variety of factors that you would have to have been there to fully comprehend, and turn out to be beyond the scope of what is needed to understand this vision. The leader of the ten accepts the offer but informs the two that their very act of explaining the plan for how the repair and construction project would proceed was very helpful, then hands over some food. Therefore, if anyone would take this theory with even a trace of seriousness, it not only would involve a sequence in which architecture would be the world's oldest profession, it would also posit construction to be the world's second-oldest profession.

Next, here is a vision of a Planet Earth in which food provision is the world's oldest profession. Imagine this: A couple, one of them a cisgender female and the other a cisgender male, approaches a group of people who had kidnapped their only child. The kidnappers did not do this for ransom; rather, they wanted to keep the child as their own. Furthermore, the kidnappers numbered eight, specifically, three men and five women, whereas the parents of the kidnapping victim numbered two. Suddenly, the couple arrives to find the eight kidnappers and the couple's only child. They offer the kidnappers some food, but only on the condition that they get their child returned to them. The kidnappers negotiate that they would be willing to return the child on the condition that it would be twice as much food as the initial offer. The parents of that child then counteroffer in the amount that is one-and-a-half-times-the-size-of-the-initial-offer, in other words, 3/4-the-size-of-what-the-kidnappers-counteroffered, and the kidnappers accept it. In the wake of that, the kidnappers get the idea that they could kidnap other children and hold them for ransom. That would be a scenario in which food provision is the world's oldest profession and kidnapping-for-ransom is the world's second-oldest profession.

Finally, behold a scenario in which transportation is the world's oldest profession. An early hominid fellow of exceptional strength and endurance was in an area when, nearby some fighting broke out. A young mother carried her three-year-old child with her while fleeing the fighting. She could tell that if she would continue fleeing in that manner, then she would soon become exhausted. but maybe the strong man nearby might prove very helpful. She asked him to carry the child and accompany her in order to more completely escape the scene of the fighting. He refused, then started to get an idea. He then offered that if she would agree that he could adopt the child, enter a long-term, committed, monogamous romantic relationship with her, including that they could routinely have sex with each other, and that they could therefore form a family, then he would agree to lift the child into his arms and help carry the child as part of how the woman and her child were fleeing. By the way, the child happened to be feeling weak due to an unknown medical condition at the time, and that is a large part of why the child was not performing the child's own walking during that process. The lady agreed to the gentleman's proposal, they fled together as a family, and, miraculously, upon waking up the next morning, the child's feeble condition had vanished, replaced by the child returning to being very energetic and very capable of plenty of walking and running, even over extended periods of time. In that version of Earth, perhaps some might combine it with added details to posit that transportation is the world's oldest profession, the provision of so-called mail-order brides predates the advent of mail ordering, marriage proposals predate the formal conceptualization and societal recognition of marriage proposals, and the inception of what was de facto an early marriage combined with an early adoption of a stepchild correlated closely in time with that child somehow miraculously healing from a mystery illness.

Some readers might at first blush after encountering the passages that started with the beginning of the ninth part of the fifth section of the tenth chapter of this book and ended with the paragraph preceding this one, think toward me, especially if they read out of sequence and out of context while knowing very little about my life beyond the fact that I wrote the aforementioned preliminary ninth-part-of-fifth-section passages, *You fucking idiot! What a waste of time it was to read what you wrote! What a goddamned loser, moron you are! I don't think you've ever had sex with anyone, or, if you have, then it would have been limited to hiring illegal hookers to have sex with you. You're clearly too fucking stupid and idiotic to have ever even been good enough in life to reach the level of hiring a legal prostitute in a way of obeying the law. Also, you're clearly not good enough to be one of those extreme religious people who voluntarily abstains from sex for long periods of time as a voluntary celibacy way of life. You hideous, sorry excuse for a human being, maybe it would be best if some drug cartel member tries to shoot at a group of rival drug cartel people and winds up accidentally fatally shooting you, because the world is probably better off with having you dead. You dirty, goddamned bastard, idiot fool, you low-life loser! Also, there's probably no way you could be a homeowner, whether co-owning a house with someone else or in any other way, because I can tell by the way you wrote that set of words that you are not good enough to be a homeowner.*

Of course, in a little while, I will address each part of that set of hostility.

In addressing that, the answers will go point by point, line by line, area by area, volume by volume, etc. However, let us imagine letting people thinking along those lines continuing onward completely unfettered for a while, such as to be granted enough rope to hang themselves. They could continue, unsuspecting of how reality would be about to sooner or later hit them and hit them hard. A possible continuation of how some of them might run with the premises of their impressions would be to think toward me, *Furthermore, if you have ever held a steady job, of which I am skeptical, then you had to have always been a bottom-of-the-barrel, terrible worker. It simply shows from the way you wrote. And another thing, if you ever have or ever will get into a conflict with any employer, however much there might be any argument for why anyone should deem their behavior to have been unjust, then there's no way in hell, no way on earth, no way in heaven, and no way anywhere else that you would ever be capable of fighting back against them strongly enough to appear on talk radio over a span lasting over five minutes, stating your side of the story. There's also no way that you could ever become the author of any published book that would state your case about this, . You are too much of a sorry excuse for a human being to accomplish any of those kinds of things!*

Now for some bullet points refuting some types of the disrespect exhibited in those descriptions:

- I appeared on the August 6, 2021 morning edition of *The Michael Berry Show* in order to present critiques of 1) The Financial Advisory Group, Inc.'s methods of dealing with the conflicts that happened between Natasha McDaniel and me, the conflicts that happened between Steve Estrin and me, and additional portions of the interactions that happened involving both the time in which I was an employee of that firm and some of the aftermath; 2) Bill Walker (who had never been an employee of The Financial Advisory Group) having gone way over the top in his hostility toward me on multiple occasions; and 3) how some of the patterns involving Saul Alinsky's indoctrination of other people have been highly problematic and quite pot-entially part of the root causation of the con-flicts between The Financial Advisory Group and me, between Bill Walker and me, and between The Democratic Party and The Republican Party. I refrained from saying the name of The Financial Advisory Group on air during that as a courtesy to the firm and as a way to not create excessive distract-ion during the call, yet I followed up by going to *The Michael Berry Show*'s Facebook page, and, using my own legal name on Facebook, responding to a few of the general public's reactions there to my phone call to Michael Berry of that day. That made it blatantly obvious to anyone who might have chosen to follow up by looking up my information on the Internet to know precisely that I was talking about The Financial Advisory Group as located in Houston, Texas during that phone call.

- About five days later, I called again, speaking only briefly. That was shortly after receiving on August 10, 2021 a libelous letter dated August 9, 2021 from Gray Reed & McGraw (using the name Gray Reed) on behalf of The Financial Advisory Group, then sending an e-mail message to the commissioners of the U.S. Securities and Exchange Commission and the attorney who had signed that libelous letter, explaining to the attorney and the four commissioners exactly how it was that the letter was libelous plus several related salient points. On air, a little less than a week after the previous call, I spoke briefly about how I had received that threatening letter yet figured out quickly that it was defamatory toward me. Chapter Nine included a copy of the e-mail message referenced, and a more complete discussion of that and other things appears after this set of bullet points.
- I am a homeowner. I co-own the house that serves both as my residence as of the time of this book going to print and as the publishing house mailing address for the publisher

of this book. Furthermore, there is no mortgage on the house; my family compl-etely owns that house, not beholden to any bank mortgage situation in connection with it.

- I have had sex with a few women, though, on account of the fact that I have never been married, it could be debatable about wheth-er this should be a reason to respect me more, respect me less, or respect me with a combination of in-some-ways more and in-other-ways less. There are many different lifestyles that work well for many different people, and, at a deeper level of reality, we may all perhaps admit to at least a little uncertainty about what could or should con-stitute the proper ethics about the regul-ation of human sexual activity—both the government regulation of sex and the pers-onal regulation of sex by each individual, each couple, each group, etc. A more in-depth discussion of this will appear later in this "Part Nine."
- Of the women with whom I have had sex, only one of them did I know to have been a prostitute, and that one was a legal prost-itute in a legal Nevada brothel where I hired her on July 30, 2022 in order to take the full range of the sexual experiences in my life to go further than where they had gone before, partly on account of some of the Vajrayana

Buddhist tantric sexual energy coordination methods, and partly on account of how previous sexual encounters with women had gravitated toward the sexual partners being much more timid and inhibited than what my entire energy system had yearned to experience. An analogy that I have expressed to a few people is that there could be thought a parallel in which the previous women with whom I had experienced sex were like drivers of a car that the owner requested to be taken to somewhere very close to its top speed of 335 mph, yet none of the drivers had been willing to go faster than about 160 mph, and the car and the owner seemed to be dying for faster speed. Finally, the owner decided to hire a professional race car driver and to tell her to go ahead and take it to an incredible speed if she could, and he and the car accept it that there could be a risk of an accident that might total the car. Sure enough a suitable automobile-racing-competition professional driver found employment by the vehicle owner, and she took the vehicle to about 312 mph, not quite as high as the 335 mph top speed that it was capable of, but still much more thrilling and complete than the 160 mph maximum that the previous drivers—all of whom were volunteer drivers rather than paid ones—had been willing and able to reach while driving the car. The hiring of the driver and the process of the fast racing went well and mutually beneficially for the professional driver, the vehicle owner, and the vehicle. (More of the context will appear later in this "Part Nine of Section Five of Chapter Ten," yet right here a few more comments will suffice.) That lady who served as a legal courtesan and paralleled having profess-ionally sped an automobile to around 312 miles per hour without crashing goes intent-ionally unnamed in this book, though I am aware of several of her aliases. Part of this decision is to be slightly more gentlemanly than I would be were I to label her by any of her known aliases here. Also, she is among the many former lovers and almost-lovers whom I consider to maybe be possible as a potential future wife of mine if things were to somehow miraculously sort themselves out such as to make it correct. Yes, I am aware that Sidney Poitier (1927-2022) and Lucille Ball (1911-1989) would probably take an extremely dim view of what I just stated here, unless they would flex their minds away from some of what they por-trayed way back when (Cf. *To Sir With Love* (1967) and portions of *The Tonight Show Starring Johnny Carson Show* (1962-1992)), whereas Richard Gere and Julia Roberts would probably find it either reasonable or, perhaps, very reasonable (Cf. *Pretty Woman* (1990)). On a related note, earlier in the year 2022 I sent an e-mail message to Master Lian-Yuan of True Buddha School, composing that message as an alternative way to apply for employment with that religious organization, and my intentions were to find out if they might accept me as a monk, to join as an employee among the professionally-paid clergy if a combination of me getting accepted by them for that role and them getting accepted by me for that monastic relationship, and appropriate follow-up steps. Although I am quite aware that some who read this will likely think very negatively about my having resorted to hiring a legal Nevada brothel courtesan to engage in multiple types of coitus, fellatio, foreplay, and other intimate physical activities with me, as a supplementation and augmentation of my rare previous experiences with foreplay and sex, but bear in mind that: 1) Sublimating sexual impulses were such that as of FEB 2022 I planned a scenario of becoming a monk and seriously limiting or eliminating sexual activities, unless and until to change for spiritually legitimate purposes, such as if leaving the True Buddha School clergy in order to get married, then later on either staying out of the clergy or later on rejoining while still married to a woman. 2) TBS allows for single people to join the ranks of its clergy, but on the condition that they remain single thereafter as clergy unless they exit the clergy to get married, later eligible to rejoin while married—in other words, if you join the clergy single, stay single while continuously among the clergy, but you can get married if you leave the clergy in order to get married, and, if you do that and decide you would like to return to the clergy, then you may apply to rejoin, and, while you are at it, maybe your spouse would consider also applying to join the ranks of our professional monks, nuns, masters, etc. 3) Many tantric practices, including some portions of the Vajrayana Buddhist general guidelines, have it that sex outside of marriage between consenting adults can generally be spiritually legitimate and correct activities if handled properly, in contrast with how many of the strict versions of many of the other religious and/or spiritually-based practices and guidelines at times condemn any sex that ever happens other than between a husband and a wife who are married to each other at the time that the sex occurs. 4) some portions of Vajrayana activities indicate an approval that in at least a few cases prostitution can be a spiritually correct activity for people to engage in. 5) Master Lian-Yuan, also known as Tienling Chen, did not directly respond to the message I sent him as an job application to become a monk with TBS, tantamount to a silent rejection. 6) In some ways, that might not have amounted to an official application as deemed by True Buddha School {also sometimes abbreviated TBS} officials, because I applied by directly e-mailing a master-level monk rather than by using an officially-structured formal employment application process. 7) Although people sometimes jump to a conclusion that if someone else's energy system and whatever else lead to the person legally engaging in an activity that some areas of society unequivocally condemn and judge to never have any legitimate reasons or explanations to support them and which various of the strictest of mindsets among some of the people wind up deeming to be clearly sinful, unethical, pathetic, and detestable, then perhaps they should also take a mirror to considering the totality of their own lives and everything they have ever done and also, look back toward others, and consider how certain they really are about anything. They could then also consider how the author Salman Rushdie, upon whom the long-time Iranian religious leader Ayatollah Ruholla Khomeini (1900-1989) pronounced a fatwa death sentence against in 1989, and narrowly survived an assassination attempt in 2022, said on *The Stephen Colbert Show* as broadcasted to the public on April 15, 2024 via CBS, that an unnamed "American humorist" had characterized, "that Puritanism is the deep fear that someone somewhere might be happy."

- Although I have experienced physical romance, including but not limited to mouth-to-mouth kissing with women, foreplay with women, sex with women, etc., those experiences have been rare. Rare with respect to regular observable reality, but how are the living to know how much some of the dead might ever have sex the living? Nevertheless, I believe a the main trend in my life was toward much major sinfulness and sexual impurity of actions prior to April 19, 2001, then a shift toward reduced nonsexual sinfulness in some ways, increased nonsexual sinfulness in other ways, and nearly an extinction of sexual sinfulness (not only in terms of physical manifestation, but also in terms of sinful thoughts and sinful intentions) during and in the wake of the April 19, 2001 end-of-tax-season-internship interview with then-Arthur-Andersen-LLP partner Amin Nosrat. Later, in portions of April-to-November 2003, there came seismic shifts in the direction of nearly a total extinction of most sinful acts and attitudes within me across the board, yet a huge part of that involved recognizing the major degree of illusion in the very concepts of "I," "me," "myself," "mine," "thine," "thee," "you," "yourself," "self," "nonself," "existence," "us," "them," "unity," "nonunity," and "nonexist-ence." As expressed by many sciences, religions, and philosophies over the eons, such illusions underscore such realities. Some who have known me during that period might think to some episode or two or twenty of interacting with me and believe them-selves to have Ouspensky-style psychological, unrefutable proof of this being patently false, yet I shall point out something: Take virtually any movie in which you feel complete proof of something, then imagine an incomplete version of that movie appearing to be psychological proof to someone of something, especially when supplemented by something else that was not in that movie, yet which you believe yourself to *know* to be a patently false way of relating to that. For example, we can put together a CERN-style supercollision of two items. In this case, the first item is how on *The Michael Berry Show* as broadcast in at least one episode sometime around the period from June 2019 to July 2021, Michael Berry spoke of some woman who had made some strong accusation against a person or organization, then remarked how the woman had later retracted in connection with admitting herself to having had a severe psychiatric diagnosis and believeing herself to have been affected by the severe psychiatric condition described by the diagnosis such as to have resulted in her bearing false witness against the accused, and Berry publicly characterized via that episode that the connection of that woman with that diagnosis is such that, "we cannot believe anything she says," or words essentially identical to that effect. The second item is the motion picture film *Day of the Woman* (1978, nowadays more generally known as *I Spit on Your Grave*), for which some of the advertising states, "*THIS WOMAN HAS JUST* CUT, CHOPPED, BROKEN, and BURNED FIVE MEN BEYOND RECOGNITION... *BUT NO JURY IN AMERICA WOULD EVER CONVICT HER!*"

Watching that film seemed psychological proof to me of how cruel, unjustified, and horrible the behavior of several male characters was toward the female protagonist in it, and how it seems plausibly-justified that she did unto them what she did unto them. Consider, though, beyond the observable part of that film, if someone dealt with a person whose life seemed a hybrid of the female protagonist, as portrayed by Camille Keaton in that film, and the male protagonist—in some ways very different, in other ways, not so different at all—as portrayed by Joachim Pheonix in *Joker* (2019), then related the entire pattern to the idea of choosing consistent disbelief toward people who have ever been diagnosed with a severe psychiatric condition. One problem you may confront is when a person, whether a cisgender hermaphrodite, a cisgender female, a cisgender male, a transgender female, a transgender male, or of any other set of gender, biology, and other aspects, genuinely experiences being extremely reputationally violated or very physically violated or both by another person, several people, an organization, or multiple organizations, and the person truly accuses the violators of having violated in the ways that they had violated, yet some of those who evaluate the situation automatically believe themselves justified to disqualify and completely disregard the possibility that the accuser is, in fact, accurate. In other words, those evaluating the situation would be jumping to a conclusion of siding with the accused, and they would be dead wrong. A somewhat opposite type of problem you may confront is when a person, whether a cisgender hermaphrodite, a cisgender female, a cisgender male, or of any other set of gender, biological reality, and whatever else, does not genuinely experience being extremely reputationally violated or very physically violated or both by another person, several people, an organization, or multiple organizations, and the person falsely accuses the alleged violators, and the accused deny the alleged behavior, yet some of those who deal with the situation automatically believe themselves justified to disqualify and completely disregard the possibility that the denials expressed by the accused are accurate. In other words, those evaluating the situation would be jumping to a conclusion of siding with the accuser, and they would be dead wrong. People can reasonably listen to someone and empathize with them while still acknowledging to themselves, whether spoken out loud or not, the boundaries of that of which they truly know, that of which they are certain, that of which they truly do not know, and that of which they are uncertain, as well as the possibility that at least a few of their perceived boundaries of certainty-versus-uncertainty might not accurately reflect the absolute truth of where those boundaries are. Any snap reaction of absolutely going one way could well be a recipe of disaster. With that stated, though, yes, there is a concession that someone, for example, an attorney serving one side of a legal battle, the spouse of a person on one side of a war of any kind, or a jury member whom a court demands to arrive at one of several possible verdicts in a court proceeding, could thoroughly side with whomever seems appropriate in context, yet even such a person or organization might wind up in a trap that Abrahamic perspectives could label as an "idolatry" of the side chosen and that some Dharmic perspectives could label as a mixture of "attachment" to the side chosen, "aversion" to the side not chosen, and "indifference" to vital facts, truths, and factors involving the situation. Having said that, though, bear in mind that those falling into such a trap may later find opportunities for course correction. It is one thing to be almost absolutely certain of knowing something that you do not in fact actually absolutely know with certainty; it is quite another thing—and potentially lethal—to think and feel and believe yourself to be absolutely certain of absolutely knowing something that you do not in fact actually absolutely know with certainty, *especially if you are dead wrong about it!!!!!*

- At the risk of being accused by some of at least temporarily drifting into becoming an avatar of Captain Obvious, I shall state the following: There have been many cataclysms in my life and the lives of others from December 2003 onward, and the remainder of this part of this section of this chapter of this book shall take a deeper dive, a higher flight, a broader panorama, and a longer look at the totality of elements of everyone and everything.

At the beginning of the humans of Earth, many things happened, and diverse people of the present have many disagreements with each other about what they believe about the origins of the entire set of human beings.

In 2003 there was much controversy over how the television broadcast of *Hitler: Rise of Evil* occurred and how due in movie theaters the next year was *The Passion of the Christ.* In 2004, besides how *The Passion of the Christ* reached movie theaters and garnered much controversy, the television show *South Park* presented a spoof of Mel Gibson, that movie which he worked on, and many societal issues, including sometimes-strained relationships between non-Jewish Christians, non-Christian Jews, ambiguously-related-to-Christianity Jews, Jewish Christians, and large numbers of other types of people. Also, all audiovisual presentations, however artfully done or disconcertingly done—as perceived and experienced by any given beholder in any given instance—can be thought of as relating to all beings, to whatever degree any of those beings might be of any type, any combination of types, any transcendence going beyond all types, any hybrid of the aforementioned, or anything else. Previously, on July 4, 2001, *South Park* had an episode that portrayed a team of Moses, Jesus, Mohammed, Buddha, and others battling against David Blaine. Although many Muslims consider visual portrayals of The Prophet Mohammed, also known as The Prophet Muhammad, to be forbidden to modern people, *South Park* handled that situation tastefully enough that the two men who mainly run that show, namely Trey Parker and Matt Stone, did not get into any immediate major backlash from Muslims over their visual portrayal of Mohammed in that episode, titled, "Super Best Friends." Also, the regular, real world illusionist David Blaine evidently did not worry or complain very much about the "coincidental" similarity of name and likeness between the *South Park* manifestation of a professional illusionist David Blaine and himself, as well as the contrast between whatever he had going on in his heart, mind, soul, and life and what that episode portrayed in connection with its version of David Blaine. From the time of the July 2001 *South Park* episode "Super Best Friends" to the time of the March 2004 *South Park* episode "The Passion of the Jew" to the time of the February 2024 *Law & Order* episode "Freedom of Speech," Jewish-Muslim relations, Christian-Muslim relations, Jewish-Christian relations, Buddhist-Christian relations, Buddhist-Jewish relations, Buddhist-Muslim relations, Buddhist-Hindu relations, Agnostic-Atheist relations, Atheist-Christian relations, Protestant-Catholic relations, and various international relations had many transformations. Some in America believe that some of the most toxic developments have involved a hyper-polarization and an escalation of hostility between Republicans and Democrats in the United States.

From time immemorial, Abrahamic religions and Dharmic religions have consistently condemned the ways that some people sometimes hold on too tightly to favoring those whom they believe themselves justified to favor—when taken that to the point that they repeatedly violate those whom they disfavor. Also, there are some strains of thought in which a given generation of a family can be thought of as passing karma down to each later generation, whether permanently or for some limited number of generations. In Western cultures, perhaps the most often cited phrase in relationship with this is, "The sins of the fathers shall be visited upon the sons." Although many people pussyfoot around many of the things that under the surface are most upsetting to themselves and others, once in a while someone says something that gives a tell about what the people are repressing themselves from saying out loud.

Even without literally and knowingly doing some telepathic mind meld technique, we can be highly confident about what were some of the underlying thoughts of many Democrats, Republicans, and Independents as of April 2024. Perhaps including the following item is a highly risky thing for the publisher and me to present, yet here it is:

"A Fictional Exhibition Intentionally Similar to Alleged Select Nonfictional Hidden Exhibitions as of April 2024"

## PART ONE OF THIS FICTIONAL EXHIBIT

A group of twenty-five Americans on April 16, 2024 were each of them located at least 25 miles away from the other twenty-four.

In most regular senses, they were not a group at all, for the only main way of organizing them into a group involved the remote telepathic dynamics that happened between their minds. Somehow across the statics and dynamics, related in ways to the "minds-communicating-across-the-ether" symbolic expression that some conceive, their minds shared a deep conversation. That is, with referring to "ether" in a very different way than the generally-refuted "ether" of the ether theory of optics that fell by the wayside when the special relativity theory of optics came to be consistently objectively proven in physics according to measured data. Refer, if you will, to information involving Albert Einstein, Special Relativity, Hendrik Lorentz, and, taking things into another direction. Consider the notion of at least a little trace of telepathic influences via mysterious levels of people's minds, expressed in *The Law of Success* by Napoleon Hill.

The minds of the 25 remote beings took turns transmitting. They shared a profound subconscious and semiconscious telepathic conversation.

## PART 2A OF A FICTION EXHIBIT WITHIN THE CONTEXT OF A NONFICTION BOOK

Two of them merged portions of their minds for a few seconds, then separated again. One of those two transmitted to the other and all the rest of the other members of this "group."

The first transmitter described here thought thusly, *Long ago, I felt strong empathy for Donald Trump. Poor rich dude, all that money and yet having to deal with the legacy of being the son of a klansman. Donald Trump's father, Fred Trump, was a member of the Ku Klux Klan. Poor rich man Donald Trump, so tragic that he had to be born into that family. Maybe, if he was more fortunate, he might have been born into a Black Panther family, whether as one of those Black-rights activist Black Panther group's families or as, literally, a black panther animal in the wild, or as, literally, a character in the Marvel Cinematic Universe involved with Wakanda, or maybe something else that might have spared that Donald Trump the grave misfortune of being born the son of a klansman. Gee, if I was born into his situation maybe I might consider shooting myself dead as a punishment for ever being born!*

## PART 2B OF A FICTION EXHIBIT WITHIN THE CONTEXT OF A NONFICTION BOOK

After a brief pause, the first transmitter continued:

*However, I lost almost all my empathy for him when I found out he had stepped down from that elevator in mid-2015 to announce that he was running for president, and, to add insult to injury, making sharp criticism of a large number of Hispanics part of his campaign platform. The nerve of that dirty moron! How dare he run for president! How dare he try to profit from stereotyping many Hispanics by associating them with the few who combine immigrating here without proper documentation with committing murders, rapes, and other heinous crimes! Just because some people of a group do something, it doesn't mean that it gives you the right to exploit that in a way that diminishes everyone of that group! Especially, if you're the son of a klansman. I mean, really, although Trump technically had the right to run for president, his family's background disqualifies him from being a legitimate president. The sins of the father are visited upon the son!*

## PART 3A OF A FICTIONAL EXHIBIT WITHIN THE CONTEXTS OF A NONFICTION BOOK

The second telepathic transmitter sent to the first transmitter and the rest of the group agreement, but the third and fourth disagreed.

The fourth transmitter described here thought thusly, *Check your double-standard hypocrisies in at the door! Look into a freaking mirror! Come on, man! Although it is detestable that Fred Trump, or anyone else, ever was, is, or ever will be a Ku Klux Klan member, you cannot permanently hold that over on President Donald John Trump! By a similar reasoning, you could hold it over a huge percentage of the entire Democratic Party that it has a heritage of long ago working in cahoots with that infamous KKK organization!*

The first transmitter retorted telepathically, *You're doing something much worse than comparing apples and oranges, you're doing something much more like comparing a bag of apples on sale in a grocery store and a group of Middle Eastern Muslim fanatics performing clitoridectomies!*

The fourth transmitter fired back, *What about this entire thing? You brought up acts of genital mutilation. Penectomies: probably almost always unethical. Clitoridectomies: probably almost always unethical. The practices of the modern Democratic Party: probably almost always unethical!*

The first transmitter responded, *Again, you are simply confusing things! Yes, both the Democratic Party and the Republican Party have a checkered past, with mixtures of godawful, terrible actions and affiliations. However, the Republican Party has veered into absolute hideousness, and its embrace of having the son of a KKK member as its main leader is beyond bad, it is sheer insanity!!*

## PART 3B OF A FICTION EXHIBIT WITH THE CONTEXT OF A NONFICTION BOOK

The third transmitter intervened on behalf of the fourth and anyone else who might be of like mind. That third proceeded, *Look, if we look at anyone's background, we could say, "Aha! Disqualification! No way in Hades can that person ever be qualified to be U.S. President!!" That doesn't necessarily make it the case. Just because anyone has just about any background, it doesn't automatically disqualify the person!! If your father shot Jack Kennedy, then that wouldn't necessarily mean that everyone should shit on you! If your father was a descendent of the soldier who pierced the side of Jesus of Nazareth while he was being crucified, then that wouldn't necessarily mean that we should hold that against you, either!*

The first responded, *That line of thinking would generally be true, but this is different. I mean, for one thing, we can all be pretty much sure that Lee Oswald acted alone in shooting Jack Kennedy dead that November day in Dallas long ago, and, for another, there are huge differences in one version of bad and another version of bad. If someone's father had this bad thing or that bad thing, or, for that matter, if someone's mother had this bad thing or that bad thing, or whatever, that's one thing. But this situation is a whole other slaughterhouse!*

The fourth rejoined, *Though slaughterhouses do what slaughterhouses do, you do not know what you do not know, I do not know what I do not know, and no one knows what no one knows! Further, we may simply have too big a divide on this. You are totally locked in to the idea that Donald Trump was born into being technically eligible for U.S. Presidency but ethically inherently disqualified from eligibility for U.S. Presidency. I believe he was not ethically inherently disqualified from birth from U.S. Presidency. We can agree to disagree, and we can segue to something else, can't we?*

The first stated, *Fine, let's shift over to discussing The Beatles, The Rolling Stones, and the individuals who are or ever were members of those two music groups, if those sharing in these telepathies can reach consensus agreement to join in such a shift.*

The second, third, fourth, eighth, twentieth, and twenty-fifth agreed and concurred emphatically. The other members wavered, except for the fifteenth, who telepathically tuned into the mysteries of "A Day in the Life" and totally spaced out for a few seconds.

## PART 4A OF A FICTIONAL EXHIBIT WITHIN THE CONTEXT(S) OF A NONFICTION BOOK

Within those few seconds of the fifteenth spacing out were many worlds of telepathic conversations.

The zenith of conflict within that—the most emotionally-intense-yet-infinitesimally-microscopic portion of it—was a telepathic dialogue that transpired thusly:

The eighteenth stated to the rest, but most especially the fourth, eighth, and twenty-fifth, *To me the problem with The Beatles begins and ends with how John Lennon had the nerve to perform, record, and allow to be released to the public that song of the title "God" that became the tenth track on his solo debut after the demise of the group. Such blasphemy! Sure, it's admirable that he stated that he did not believe in Hitler, and in some ways maybe it's touch-and-go with whether or not it made sense for him to state that he did not believe in Kennedy and some of the others, but for him to directly, point-blank express disbelief in Jesus, The Bible, and Kings in a song that he called "God" and dared to go onto an album to be sold to the public?? Are you freaking kidding me? You're not freaking kidding me, and he was not freaking kidding anyone. Steely Dan rebuking "Imagine" via "Only a Fool Would Say That" also in some ways was rebuking that other song I was just now criticizing. How could Lennon dare to make that "God" song with such patently blasphemous lyrics and unleash it on an unsuspecting public!*

## PART 4B OF A FICTIONAL EXHIBIT WITHIN THE CONTEXT(S) OF A NONFICTION BOOK

After a brief pause, the eighteenth transmitter continued thusly:

*Even though Mark David Chapman has gone on to blame himself for assassinating John Lennon in December 1980, maybe we should all blame John Lennon himself for how his lyrics in that 1970 "God" song were more primarily to blame than the assassination done unto him by Mark Chapman. That John Winston Lennon! Didn't he get it that Christianity is the only true religion, and that there are only two correct ways for anyone to declare religious affiliation, namely to call oneself a Christian or to call oneself a Jew, with a degree of transformability between the two for at least some people some of the time, but that John Lennon went into extreme blasphemy. I wonder if he rued the day he made that song while he was bleeding to death from the bullets that Chapman fired into his body. Putting together that 1970 "God" song, the nerve of that singer-songwriter! That may have been one of the worst decisions anyone has ever made in the history of existence!!*

The twenty-fifth responded, *I'll take a totally Pyrrhonist approach to this. What the fuck do we really know about anything?! Maybe it was one of the worst decisions anyone has ever made, maybe it was one of the best decisions anyone has ever made, maybe it was both! And your notion that there are only two correct religious declarations that anyone can ever make? You bigot!*

## PART 4C OF A FICTIONAL EXHIBIT WITHIN THE CONTEXT(S) OF A NONFICTION BOOK

The eighth added a twist before the eighteenth or anyone else could answer the twenty-fifth. Thus telepathically transmitted the eighth: *There are alternative angles to that song. Some Christians, Buddhists, Hindus, Jews, Muslims, Sikhs, Jains, Atheists, Agnostics, Scientologists, Democrats, Republicans, Independents, and others will tend to find it agreeable some of the time. Others will sometimes find it perhaps the most disagreeable song ever devised. As for me, I sometimes oscillate along the full spectrum of favorability, unfavorability, and neutrality toward it.*

## PART 5 OF THIS FICTIONAL EXHIBIT WITHIN THE CONTEXTS OF A NONFICTION WORK

After the fifteenth snapped out from spacing out, having been tuned out from all but a microscopic trace of deep collective unconscious awareness, that fifteenth quietly and telepathically listened as several of the others took the Stones versus Beatles debate into more directions.

The 24th stated, *What about Brian Epstein, that fellow who helped them so much in the beginning but fell by the wayside with all the stuff he was dealing with and eventually dropped dead?*

The 22nd responded, *What of him? He served a world-changing purpose for a while, his work was reasonably complete, and he moved on from this world.*

The 13th chimed in, *That sounds rather naïve. You're kind of presuming him to have passed from this world into some afterlife realm. We don't really know if that happens for anyone! Maybe it happens for some people sometimes, maybe it doesn't! There was even a show or two where if someone with a different kind of naivety watched it, then that someone might jump to the conclusion of knowing with certainty that there's nothing but nothingness awaiting all of us when we reach the end. You don't know, I don't know, nobody knows!*

The fourteenth transmitted, *Ah, but maybe it would be more productive to turn attention now to The Rolling Stones. What were they thinking, after one of their members died from overdosing on LSD, with putting together that song "Sympathy for the Devil," yes, what were they thinking? Sure, it's a great song, and I've enjoyed it many times, but what kinds of thought processes did they have in composing and first performing such a thing?*

The sixteenth stated, *Maybe only they know. Or maybe they've revealed a bunch of it in interviews?! When artistic types express answers about works they've created, who's to say that their answers are anywhere near complete?*

## PART SIX OF THIS FICTION EXHIBIT WITHIN THE CONTEXT OF A NONFICTION BOOK

The fifteenth transmitter jumped in and stated to the others through a silent, telepathic mixture of subvocalization and other means something that transcended all language, but which approximate to, *Reality transcends all thought, even thoughts involving the concept of reality. Mystics both East and West have described this in multitudinous ways, and every way is best, and every way is worst, and every way is in the middle, for where whatever is actually is what transcends all words and concepts and idea structures, where is "middle," where is "left," where is "right?"*

...

## PART SEVEN OF A FICTIONAL EXHIBIT THAT PROVIDES SUPPLEMENTAL PERSPECTIVES ON THE CONTEXT AND CONTEXTS OF A NONFICTION BOOK

The sixteenth transmitter offered alleged rebuke toward nearly everyone and everything, stating, *It is very real when someone steps out in front of a moving vehicle from a hidden spot, and, with the moving vehicle traveling too fast for its driver to stop or swerve in time to avoid tragedy, splat.*

*'Tis real indeed also when groupthink leads to people in a group presuming some person or some group they view as having some fatal flaw of life-style or belief system or what-have-you treat those out-of-favor with extreme disrespect.*

*Earlier, Transmitter Number Eighteen indicated a belief in there being only two correct ways for anyone anywhere to ever declare that being's religious affiliation, videlicet Judaism and Christianity. Transmitter Number Eighteen expressed a belief that some beings could transform back and forth between a primary religious identity of being a Jew and of being a Christian, whereas others might go with a consistent primary of being a Jew, and, yet others still, might go with a consistent primary of being a Christian, but TN18 was adamant that there are no ways that anyone anywhere is actually anywhere near justified to identify with being of any other religion, presumably on the premise that there is absolutely no legitimacy in any of the other religions whatsoever.*

*Soon after that, we telepathically witnessed Transmitter Number Twenty-Five think critically and with objection to that telepathic statement of Judeo-Christian-theology-or-else mindset, even going so far as to label Transmitter Number Eighteen a bigot. I believe that reality has much greater subtlety and dexterity than either TN18 or TN25 admitted to in their little row from a little while ago.*

*From what I have experienced, it sure seems like that Twilight Zone model of reality and that Indiana Jones model of reality—when taken expansively enough to include many different primary religious expressions weaving their way into and out of forcefully affecting folks, yet sometimes demanding for people to narrow down their faith and practices when just one religion shines with some totality of energy upon them in some localization of space-time and mind. "Straight is the path, and narrow the way." Sometimes it could well be that Jesus is the only way. Other times it could well be that Buddha is the only way. Yet other times still, maybe we could only go directly with Yahweh or only with Allah or maybe with some middle way between conceiving of the ultimate level of reality as being best expressible in speech and writing as Yahweh and as being best expressible in speech and writing as Allah. I have experienced stuff that was either clearly paranormal or clearly in that range where people could argue the semantics of whether to best use the word "paranormal" for it or to use some alternative word or phrase, such as "supernatural," "ultra-bizarre," "really, really, super, super weird," "paranormalesque," "unbelievably strange," or "surreal."*

*Something problematic for the various people trying their damnedest to proselytize me, though—and, for that matter, also trying their damnedest to proselytize others who have had diverse surreal experiences for which Occam's Razor seems impot-*

*ent to give any smooth path toward a plausible way to debunk from being in the paranormalesque-to-totally-paranormal range—is that, although those experiences seem proof-positive of there being a deeper and more profound spiritual reality than "the basic, obvious world of the five senses," so to speak, they do not seem to provide any clear specification of which religion or combination of religions might be totally correct.*

*So TN18 expressed a belief in Judaism and/or Christianity as the only range of correct religion. So TN25 categorically rejected that view as a form of religious bigotry. So a bunch of beings could gang together with agreeing with each other to conform to TN18's expression of that severe circumscription of beliefs and practices, while a bunch of other beings could gang together with agreeing with each other to conform to TN25's expression diametrically opposed to TN18's expression of that. There could be many other such expressive conflicts, and...*

PART 8 OF A FICTIONAL EXHIBIT SUPPLEMENTING PERSPECTIVES ON THE CONTEXT AND CONTEXTS OF A NONFICTION BOOK

After a brief pause, Transmitter Number Sixteen again dished out a mixture of criticism and praise toward many ranges of ideologues:

*I shall now endeavor to elucidate a few of them by tapping into transmitters beyond our present telepathic set of twenty-five.*

*Similar to that recent TN18-vs.-TN25 back-and-forth, consider the following set of religious claims and counter-claims:*

- *Christianity is the only true religion, and there are only two correct ways for anyone to declare religious affiliation, namely to call oneself a Christian or to call oneself a Jew, with a degree of transformability between the two for at least some people some of the time.*
- *Buddhism is the only true religion, and there are only two correct ways for anyone to declare religious affiliation, namely to call oneself a Buddhist or to call oneself a Hindu, with a degree of transformability between the two for at least some people some of the time.*
- *Buddhism is the only true religion, and there are only two correct ways for anyone to declare religious affiliation, namely to call oneself a Buddhist or to call oneself a Jain, with a degree of transformability between the two for at least some people some of the time.*
- *Buddhism is the only true religion, and there are only two correct ways for anyone to declare religious affiliation, namely to call oneself a Buddhist or to call oneself an Esoteric Christian, with a degree of transformability between the two for at least some people some of the time.*

- *There are no true religions, yet all religions are at least partway true.*
- *Islam is the only true religion, and there are only five correct ways for anyone to declare religious affiliation, namely to call oneself a Muslim, to declare oneself a Jew who acquiesces to reasonable respect for the truths of Islam, to declare oneself a Christian who acquiesces to reasonable respect for the truths of Islam, to declare oneself to be of some religion other than Islam, Judaism, and Christianity, yet to acquiesce to reasonable respect for the truths of Islam in such a manner as to be de facto one of The People of The Book, and the rest of the just and good.*

PART 9 OF A FICITON EXHIBIT WITHIN THIS NONFICTION BOOK

All 25 transmitters went silent for one minute.

PART TEN OF THIS FICTION EXHIBIT WITHIN THIS NONFICTION BOOK

Four of the twenty-five transmitters suddenly died of heart attacks. And then there were twenty-one.

THE END.

[The previous line concluded the short fiction story "A Fictional Exhibition Intentionally Similar to Alleged Select Nonfictional Hidden Exhibitions as of April 2024" (by the author of this nonfiction book in which it serves as an exhibit).]

Reflect on how Visigothic and Mozarabic practices were tolerated by the Moors in Spain long ago, until Roman Catholicism retook Spain and extirpated many of those practices, though some Visigothic and Mozarabic patterns were able to persist via the oral tradition, assimilation, and transfiguration.

Cf. "The Message of The Monks," by Bruno Stäblein, translated by Stewart Spencer, in the CD booklet portion of *The Mystery of Santo Domingo de Silos* (Polydor CD 445 399-2).

Though hardly anyone ever dares to state it very directly, consider how an extinction of all religions together with degrees of persistence via the oral tradition, via assimilation, and via transfiguration occurred in many places on Earth at many different times prior to the December 2007 publication of Clarke & Baxter's masterpiece *Firstborn.*

## PART J OF SECTION 5 OF CHAPTER 10

Here is a transcription of an outtake on an April 19, 2024 LinkedIn response from me to an executive recruiter who initiated contact with me ten days earlier (i.e., on April 9, 2024):

---

Darcy,

Although I am thankful for the thought of opening back up the possibility of my primarily working in the tax area of business activity, I am not presently open to primarily working in that and will most likely remain closed toward it during the remainder of this lifetime.

No thanks at this time on the idea of applying for that position.

Early in my undergraduate studies (i.e., the early portion of the August 1994 - December 1998 period), there were several forks in the road, and part of it involved my walking away from STEM career possibilities largely due to deep disagreements with much of the trend in American academia across philosophy departments and natural science departments in terms of the high percentage of professors who leaned heavily toward rigid adherence to views that--as I perceived them--insufficiently acknowledged the roles and realities of minds and freedom of the will, whereas in business academia (to include economics, in which I ended up majoring) sufficient acknowledgment of the roles and realities of minds and freedom of the will tend to be taken as a given. Eventually, I worked in tax and accounting roles mainly as a profession of convenience, though I sometimes adapted into genuinely enjoying that work.

Further into developments, I eventually transitioned completely outside of tax and accounting as a profession. My heart is not in currently it with performing tax and accounting as a primary work activity, and it never was fully in it with that. Even when I sometimes enjoyed that work and performed moderately well at it my heart was never more than about 85% in it. True, many a successful tax and accounting professional also never gets to having more than about 85% of heart in it, but there came a time when the one thing that held all of that together, viz. being able to have unlimited ferocity of competition outside of work-- in that case with U.S. Chess Federation activities as a primary hobby coordinate with performing in tax and accounting as a primary profession without any sharp conflict between the two came to an almost-instantaneous halt, specifically with one conversation that occurred on November 18, 2018. As I mentioned in one of the follow-up comments to my September 2022 article on this very networking platform (i.e., LinkedIn), I consider it astronomically unlikely that I will ever choose to work in tax and accounting again as my primary professsion and also astronomically unlikely that I will ever choose to enter another federation chess tournament, as seasons have changed in my life regarding those activities.

This message that I am sending to you in response to your initial message to me will probably be either the last communication that we share in this lifetime or the second-to-last communication that we share in this lifetime.

Experience shows that I may already be wearing out my welcome with you by providing as much detail as I am providing in this message, and, with how busy you are and how little I have tended to be valued by the vast majority of people in many settings in this life, it would probably be asking too much from life itself for me to try to set up further rounds of communications with you. Therefore, I recognize that you will either most likely decline to send any response to this response or send one final response that provides closure to the totality of the direct interactions that you and I share in this lifetime, and I accept that with total peace of mind.

That being stated, though, I do plan to include a copy of this response to you--devoid of the original message in which you suggested that I apply to a tax manager position, devoid of revealing your surname (i.e., the family name that you presented yourself in connection with), devoid of revealing the employer for which you serve as a recruiter, and devoid of revealing the industry in which that employer primarily operates--in the forthcoming nonfiction book ALTERNATIVE BEGINNINGS AND ENDINGS OF ALL THINGS: SCIENCE, RELIGION, POLITICS, AND CARDS, HYPER-VOLUME II.

On another note, some might question whether there is much legitimacy at all to my forays into being an author, for example, given that eighteen days ago (on April 1, 2024) I finally joined X (formerly known as Twitter) and have since, with a modest amount of activity, not convinced anyone to follow me on that platform (as of a few minutes past 9 A.M. CDT on April 19, 2024), yet this is not as much a rebuke on the legitimacy of my forays into being an author as a rebuke on much of the relevancy of my entire life to others. Although I know that I am relevant to some people some of the time, clearly, up to the present time, there are huge degrees to which I have been of little or no relevancy to nearly everyone, in large part due to the judgment of others to deem me that way. This is part of what I am factoring into how my C corporation (i.e., the aforementioned publisher, for which I serve as CEO) and I are crafting the aforementioned forthcoming book, as well as why I am looking into multiple options for additional work that I may legally and ethically perform in the future while reasonably feeling that my heart is in the work and reasonably knowing that the work is completely relevant to at least a few of those whom it serves.

Regards,

Maurice Blair
Chief Executive Officer
Synapsid Revelations Press Corporation

X (formerly known as Twitter): @M_James_Blair

{That outtake showed Nov. 18 where it intended Nov. 21.}

Having presented that outtake, here is a transcription of what I actually decided to send in that context as an April 19, 2024 response to an April 9, 2024 message:

Darcy,

Although I appreciate your reaching out to me to present the thought that I might open back up to the possibility of primarily working in the tax area of business activity, I am not presently open to primarily working in that and will most likely remain closed toward that during the remainder of this lifetime.

No thanks at this time on the idea of applying for that position.

Take care.

Regards,

Maurice Blair
Chief Executive Officer
Synapsid Revelations Press Corporation

---

Part K of Section 5 of Chapter 10

Consider the following list of names, in relation to everyone who ever has or ever will have any of those as part of any interpersonal identification processes: Amanda, Michelle, Scarlett, Roger, Edwin, Bruce, Carisa, and Bo.

---

Part L (in this case, the twelfth part, rather than the fiftieth part) of Section 5 of Chapter 10

On January 12, 2024, I sent a message to a woman whom I have only met in portions of the first half of 1995, her father, and six people with whom I primarily became acquainted via the Chi Delta Chapter of Psi Upsilon Fraternity. I sequenced that lady first among the recipients and her father seventh.

Here is a transcript of that message:

Liza, Michael, Roger, Dave, Jennie, Dan, John, and Tri,
Although I originally planned to either inquire directly to David Nieves (also known as Dave Nieves, not to be confused with the David Hoffman also known as Dave who is among you) about this or to carefully decide whether to include one or more cc-line-style recipients with Dave Nieves as a to-line-style recipient, it seems to me that he probably fits into one of three categories for Facebook usage: 1) not having any Facebook account, 2) having such an account though virtually inactive, or 3) having a reasonably active Facebook account while having blocked me on this networking platform. Several of you know very well some details of what I was setting out to ask Nieves about, though, perhaps no one on Earth knows anywhere near a complete amount of it. Soon after a mixture of behavior by Liza (who was my date) and her female friend (who was Tri's date) at the Psi U Formal in April 1995, Liza and her female friend left the event early. At that instant I felt extremely favorable toward Liza. However, soon thereafter one of the fraternity brothers pulled me aside from the rest of the festivities and spoke with extremely harsh criticism

toward Liza's behavior at the event. Although my memory for many years was very unclear about the identity of the brother who had done that, my memory around more-or-less two months ago started to point toward about 85%-95% chance that it was David Nieves. Even if one of the people who was there at the time, even Nieves himself, were to tell me that it was Nieves, then I still might not decide to believe it at 100% at this stage, because there could be an outside possibility of receiving misinformation from whomever would be telling it; whereas, if my memory ever clears up to reach an absolute 100% level with that, then I would accept it as it is. Although it could be easy to analyze this entire situation with an enormous quantity of idea structures, at this stage I am not overly concerned with blaming anyone connected with it for any specific things of any types, as the patterns have, in the long run, transformed their effects on my life in a very constructive and very favorable way. With that said, although none of you are named in the new, free book (with print copies to go to yet-to-be-determined recipients and with flipbook available recently at https://mixam.com/share/659351615dddc94c958bb985 online) *Impact* which my C corporation published on New Year's Day (eleven days ago), that work is one of the kinds of things that could lead people who "do not get it" with how and why I've communicated what I've communicated in many of the situations of recent years, to have a clear-though-challenging path toward getting it. For example, it can provide some of the supplemental context that might allow Dan to eventually "get it" regarding the communication last year in which Psi U Brother Dan Lerner told me that he "did not get it" with why I inquired with him about how at the time my memory had pointed toward a likelihood of it having been either him or Psi U Brother Dave Nieves who had pulled me aside and sharply criticized Liza's April 7, 1995 behavior. At that time, I believed it best to sidestep much of Dan's telling me he did not get it, but I eventually changed my mind to believing it best to give him and other beings an extra chance or twenty to understand what they might not otherwise have understood. On another note, about 14 or 15 months ago, I noticed a several-years-old Seattle-area newsletter on the Internet that would seem to point toward Liza having been most likely a married woman as of December 2017, and if Liza is currently married, then for clarification, I am not trying to cause any problem for that marriage. Also, as clarification, considering the fact that she has been silent toward me (in terms of one-to-one communications) since after accepting my LinkedIn invitation to join networks a little over a year-and-a-half ago, I am neither seeking nor expecting any direct response from her regarding this, yet I decided it would be best for her and her father John to be included in the loop of this communication. As a parting thought, several times in the past six weeks or thereabouts I considered a hypothetical scenario in which "THE LORD" might go to a given human being and request a designation of eight people to select as survivors of a new mass extinction of nearly the entire human race and decided in those cases that upon receiving such an inquiry I would select as follows: 1) to choose Liza to be one of the survivors, 2) to give Liza three of the remaining choices, 3) to give HH the Fourteenth Dalai Lama two choices, and 4) to give GM Sheng-yen Lu two choices. Yes, I admit that currently lacking any long-term romantic relationship and lacking any known biological descendants affects some of this, and, yes, some of you might consider this to be excessively pro-Liza Darnton, yet consider this: There were several times I considered the same scenario from mid-2022 to mid-2023 and thought of an answer of simply giving all eight choices to Liza! You might wonder why I did not choose myself to be among the designated survivors, leaving it to others to decide whether or not I should be among them. A huge amount of how someone could understand that better could emerge from studying stuff like ancient religious wisdom literature (of any of the major religions) or with a variety of well-performed science fiction with themes similar to ancient wisdom literature, as well as considering how a high percentage of the time - though not all of the time - over that span, I have felt that I have lived a reasonably good and reasonably complete life. I also respect that some people in some situations could be making a correct decision with selecting themselves to be among the designated survivors of such a hypothetical scenario, and I can use a flexibility of mind to let go of past answers to that for future considerations of that. Michael, Roger, David, and Jennie, as you are already among my Facebook friends and will likely continue to be, and, Liza, as you are among my LinkedIn network persons and will likely continue to be, this is not very likely a farewell address to any or each of you, though it could very well prove to be the last direct message that I send to each of you. Although I feel like there's a major likelihood that I might live for several more decades, given that the Tri Nguyen, the John Darnton, and the Dan Lerner recipients of this message are not directly in my network on any social networking platform at this time, are unlikely to ever be in-network with me in that way, and are unlikely (as far as I perceive the probabilities at the time of sending this) to either initiate or receive another direct communication with me in the future in this world, the Tri, the John, and the Dan recipients of this, to each of you this can function as a brief farewell address. Take care, Jim Blair

---

To clarify who directly recieved that 12 JANUARY 2024 electronic message, here is a list of them: Liza Darnton (who, along with the author and a variety of other persons, attended "Introduction to Modern Philosophy" class as a student in the spring semester of 1995 at Duke University in Durham, North Carolina), six of the Psi Upsilon Fraternity Brothers of the Chi Delta Chapter, and John Darnton (the father of Liza).

* * * * * * * * * * * *

* * * * * * * * * * * *

Almost the entire reason why I joined X (formerly known as Twitter) was to officially become a follower of Liza Darnton on that platform. On a related note, although I am almost completely certain that the human race would best be served if I were to someday die while Liza would still be alive to help the human race, recently, I occasionally think and feel like this:

*God help the rest of the human race if I were to someday be alive after the passing of Liza Darnton, the person I consider to have treated me with the most overall respect thus far in this life, even given that some of her excellent treatment of me was due to some mysterious patterns of serendipity, rather than conscious effort.*

*This is also even with how the furthest that she and I ever went with physical contact with each other was a brief amount of mouth-to-mouth kissing, in contrast with how some women went much further with me in terms of physical intimacy.*

*Yes, there have been women with whom I have experienced actual sex.*

*No, Liza Darnton is not one of those sexual partners, and she will probably remain outside of that set of partners during the remainder of when she and I are both "alive," in other words among what some would call, "the undeparted living of the realm of regular, historically-observable reality."*

*Furthermore, she and I probably will not meet each other again in person for as long as we are both still alive. Thankfully, since joining each other's LinkedIn networks in June 2022, she and I have maintained being on good enough terms with each other to both avoid throwing the other out of LinkedIn network. As far as I know, she has not blocked me on any social media or other accounts, and I know that I have not blocked her on any social media or other accounts.*

*Even in the absence of more thorough direct physical contact, her intellectual and emotional effect on me, in the long run, have proven extraordinarily helpful, and she has had quite an effect on other people as well. Considering the full set of her interactions with me and the miniscule sliver of observation I have had of her interactions with others, such consideration has the result that I feel the utmost respect toward her, and, yes, I continue to admit the chances extraordinarily remote that she and I meet in person again between now and when at least one of us dies. I also recognize that, although she has continued to refrain from throwing me out of her LinkedIn network, she has declined to follow me on X since I joined it early in April 2024, and she will almost undoubtedly continue to refrain from following me on X. That serves, in this case, as a huge part of the rebuke, Lord, that I recognize that the general public has delivered to me through extreme silence toward my public social media posts in a high percentage of cases, as well as other specifics of how the public has interacted with me, not only in recent years, but through nearly my entire life. Yes, to many people my best has never been good enough, and I continue to do what I can to get things to work out. Tough. Lord, to whatever degree Thou manifesteth as Adibuddha and to whatever degree Thou manifesteth as God, this I know not, yet I deeply respect the most powerful sources of Reality Itself, and I respect Reality Itself.*

*Dear Lord, my visceral reaction in recent times of, "God help the rest of the human race if I were to someday be alive after the passing of Liza Darnton," as mentioned a little while ago, might best be placed into perspective. As you know, my sense of fondness toward her rose exponentially the instant I found out in June 2022 that she had accepted my LinkedIn invitation.*

*Let us consider more closely that concern about the possible scenarios in which I might wind up still among the living after her eventual passing. Much of it is because, if that ever happens, then that will probably be to me personally an even bigger version of one of those days when everything changes, including some profound recognition of the loss from this realm and transition to the mystery of the beyond of someone who has had an at-times extraordinarily helpful effect on my life, yes, an even bigger version of a day that everything changes than were: 1) the day when I saw the bottom line news flash scroll by a television screen broadcast to inform humans, including me, that Arthur C. Clarke had died; 2) the day when I received the phone call that informed me that my father, Maurice A.T. Blair, had died, and 3) the day I learned that the singer Olivia Newton-John, the music artist whose music I have tended to most consistently enjoy at a maximal level in recent years, had died (which was one day after her death).*

*Although my mother, Ming Y. Blair, is still among the living, if I someday learn of her death, although it will in a few ways likely affect me more than Liza's passing would, my mother's death will in many other ways, including many of the most vital ways of emotional resonance, most likely affect me at nowhere near the magnitude that learning of Liza Darnton's death would affect me. A strong visceral feeling affects me with the mere thought of it.*

*If I had to vote at this time for only one human being to have earned the right to stay among the living, then I would vote for Liza Darnton.*

*Also, if she was running for President of the United States as a Republican, a Democrat, a Green, a Libertarian, or an Independent, then I'd definitely consider very seriously the possibility of voting for her, because my personal level of respect for her could overshadow many of the specifics of policy platforms and the existence of political parties. Yes, in that scenario, I would seriously consider the possibility of voting for her to become the U.S. President, because I currently respect her more than I currently respect any other regular-realm-of-the-observably-historical-reality living human being, even though some people may find it rather bizarre for me to hold her in such high regard.*

*Lord, to whatever degree Thou might be what some religion or combination of religions presenteth Thee to be, to whatever degree Thou might be beyond what any religion or combination of religions presenteth Thee to be, I thank thee for the presence of Liza Darnton, Arthur C. Clarke, Olivia Newton-John, my ancestors, and my life within this set of space and time and mind spanning from the origins of this universe I am presently in and any other universes, if any, involved with subsequent developments. This includes thanking Thee for how these and everyone and everything else might relate to all ranges of hyperspace, all ranges of space-time, all ranges of mind, and all that might be utterly beyond all of this.*

---

---

---

Part M of Section 5 of Chapter 10

Consider the following list of names, in relation to everyone who ever has or ever will have any of those as part of any interpersonal identification processes: Attita, Ananda, Mustafa, O'Brien, Winston, Lucien, Lucille, Wanda, and O'Reilly.

---

Part N

If you take infinity and raise it to the nth degree, then factorialize that, then one way of transcribing that quantity would be "$(\infty^n)!$" and another would be "$\infty^n(\infty^n-1)(\infty^n-2)(\infty^n-3)\cdot(\ldots)\cdot 5\cdot 4\cdot 3\cdot 2\cdot 1$."

---

Part O

Although I choose a reasonably degree of respect for Oprah Winfrey's professional success, I choose to compare and contrast much of how she has at times expressed the value of a very civil approach to life and how some people, including the writers, producers, and actors who crafted the episode "Blowback" (which first aired in March 2010) of the TV series *Flashforward* (2009-2010) expressed the value of unleashing our inner monsters when times and seasons call for unleashing monsters.

---

## Part P

Marcus Padow is the government man of the name redacted (re: 2021) in Chapter Nine. I do not know whether he is alive or dead at the time of this book going to print. Although I decline to specify here in which part of the U.S. Federal Government he worked in when I sent him an e-mail in 2011 and multiple e-mails in 2021, I shall reveal here this: On August 1, 2011 I included a reference to him in a Facebook post, and one of my friends, a man named Geoffrey Williams (a.k.a. Geoff Williams) invited me to get back into contact with Marcus. I accepted that opportunity, and it may have saved my life on at least a few occasions.

Some might question whether it makes sense for me to reveal in this book the name Marcus Padow and some of the related context. However, in response to that I will point out a few things in favor of considering it appropriate: 1) Geoff Williams already revealed an update for any of my Facebook friends to see soon after my August 1, 2011 post—he gave an update that Marcus was as of the time working for the Federal Government. 2) Geoff revealed on Facebook extra levels of the specifics—extra levels which I am declining to relay here. 3) Synapsid Revelations Press Corporation and I have designed this book to conceal Padow's name until many pages later than when which I introduce him without presenting his name. 4) Many people in recent years have demonstrated an attitude of derision, contempt, and total dismissiveness toward my life, the facts about my experiences, my descriptions of things that truly happened, etc. If I were to completely omit his name, then those who have seemed hell-bent on having that attitude of total derision, contempt, and dismissiveness might jump into continuing to repeat the history of harming themselves and others in the long run, rather than snapping out of it, due to the trap of thinking along the lines of, *That terrible writer, I'm pretty sure that he declines to name that alleged person because such alleged person does not actually exist in any way, shape, or form. Freaking figment of his imagination, that writer's such a loser! Why the hell does anyone ever take him seriously? Why doesn't God or what-have-you simply freaking kill him before he presents to the public another book? Why God, why don't you freaking execute him before he gets to author any more books?!*

Hopefully, the act of providing this information here affords such readers—however much or little they might have had previous conflicts, if any, with me—better chances to improve their lives. Therefore, to answer the question, "Is it appropriate to reveal the name of that federal employee in Part P of Section 5 of Chapter 10 of this book?", I state clearly, "Yes, I truly believe that it is appropriate!"

Also, while I neither confirm nor deny here which government entity or entities I know him to have been part of during portions of the 2011-2021 period, if the U.S. federal government itself, any given U.S. President, any given U.S. Senator, or anyone else—even Liza Darnton, Tenzin Gyatso (i.e., His Holiness The 14th Dalai Lama), and/or GM Lu Sheng-yen, the three people I respect the most as of the time of the final stages of composing this book (relative to my frame of reference of that time, the three most respectable people out of all living human beings of the regular reality), *in precisely that order*—or even all three of them plus Marcus Padow himself were to complain about this, then tough. *Such a huge percentage of the human race has cared so little about the reality of my life in many ways in recent years, and I am pushing back.*

Marcus had plenty of opportunity from August 2011 onward to at any stage send me a message to discourage me from using unfettered discretion to someday reveal to others in writing about the fact that he joined the federal government many years ago as an employee. *SOMEDAY COMES* with the publication of this book, and that rather closely *parallels* in some ways *Geoff Williams' Q3 2011 revelation* of Padow's career update to anyone on Facebook who would chance upon finding that response. Shifting, consider however much any observer may consider any given communication: 1) to be, 2) not to be, or 3) to transcend being vs. not being:

a) a message

b) many messages

c) information by which the guilty—whether of crimes against human law, crimes against divine

law, or crimes against both—get exactly what they have coming to them, more swiftly than they might otherwise have reaped what they had sown
d) an action to enlighten and empower readers and listeners—whether directly through items #a, #b, and #c, directly through other means, or indirectly
e) catalysts for processes to serve the ABSOLUTE, TOTAL, ULTIMATE REALITY, AS WELL AS WHOEVER AND WHATEVER, IF ANY, IS MOST PRIMARY TO THAT ABSOLUTE, TOTAL, ULTIMATE REALITY, to whatever degree THAT may manifesteth as "YHVH," "God," "Adibuddha," or whatever else.

Sidenote: To be clear, I am not trying to proclaim Liza Darnton to be better than Jesus (i.e., Jesus Christ, as labeled by Christians and some others / Jesus of Nazareth, as labeled in general sometimes by people of nearly every demographic, including many Jews and many Gentiles / Jesus, the Spirit of God, as sometimes labeled by Muslims).

Likewise, I am not trying to proclaim H.H. The Dalai Lama to be better than Shakyamuni Buddha. Also, I am not trying to proclaim Lu Sheng-yen to be inherently better than George Washington, etc.

In many respects I am choosing nonjudgment toward each of those notions. I am continuing to aim to perfectly render whatever respect is due to each and every being and, hopefully, if and when appropriate, finding ways to more perfectly render the proper amounts and kinds of respect to each and every sentient being.

# PART Q

Three books that I have only read partway up to the time of the initial publication of this book are *The Democrat Party Hates America* (2023) by Mark R. Levin, *American Psychosis: A Historical Investigation of How the Republican Party Went Crazy* (2022), and *Recovering Sanity: A Compassionate Approach to Understanding and Treating Psychosis* (2003) by Dr. Edward M. Podvoll.

Legend has it that Shakyamuni Buddha dared to present to the general public in the sixth century B.C.E. many of what were then revolutionary ideas and methods. Here are some of them:

1. "Hatred does not cease hatred, but by Love alone is healed."

2. "Free yourselves of mental intoxicants."

3. "Utilize correct views, correct resolve, correct actions, correct occupations, correct zeal, correct meditations, correct speech, and correct attention."

______________________________________________

______________________________________________

______________________________________________

______________________________________________

______________________________________________

______________________________________________

## CH. 10, SEC. 5, PART R

Both current main U.S. political parties have portions of themselves that can be thought of as toxic, though many people sharply disagree with each other about which portions are toxic.

In some ways, some might respond by echoing one of the catchphrases that one of my elementary school classmates was fond of sometimes saying in the 1980s: "No shit, Sherlock!" However, contemplating more thoroughly may uncover intricate nuances.

One example of this was how, at around 11:27 AM U.S. CDT (i.e., around 12:27 PM) on April 23, 2024 *The Clay Travis & Buck Sexton Show* presented that we can think of part of the Democratic Party as it existed at that instant as having a strained internal struggle that one could characterize as an "Oppression Olympics" that in theory can hold together and sometimes does hold together in practice, yet which tends to fray and sometimes collapse altogether when advocates of the oppression-oriented worldview have to take sides between Israeli Jews and Palestinians, between cisgender females and transgender females, etc.

Another example of this occurred in one of the debates for the Republican nomination for U.S. President in connection with the 2024 general election. Specifically, that was a 12/06/2023 debate. In it, there was a critical juncture in which the Republican coalition of what some might deem a "Laissez-Faire Olympics" reached a head for a little while, as witnessed live by many people via television and others live via being in the audience. People recorded it for posterity. Specifically, attention turned to the tensions between the different priorities of different Republican voters, and some of what happened was incindiary. There was an exchange that addressed conflicting ideas of how people from any continent or anywhere else might relate to masculinity, femininity, comparative religion, etc. Nikki Haley and Vivek Ramaswamy expressed sharp criticisms toward each other and millions of other sentient beings. Things reached a point at which Vivek Ramaswamy said, "This is a symptom of a deeper cancer in American life. Identity politics, this new religion that says your race, your gender, and your sexuality are your identity. It is anti-American. And it is dividing this country to a breaking point."

---

Cf. Both of the following URLs, as accessed 4/23/2024:

https://www.newsnationnow.com/politics/debates/ramaswamy-haley-religion-alabama-debate/

https://www.newsnationnow.com/politics/debates/gop-debate-alabama/ (esp. 1:09:26-1:12:01)

---

I watched portions of that debate live on television, mostly thinking and feeling in a rather neutral and Zen way toward the most statements from each person.

However, I felt enthused upon hearing Ramaswamy say, "Having two X chromosomes does not immunize you from criticism." I gave that brilliant statement a brief and fully enthusiastic one-man standing ovation from home!!

Yes, there are times when chivalry and similar ideas along the lines of "Viva la difference" can be great for people, even including some men putting some women on pedestals during some ranges of reality, but there are also times when men should go hardline in the way that a male character compelled a female character to face justice in *The Maltese Falcon* (1941).

Had The Financial Advisory Group, Inc. or Gray Reed & McGraw been able to tune in very much to a major amount of the reality of my life, after I had given them plenty of opportunity to understand and respect that reality, then maybe things would not have resulted in this book expressing such thorough criticism of them. They did not seem to have enough of that toughness of dealing with the situation that might have led to this book landing less criticism toward them and more toward other people and organizations. Although there were many junctures at which they could have chosen differently, many junctures at which I could have chosen differently, and many junctures at which third parties could have chosen differently, perhaps the most crucial occurred on August 9, 2021, as referenced in Chapter 9. After I had endgamed Steve Estrin, Natasha McDaniel, and Juan Martinez on July 19, 2021, they had a chance to immediately cease and desist any overt showing of hostility by shutting up toward me and to thereby let me drift off into the sunset. In such a scenario, maybe I might possibly have gone on to still wind up calling into *The Michael Berry Show* on August 6, 2021 and having that call proceed identically to the way that it indeed proceeded.

Then, in that scenario, they could have continued to shut up toward me and to let me drift off into the distance, accurately gauging that a fellow with the totality of what I had communicated with them, together with expressing via Facebook both an affinity for The Ark of the Covenant and an affinity for Yamantaka, together with having described to them in the spoken word some of the details of the July 10, 2005 rather paranormal-or-paranormalesque experience that I later described in length in *Science, Religion, Politics, and Cards*, to refrain from initiating a new round of picking a fight with me. Or, as an alternative, they could have called me and requested to arrange to pay me a handsome sum for a nondisclosure agreement, in which they would admit that there was something totally FUBAR about how they had dealt with me, and that they respect much of the reality of my life, and that they might like to negotiate with me that I might wait until something like April 2042 at the earliest to reveal a bunch more stuff about interactions with them to the general public, while being paid an annuity from them in a moderately handsome amount, with the threat that failure to wait until something like April 2042 would result in cancellation of what would otherwise have been the remaining annuity payments.

In contrast, somehow, as relayed in another context in a portion of Chapter Nine of this book, attorney Michael Kelsheimer of Gray Reed & McGraw sent me a letter that attempted to intimidate me into shutting up about them. NO WAY IN HELL!!!!!!!!!!!!

If anyone who encounters this book, whether an attorney, a district attorney, a former coworker, a former supervisor, a former acquaintance, a former lover, a former friend, or anyone else believes it best to pursue civil litigation against me, a criminal probe against me, a criminal justice proceeding against me, civil litigation against any other anyone else, a criminal probe against any other anyone else, a criminal justice proceeding against any other anyone else, to go to all-out war against me, to go to all-out war against anyone else, then bear in mind how Synapsid Revelations Press Corporation and I hereby reiterate to any such person or organization something we stated on the copyright page: The information herein is accurate to the best of our knowledge as of the time of going to print. This does not constitute specific advice on which decisions, actions, and judgments the reader should choose; consult the most relevant experts if appropriate.

* * * * *

Think about it from my perspective. Although there is a degree of truth in the notion that no one can ever absolutely completely know what it is like to be another, there is also a degree of truth in the notion that, with effort, we can somewhat know some of what it is like ot be another. I can and often do try to—metephorically speaking—put myself in your shoes, put myself in her shoes, put myself in his shoes, put myself in their shoes, etc. Here is a recommendation that you—metaphorically speaking—put yourself in my shoes, put yourself in his shoes, put yourself in her shoes, put yourself in their shoes, etc.

This is going to take a while in order to adequately convey. The effort to place this narrative, and to compare and contrast it with any other relevant narratives, could prove priceless to a person who truly treasures accuracy, understanding, and insight.

* * * * *

Consider counting to ten, pausing, then counting to twelve, then proceeding to the ensuing autobiographical narrative.

* * * * *

This will start to make sense if taken step by step, piece by piece, journey by journey.

* * * * *

Perhaps the best place to start shall be when I was working in Charlotte, NC in portions of mid-1994 at a carryout-and-delivery restaurant called "The Call 'N China." That was after graduating from high school in El Paso, TX, but before my Freshman Year of college in Durham, NC.

Picture in your mind Charlotte, NC in portions of June-to-August 1994. Next, think about scenes at carry-out-and-delivery restaurants. To reiterate, I worked at The Call 'N China for about seven weeks or so from something like mid-June 1994 to something like early August 1994, a little ways ahead of when I proceeded to start my baccalaureate studies at Duke University. Imagine The Call 'N China restaurant.

There I faced a great many challenges as a meal order taker. The main duties included answering customer calls, taking notes about what they were ordering to be delivered, addressing walk-in orders, finding grid coordinates with which to facilitate deliveries, and more. I went through many changes.

The thing perhaps the most relevant to decades-later FUBAR situations is how a Caucasian delivery driver who presented himself as "Mike" spoke to me about honesty, and how I contrasted it at the time with various sitcom episodes from television, plus how I later changed to often approaching the issue of purity of speech in a way similar to the extreme adherence to honesty—even in the face of social pressures—as Mike had presented.[4]

Although impressions from many sitcom episodes I witnessed from the mid-1980s to mid-1994 had influenced me to believe that many social situations required lying in order to get them to work well, I suddenly heard and listened to Mike say in approximately July 1994 something that equated to, "It is never a good idea to lie. I trust in 'the good book.' After I found Christ, I decided to stick with always telling the truth."

My immediate reaction was to think of him as a moron. I had believed that TV shows like *Night Court* (1984-1992) and *Three's Company* (1976-1984) had proven that a very sizable amount of lying would be necessary in order to get the gears of society to work reasonably smoothly and properly. Considering how that restaurant food delivery driver expressed his religious zeal to involve him daring to say that he believed in some kind of Legend-of-Honest-Abe absolute adherence to telling the truth smacked me at the time as a case of him having gone into some totally ridiculous behavior out of religious brainwashing. I perceived him to be an excessively-anti-charlatan Charlottean who had been influenced by manipulative charlatans who had presented him some religious pretext to make him steadfastly believe in an excessive degree of honesty.

*Many years later, I embraced GM Lu Sheng-yen's advice to range from absolutely and completely honest to being extremely close to that, become what I previously had considered moronic and totally ridiculous! That being said, after my October 2003 to early 2004 transformation into being extremely-pro-honesty, I did at times become rather ready to feel within the fibers of my being an extreme viciousness toward deception in a way that might have sometimes been a bit excessive.* There were times in 2015-2016 that I felt extra hostility toward Donald Trump for how his choices of speech at times fell way short of some ideal level of extreme honesty. After he became President Donald Trump, I then noticed how Mark R. Levin on *The Mark Levin Show* on the radio in 2017 provided sharp criticism of President Barrack Obama's administration's use of FISA warrants to have the federal government perform surveillance on Donald Trump's 2016 U.S. Presidential campaign. *For a while I completely bought into Levin's radio presentations that characterized that set of surveillance by the Obama Administration against then-candidate Trump as having been many times worse than Watergate.* I shifted to viewing Trump's sometimes-impressionistic speech patterns as plausibly justifiable and his at-times seemingly Xenophobic policy statements as fully justified as part of fighting back against what I came, for a while, to view as a menacing and extremely evil set of behaviors by The Democratic Party in portions of multiple decades, escalating into President Obama having become much worse than President Nixon ever was. *(To many of the Democrats reading this Obama-vs.-Nixon evaluation, this will seem patently absurd. To many of the Republicans reading this Obama-vs.-Nixon evaluation, this will seem the gospel truth.)* Eventually, I have settled on a degree of agnosticism toward it. To me, it has become very much like one of those optical illusions in which, if you use your mind one way, you can see the pattern translate a mainly-2D-space item into one mainly-3D-space cognition, whereas if you use your mind another way, you can see the pattern translate into an opposite mainly-3D-space cognition. *As I have come to see it, there are huge amounts of the unknown to me in relationship with this, vast and gargantuan unknowns.* Therefore, although I plan to vote in the 2024 U.S.

Presidential general election, I will almost definitely feel uncertain enough about the situation that, much like in 2016, rather than purely cheering the winning side to accord with the side of my vote, to cheer for whomever is best in relationship with THE ULTIMATE REALITY to win, while remaining agnostic toward which side that would happen to be. Yes, many people who believe it to be clear-cut, slam-dunk, blatantly obvious that The Republican Party is best for the 2024 General Election for President of the United States will likely think of me as lame in relation to this, though thinking of me as less lame than people wholeheartedly supporting and endorsing The Democratic Party for that election. Yes, many people who believe it to be clear-cut, slam-dunk, blatantly obvious that The Democratic Party is best for the 2024 General Election for President of the United States will likely think of me as lame in relation to this, though thinking of me as less lame than people wholeheartedly supporting and endorsing The Republican Party for that election. *HOWEVER, I AM DOING MY UTMOST TO DEAL WITH THIS SITUATION AS HONESTLY, TRUTHFULLY, AND EFFECTIVELY AS I CAN, AND I AM BEING HONEST WITH MYSELF ABOUT MY LIMITATIONS.*

Perceptions sometimes change as time goes by. *To some that can go without saying, yet others may have difficulty getting it through their skulls, especially if they themselves are very rigid with the inflexibility with which to adapt to changing people and data.*

Two books that could be helpful with understanding this, both in terms of everyone else's backgrounds and in terms of my background, potentially much better are

*Science, Religion, Politics, and Cards* and *All Things under and over the Sun and Stars: Enigmas in Various Stages*. Also, the forthcoming book *The Dimetrodons, the Dorians, and the Modern World, Synapsid Critical Edition* could be relevant. Another set of approaches could involve comparing and contrasting any given set of 20th century science fiction novels of a person's choice with any given set of religious texts and any given set of scientific texts. For example, one could compare and contrast the set of Philip Pullman's trilogy of *His Dark Materials* novels, the set of religious texts consisting of one's religion's origin story (if one has a religion and if that religion has an origin story) for reality itself, and whichever astrophysics articles that emerge from casually surfing the Worldwide Web.

Now consider some semblance of portions of a circa-first-half-of-March 2024 conversation:

Courtney (a woman who was most likely of an age of 40-something-years): Although I enjoyed that TV show *Married... with Children* when I was young, I sometimes think back to it and react like, "Hey, that show could really influence young guys to be sexist and to demean women."

M.J. Blair (the man who is the author of this book): Well, many of the TV shows could help or harm a given person, depending on how the person coordinates them with everything else.

Courtney: But that show presented Al as such a... I'm trying to remember the word for it...

M.J. Blair: I think you're thinking of the word "chauvinist." You're probably trying to say something like, "Al Bundy on that show was a chauvinist."

Courtney: Yes! Yes, that's the word I was thinking of! I mean, some guys might be able to handle watching that show and not winding up degrading women, but there are many guys, especially if they watched it when they were teenagers or young adults, who could have been adversely affected, influenced to treat women terribly.

M.J. Blair: In some ways that could be true. Thinking back to that, one example of the kind of stuff you're criticizing could be how Al, on at least one episode, said to his son Bud Bundy advice about which women to try to get involved with, and Al actually said, "Hooters, hooters, yum yum yum! Hooters, hooters, on a girl that's dumb!" I do see how some impressionable youth might be affected by that in a way that could lead to them becoming more sexist than they might otherwise have become.

Courtney: Exactly!

M.J. Blair: However, a bunch of this stuff depends on a turn of the mind. For example, if someone's advanced enough, then the person could view that series in more of a light of, 'You know what, maybe one of the best things to learn about from that TV show is that *it's probably a good idea to try not to be too similar to any of the main characters on that show!*"

When I was growing up, my family went to a variety of religious places on some occasions. The church I visited most often during much of elementary school through high school was a place that in the earlier years was called Grant Avenue Baptist Church and in the later years was called El Paso Chinese Baptist Church. From about 1983 to about May or June 1994 my parents and I attended events run by that church on many occasions, though not as often in the last five or six years as in the earlier years.

One of the most controversial areas of interpreting scripture is what to make of *Genesis* 38:4-10. Here is a comparison of two renderings, followed by a takeaway:

- The Jewish Publication Society's 1917 English translation *Tanakh* ("OJPS") presents it as:

And she conceived again, and bore a son; and she called his name Onan. And she yet again bore a son, and called his name Shelah; and he was at Chezib, when she bore him. And Judah took a wife for Er his firstborn, and her name was Tamar. And Er, Judah's first-born, was wicked in the sight of the LORD; and the LORD slew him. And Judah said unto Onan: 'Go in unto thy brother's wife, and perform the duty of a husband's brother unto her, and raise up seed to thy brother.' And Onan knew that the seed would not be his; and it came to pass when he went in unto his brother's wife, that he spilled it on the ground, lest he should give his seed to his brother. And the thing which he did was evil in the sight of the LORD; and He slew him also.

- A Bible with the title *Pictorial Family Bible* and the alternative title *Holy Bible, Containing the Old and New Testaments, Translated out of the*

*Original Tongues, with the Apocrypha, Concordance and Psalms, and Revised New Testament, The Old (King James') Version and the Revised Version Arranged in Parallel Columns for Convenience in Reference and Comparison, Self-Pronouncing Edition* (National Publishing Company; Phila-delphia, PA; 1891, largely based on the 1611 *KJV* and other source materials) presented somewhat differently:

4 And she conceived again, and bare a son; and she called
his name [e]Ō′năn.
5 And she yet again conceived, and bare a son; and called
his name [f]Shē′lah: and he was at Chē′zĭb, when she bare him.
6 And Jū′dah [g]took a wife for Ĕr, his firstborn, whose name
*was* Tā′mar.
7 And [h]Ĕr, Jū′dah's firstborn, was wicked in the sight of
the LORD; [i]and the LORD slew him.
8 And Jū′dah said unto Ō′năn, Go in unto [k]thy brother's
wife, and marry her, and raise up seed to thy brother.
9 And Ō′năn knew that the seed should not be [l]his; and
it came to pass, when he went in unto his brother's wife,
that he spilled *it* on the ground, lest that he should give
seed to his brother.
10 And the thing which he did †displeased the LORD
wherefore he slew [m]him also.

e ch. 46. 12.
Num. 26. 19.
f ch. 46. 12.
Num. 26. 20.
g ch. 21. 21.
h ch. 46. 12.
Num. 26. 19.
i 1 Chron. 2. 3.
k Deut. 25. 5.
Matt. 22. 24.
l Deut 25. 6.
† Heb. *was evil in the eyes of the* LORD.
m ch. 46. 12.
Num. 26. 19.

Although there are many interpretive controversies, a recurrent theme is to endeavor to avoid getting smote.

Although many things changed at many stages of my life, much of this life has been filled with a commitment to doing the best I can to exhibit proper sexual ethics. The concepts I have had regarding sexual ethics have changed many times, and I believe that I made multiple breakthroughs of improvement, especially in the 2001-2003 period, the 2005-2008 period, and the period from 2022 to the present. Team Austerity has worked well.

Imagine the presence of multiple beings who are on the edge of total omniscience yet slightly short of total omniscience—specifically, beings who have the capacity to witness any portions of the basic five senses of data and any portions of telepathic reading of minds across all observable galaxies and all regions of space and hyperspace between galaxies, across all observable time, as well as any other regions of space-time, yet, somehow, unable to fully know answers to questions about which religion, if any, is most correct; which combination of religions, if any, are most correct; and whether there are any best answers to the most mysterious questions of ethics and metaphysics. Imagine those beings repeatedly judging everyone mentioned directly in this book and repeatedly judging everyone else, while also not always agreeing even amongst themselves about what the best judgments and actions would be.

An immense amount of the time when I would wind up having difficulty sleep in portions of 2003-2004 was spent constructively by running through mock trials in my mind in which the best I could do to tune into the perspectives of how such beings might consider things could have them and myself participate in placing myself on trial. One side would conduct a prosecution that would argue me to lack any right to live and to lack any right whatsoever to exist in any way, shape or form. The other side would conduct a defense that would argue me to have the right to live and the right to exist. I would use logic and emotion to energize both sides to the outer limits of everything forceful and seemingly relevant, then to attempt to go beyond those limits, unleashing unlimited wrath and fury aimed at myself and unleashing unlimited counter-wrath and counter-fury aimed to push back in self-defense. That was a huge part of what set me up well for making the various 2005 and onward adjustments that have improved my life, as well as finding ways to sometimes expand the opportunities for others to improve their lives.

---

As a sidenote, one of the weirdest things I experienced at The Financial Advisory Group at 5599 San Felipe St, Suite 900, Houston, TX 77056 was when about two or three then-coworkers, who, to the best of my memory at the time included then-intern Hunter Coday, asked me a bizarre question, circa July 2019. They asked about the idea they had somewhere acquired from someone, whom they declined to identify, about an alleged ban by McDonald's. Fortunately, I have never been banned from any of the locations of the fast food restaurant chain known as McDonald's. However, I have told several people over the years, including some of the people I met at The Financial Advisory Group during portions of the August 6, 2018 to August 6, 2019 period, about how there was a day in something like the 2011-2014 period or thereabouts that something truly weird happened at the McDonald's located in part of the Southeast corner of Bellaire Blvd and the West Loop of Beltway 8 in

Houston. At that time, there was also a Subway restaurant a short walk from there, just the other side of the Denny's restaurant almost adjacent.

That fateful day, whether it was in 2012 or 2013 or whatever, I went into that restaurant as I had many times before. I had been gaming their pricing scheme repeatedly by ordering multiple very cheap things and combining them with ordering a grilled chicken patty a la carte. That a la carte grilled chicken patty had been very cheap for a long time, something like $1.29, and it would go well with something like ordering a McDouble and a side salad, obtaining a reasonable meal for what seemed a ridiculously low price. However, that day, it turned out that McDonald's had ended the offering of the a la carte grilled chicken patty for an extremely low price, having adjusted it to something significantly higher. I decided, *You know what, if they're not going to let me game the system of their menu like they did before, then I'll just go over to ordering a very different meal from them.*

Therefore, I ordered a different meal from them.

*However, things got really weird. After placing the order, the person behind the counter quoted a price, and I could tell by having performed approximate math that it was a very wrong and excessively high price for what I had ordered; the quoted price was in serious contradiction with what the menu showed for the prices, plus the 8.25% tax. I objected. However, the person behind the counter stuck with the quote. After some additional back-and-forth, I decided to leave.*

The main explanation that the worker had was along the lines of, "The machine tells me this is the total price. I can't go against the machine!"

I do not know if the operator had placed some wrong input into the order-taking-and-calculating, computerized, cash register system or if there was a computer anomaly or what, but I knew that the numbers were not adding up correctly, and it had become dreadfully obvious that the person behind the counter had decided to stonewall any reasonable further inquiry into what in the world had actually happened to cause the discrepancy. Therefore, I stuck with the idea of leaving on that occasion, cancelling the order.

On my way out of that McDonald's restaurant location that day, I said, either word-for-word or almost exactly word-for-word, "I don't know if I'll be coming back to this location. Maybe I might be back a few weeks or a few months from now, or maybe not. I'm cancelling that order, since you can't seem to figure out the math problem. I'm going to go over to Subway to eat today."

I proceeded to do just that, ordering food from Subway and eating there without a hitch. That being said, it was something like about three or four months later that I decided along the lines of, *You know what, I've had many great experiences at that McDonald's location that's almost adjacent to the building where I work. I've punished them enough with avoiding them for a few months. I'll go back and order something, and we'll see how this goes.*

Sure enough, I went back there, then proceeded to place an order, estimate the math, notice that this time the price was right, ate the food, and went ahead with the rest of my life, knowing that the previous pricing discrepancy visit had been an outlier in my experiences as a customer of McDonald's.

You can probably see, though, how if one person retells another, and the next retells, and so on, then, as with many stories that get passed along, details can eventually transmorph into making it something very different from the original tale.

---

The next exhibit of Part R of Section Five of Chapter Ten is an alternate version of Footnote 15 to Part Four of Chapter Six, a copy of a message I sent to the very person referenced there as having served as a bartender on December 11, 2021 and having been present as a patron on April 7, 2022 in connection with that stuff:

[15] Cf. an inquiry sent via Facebook Messenger
From: Maurice James Blair
To: Penny Lloyd Clark
Date: April 16, 2024, 7:07 PM U.S. CDT

Penny, I tried to call to discuss a few things with you by phone, mainly what I'm about to ask here. You should find a brief, supplemental voicemail in connection with this. Before, I had been reluctant to send a written message mainly because I value your friendship on Facebook, and I perceive that bringing this up with you might cause you major discomfort. Phone would be more ideal, but you repeatedly happened to not pick up. However, there is great value in opening the door to finding out from you a little more information on the aftermath of that incident. You might recall being the bartender when the main incident described in Footnote 6 of Chapter 4 of the free ebook *Impact* [*] occurred, and

you might notice that a few spots in that chapter of that refer to you, though not by name. What I am requesting of you now is if you would sometime be so kind as to describe to me some of the aftermath of the barfight from what you observed from your perspective, whether by Facebook messenger, by phone call, or in person. The 713 number I called you from is a landline number and therefore not able to receive text messages, by the way. If the time is right for it later on, then I might someday share with you what my cellphone number is. Thanks in advance. [*] Cross Reference: the free ebook at https://mixam.com/share/659351615dddc94c958bb985
Regards, Maurice J. Blair

---

Please note that as of just before going to print, she had continued to remain silent about that incident, although, thankfully she and I had maintained friendship with each other on that Platform. She friended me on Facebook sometime in the first half of April 2024.

First, she sent a friend request from seemingly out of nowhere, then I noticed and accepted it.

---

---

---

---

---

---

---

$10^{38.5}$ ... $10^{37.9}$ ... $10^{38.4}$ ... $10^{39.4}$ ... $10^{38.1}$

---

+G, +R, -R, -B, +B, -G, -G, -G, +G, +G, -R, +R, +R

---

<, >, =, <, >,  > -B, -B, +R, -B, -R, +R, +G, -G, +R, -R

---

-G, <, >, <, =, >, +R, +B, +G, +B, +G, +B, >, >, <, +R

---

>, >, >, <, >, >, >, <, >, >, =, <, >, =, >, =, =, <

---

+G, -R, +R, -B, -B, +R, +B, -B, +G, -R, -G, +R, +G

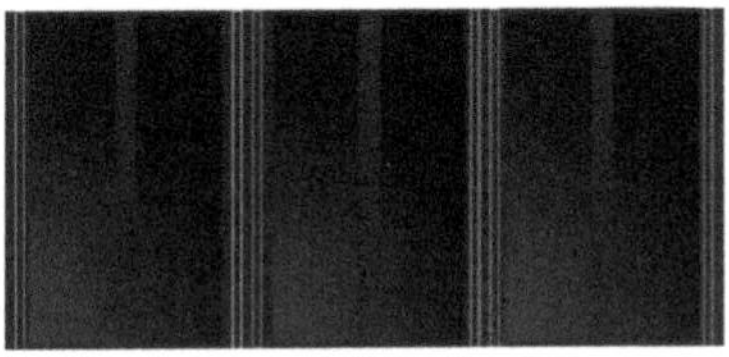

---

Finally, to close out Part R, here is an approximate transcript of portions of dialogue that happened between my mother and me at about 2:52 P.M. Central Daylight Time on April 23, 2024, redacting via ellipses a few phrases that could have otherwise proved very distracting to about 99.9% of readers:

Ming: You're not making money at this age, writing those books. When you get older your money might run out. When the money's gone, it's gone!

Jim: I'm not that worried about the risk of dying homeless, penniless, and in the street! Taking things further, I'm not that worried about the risk of if Los Zetas or MS-13 or some Feminazis or some excessively-masculine—what would they be called?—Mascunazis or some weirdos of any kind were to kidnap me and then physically torture me to death!!

What I *am* concerned about is... stuff like stomping a boot on... those bearing false witness... and helping those who bear true witness to be able to do that better. *I am concerned about reducing the bearing of false witness and increasing and enhancing the bearing of true witness, for the betterment of all sentient beings!!*

---

## Chapter 10, Section 5, PART S

The references to dates and times here are as stamped relative to U.S. Central Daylight Time. Some portions are slightly-redacted in this transcript. In it, each reference to Aron is to Aron Silberg and each reference to Maurice is to yours truly, the M.J.B. author of this book.

Preface: Aron sent me a message on April 23, 2024 at 9:14 PM, informing me that he had learned that a mutual acquaintance had recently died. He expressed grief and an openness for extended communications in general.

From: Maurice
To: Aron
Date: April 23, 2024, 9:31 PM

Oh, sorry to hear that. BTW, I had been reluctant to bring this up with you, but a while ago, there was a time when Eliza and I sent text messages to each other, and, at one stage, I asked about if she might provide information that would allow me to visit [Mario] at whichever jail or prison he is in, and she declined. Would you happen to know what Mario's family name is, what facility he is incarcerated in, etc.? I believe there could be value in if I were to someday stop by and share a conversation with him. On another note, I am not inherently talkative. Many times when I was younger I was very silent, and, many times since I have also been very silent. That being said, after some of the patterns of events in November 2018 to July 2021, I became very ready to go ballistic in communications with others early when they would seem to be headed for trouble rather than waiting for problems to fester and having to go thermonuclear later. If you are worried about imagining me to become excessively talkative during a visit to Mario while he is incarcerated, then, rest assured, I would be aiming to speak little and listen much, limiting scenarios of speaking a bunch to be more circumscribed than I would in more normal settings. What, if anything, might you be at liberty to divulge regarding that Mario?

From: Aron
To: Maurice
Date: April 23, 2024, 9:52 PM

Thanks, yeah, that's confidential. His last name is [surname redacted], I think. Could be. Yes, your talkative nature surpasses mine, but that's ok. You're a great person.

From: Maurice
To: Aron
Date: April 24, 2024, 10:02 AM

Aron, Thank you for indicating a vote of conceptualizing me as a great person, but my message was not aimed at getting you to increase approval toward me in general. For many years, almost my entire motivation with everything has energetically revolved around that ultimate level of reality--whether best described by a given religion, a given combination of religions, some combination of sciences and religions, or whatever else--and to whatever degree best left undescribed. Every so often, I work hard to make things happen. A little while ago, continuing the searches I had let go of back in July 2023, then let go again, and it seems that the Internet has a great empty void where information on anyone named Mario and convicted in Texas on that date while plausibly being identical to former coworker Mario would have shown up. Although Elizabeth [surname redacted] had indicated her then-boyfriend Mario to have been convicted on 7/7/2023 and sentenced to 25 years, I am growing partway skeptical that our former coworker was actually convicted at all; rather, I am suspecting it possible something totally different may have happened and that Eliza and other people, including you, are presenting it to me as a cover story with which to hide something different that happened.

*[Multiple Redacted Statements ensued. The publisher considers them beyond the scope of this book, and they are therefore omitted from this transcript.]*

I could look at this either way: in some ways it seems plausible that some people, including Eliza, might have found my communications disconcerting enough to them such as to make a cover story like that out of a paranoia that I might aim trouble for them; however, it also seems plausible that maybe Mario might have actually been convicted of something, yet for some reason seeming difficult to track down via Internet searches.

*[Multiple Redacted Statements ensued. The publisher considers them beyond the scope of this book, and they are therefore omitted from this transcript.]*

Although I recognize that many terrorist organizations have done many terrible things, I accept a degree of agnosticism toward the big picture of those [groups'] choices, especially in those ways of how depending on who is arguing for what there are all kinds of those arguments about who is a freedom fighter, who is a terrorist, who is just, who is unjust, who is immoral, who is moral, etc. Therefore, if G-d/God/Adibuddha/REALITY were to ask me to vote for one organization to be the most expendable organization on the face of the Earth, then I would vote for my former employer The Financial Advisory Group, Inc., because, even though they and the attorney they hired to send me a threatening letter dated August 9, 2021 shut up toward me after I refuted that letter in an e-mail message that I sent to all four commissioners (of that time) of the Securities and Exchange Commission and to the attorney who dared to sign that letter to me, still, nevertheless, neither the law office associated with sending me that defamatory letter in a lame attempt to intimidate me nor The Financial Advisory Group itself have ever taken any observable action, as far as I know of, in the direction of either apologizing to me or doing anything else to show acknowledgment of them having any more than a trace of an idea about how much that former employer had violated much of the core of my life prior to when I repeatedly fought back against that organization. I have absolutely no regret about the many times that I expressed to various people and organizations sharp criticism of The Financial Advisory Group, Inc. and the law firm Gray Reed (also known as Gray Reed & McGraw). I do not know how much of the primary driver of the terrible behavior they had toward me and their not bothering to have followed up with either an apology or another type of acknowledgment of much of the reality of the past interaction stems from only one former coworker having had extreme animosity toward me personally, an interest they might have had in coddling that former coworker, a disdain that many of them or maybe all of them might have felt toward my affinity for Buddhism, some secret information they might have somehow obtained about hidden details involving the lives of my late father and my late Grandfather Blair and an idea that some of them might have had to take a "sins of the father(s) shall be visited upon the son(s)" approach, or if something else was going on with that. However, much of what they had is not necessarily to be most heavily to blame, because if 20th century Earth had not been involved with Paul Churchland and a few other prominent philosophers and scientists having been so hell-bent on imposing belief in metaphysical materialism, then I might not have wound up ever working in the tax and accounting field; instead I might have become an engineer, a physicist, or a philosopher, or maybe some combination of those. Actually, with some of the writing I have been involved with I have become, to some degree, a philosopher and a scientist, though without having achieved much observable acclaim as of yet. Whether that former coworker Mario experienced something other than getting convicted on 7/7/2023 and sentenced to 25 years in prison or actually did experience getting convicted on 7/7/2023 and sentenced to 25 years in prison, and whether he was in actuality guilty of having done some heinous crime or not guilty of having done some heinous crime, we can focus on doing what we can about getting the future to work well. Take care. Regards, Maurice

From: Aron
To: Maurice
Date: April 24, 2024, 6:29 PM

You're welcome. It didn't have to have that purpose. That's cool. I have no idea. I'm just going by what I've heard. We're not trying to mislead anyone or gaslight, antagonize, etc. It's good that it was balanced. I've never heard of them. No one should bomb anything regardless. You were brave then and now. Their actions were uncalled for. May the dead all rest in peace. We don't know what could have happened with anyone under different circumstances. Maybe the information isn't available online for privacy purposes and clearance purposes because not everyone needs to know what prison, cell block, etc, anyone is in. What if victims want to take justice into their own hands, for example, with a convicted rapist or convicted killer? Like, say Selena's brother was able to find Yolanda Saldivar and kill her 27 years ago? What, then?

From: Maurice
To: Aron
Date: April 24, 2024, (6:30 PM or thereabouts; time not separately stated by Facebook Messenger b/c almost instantly after the 6:29 PM message)

Actually, you point out something that many people in the public might not know about, and which did not fully dawn on me until studying your latest response:

Just because many convictions that result in severe sentences become reported publicly in the news and on the Internet, it does not mean that all such convictions make the news.

From: Aron
To: Maurice
Date: April 24, 2024, 6:54 PM

I'm not actually sure, honestly, but it would make sense despite heavy security present to prevent prisoners from escaping. That, too. The public doesn't need to know the particular prison or cell block, etc, even high-profile people are in.

From: Maurice
To: Aron
Date: April 24, 2024, 7:20 PM

On the other hand, as I've mentioned to a few folks before, sometime around early 2006 I was assigned a job duty by my then-boss Tielin "Sunny" Sun to perform a work errand of visiting my then-coworker Diego Sanchez at a jail downtown, in the hopes that my stopping by would get the jail people to let him out sooner. Oftentimes, people don't need to know what cell someone is in when visiting them; they just need to know what jail or prison the incarcerated individual is in. Taking things into a whole other direction, I have noticed online sites encouraging people to become pen-pals with inmates. Maybe that could work well sometimes, but it is also maybe extra-super-high-risk. It probably results in a mixture of some great marriages, some good marriages, some bad marriages, and some excruciatingly tragic marriages, as well as some good Platonic friendships, some disastrous Platonic friendships, and many other outcomes. On another note, in something like late 2005 or early 2006 that Diego Sanchez did something most would consider unethical in almost any workplace: All of a sudden, he asked a coworker named Oscar Flamenco and me to go over to his desk and look at something he thought we should see. On his computer screen at work he then proceeded to play bestiality videos in which female human beings were getting mounted by male canines. We thought it was kind of funny, but we did not want to encourage him to show such videos to us again at work, as that was taking workplace inappropriateness to the extreme. BTW, that was not what landed him in jail; instead, it was evidently something to do with falling behind on child support payments or something very similar.

---

A sidenote to the correspondence transcript presented:

Perspectives on controversies between metaphysical critical idealism and other metaphysical theories can help people or harm people in different ways depending on how well people use and relate to them. Likewise, there are opportunities all over the place for people to explore and consider competing ethical theories and practices, though the best way to become more aware of ethics is often by facing ethical dilemmas and trilemmas in real life, especially some of the most unwanted and difficult ethical dilemmas and ethical trilemmas.

---

# SECTION T: TWISTED TRAVELS THROUGH TERRAIN

$T \cdot T^4 = T^5$. The preceding mathematical statement is either true or generally true. Yes, there can be contorted nonlinearities and nuances of unusual equations that would render it of limited degrees of truth rather than as of absolute truth. Some of this could relate to how what many would consider the commonsense notion of relative motion becomes, near the speed of light in many cases, a dead-wrong notion of how relative motion works. Sometimes, whereas many people would assume things are of an a+b pattern, experimental results repeatedly coincide with an $(a+b)/(1+(a \cdot b)/(c^2))$ pattern, rendering what seems "= a+b" in actuality "≠ a+b."

Common sense can be living-right at times, common sense can be dead-wrong at times, and sometimes common sense can occupy the intermediate zones between death and life and between right and wrong. Similarly, uncommon sense can be living-right sometimes, uncommon sense can be dead-wrong sometimes, and uncommon sense can occupy the intermediate zones between life and death and between wrong and right in some cases.

Whether you give a damn about chess or not, the next few pages present chess information.

If you do not give a damn about chess, then it is perhaps best that you glance at them as odd curiosities without straining too much, similar to if and when you flip to an unfamiliar TV program and have a visceral reaction of, "WTF are they showing on the screen now? I'll glance at this channel for a little while, but I'd best soon move along to something that makes more sense." On the other hand, maybe your unique situation might make it best for you to finally start to give a damn about chess. As with virtually any text, the works culminating in the formation of the text affords an opportunity for it to be part of new contexts—contexts beyond the surface of the text that arrives into those contexts—much as the origins of a given text involved contexts beyond the surface of the result-ing text.

In contrast, if you do give a damn about chess, then studying the next few pages will seem second-nature to you. Admittedly, if you are great at chess, then some of it might seem overly simple to you.

Whichever givings, misgivings, forgivings, and thanksgivings anyone might bring to the table regarding physical combat, psychological combat, sports, games, and everything else, here goes.

Consider online chess as analogous to regular life such that: 1) If a person has a terrible situation in life that is tantamount to some type of waiting around to die, and the languishing person refrains from committing suicide, then one could think this analogous to officially resigning a game while in a totally losing position. 2) If a person has a terrible situation in life that is tantamount to some type of waiting around to die, and the languishing person commits suicide, then one could think this analogous to someone intentionally leaving an in-progress chess game, vacating the online board, and going on to lose the game without getting back to that online board. The game loss in that case could either occur by the remaining person (viz. the opponent of the player who left) at the online board hitting a button to claim victory or occur by time running out for the leaver. This analogy could be extended by considering that a) a case of a player wishing to return to the online board and succeeding in doing so being akin to starting a suicide attempt and subsequently having a change of mind and succeeding in surviving; whereas b) a case of a player wishing to return to the online board and failing to return there in time to resume participation in it being akin to starting a suicide attempt and subsequently having a change of mind and failing to survive that suicide attempt.

3) To state the obvious, people with great situations in life could be thought of as analogous to people competing in those online games when their state of play finds them to have very advantageous chess positions.

Of course, it can go without saying that analogies such as this are quite imperfect in many ways, and it rather behooves those considering them to be mindful of multiple genuine similarities and multiple genuine differences between the regular life-and-death level and the alternatively-conceptualized abstraction level. That is, in this case, between the regular-world situation of life and death in their totality versus the abstract-world situation of the online chess game activities.

Now, consider a series of displays that combine to exhibit two April 2024 online games. In both cases, I won after an anonymous opponent left the board, failed to return, and ran out of time.

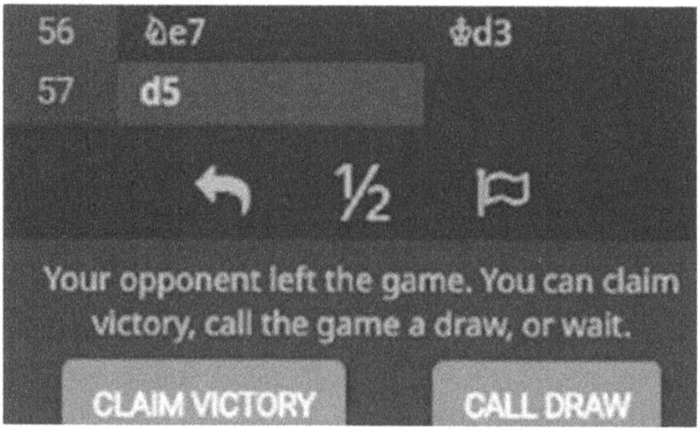

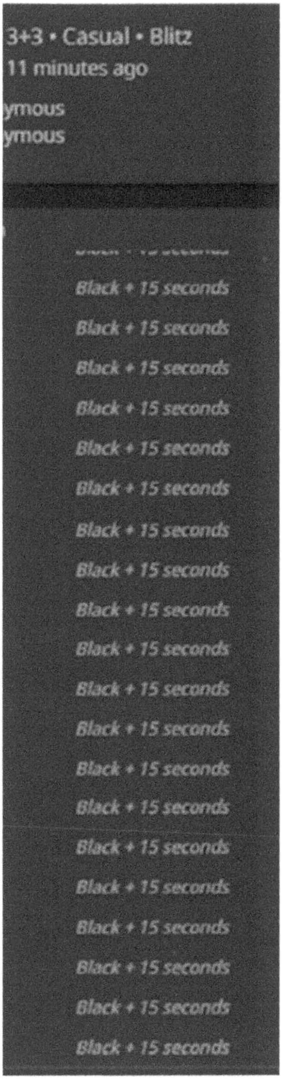
3+3 • Casual • Blitz
11 minutes ago
ymous
ymous
Black + 15 seconds
Black + 15 seconds
Black + 15 seconds
Black + 15 seconds
Black + 15 seconds
Black + 15 seconds
Black + 15 seconds
Black + 15 seconds
Black + 15 seconds
Black + 15 seconds
Black + 15 seconds
Black + 15 seconds
Black + 15 seconds
Black + 15 seconds
Black + 15 seconds
Black + 15 seconds
Black + 15 seconds
Black + 15 seconds
Black + 15 seconds
Black + 15 seconds

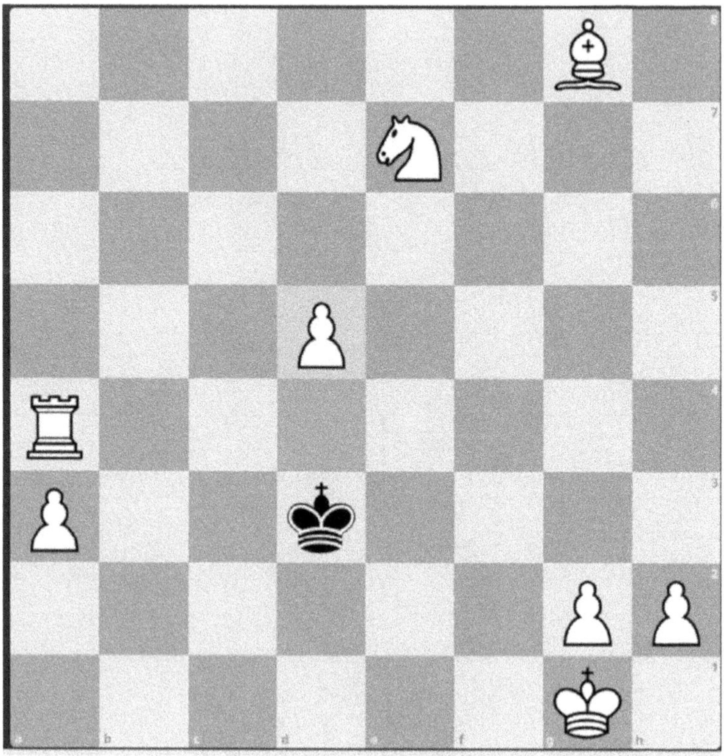

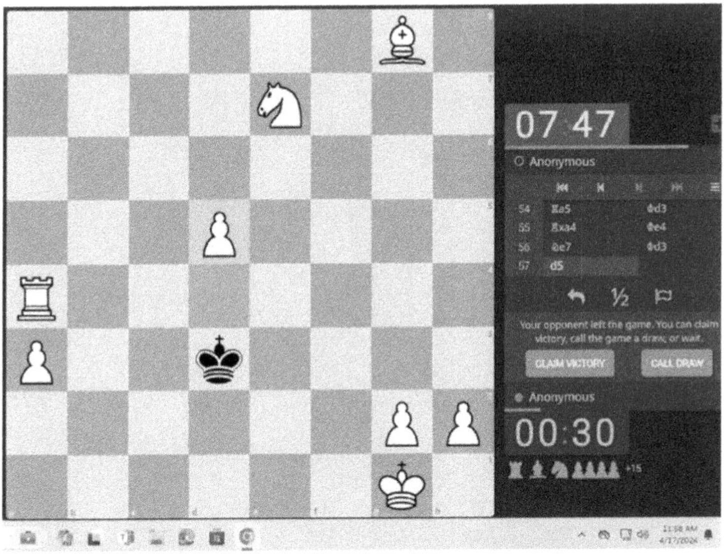
07 47
Anonymous
54 ♖a5 ♚d3
55 ♖xa4 ♚e4
56 ♗e7 ♚d3
57 d5
½
Your opponent left the game. You can claim victory, call the game a draw, or wait.
CLAIM VICTORY
CALL DRAW
Anonymous
00:30
+15
11:58 AM
4/17/2024

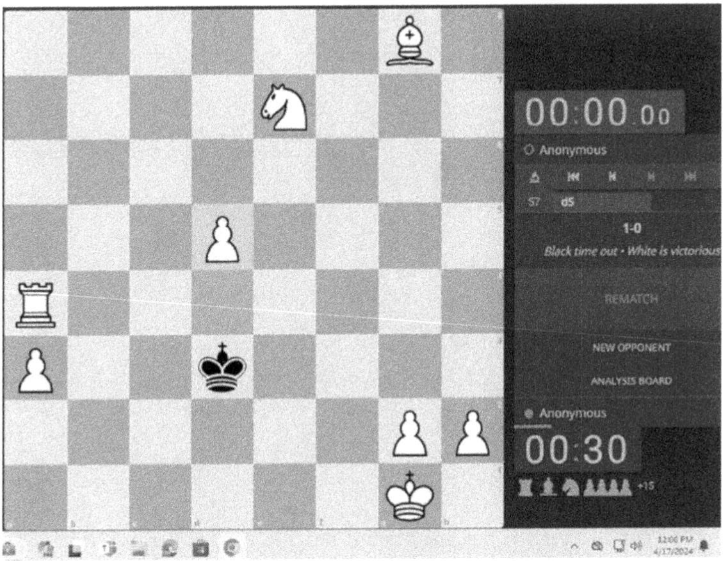
00:00.00
Anonymous
57 d5
1-0
Black time out • White is victorious
REMATCH
NEW OPPONENT
ANALYSIS BOARD
Anonymous
00:30
+15
12:00 PM
4/17/2024

| | | |
|---|---|---|
| 1 | d4 | d5 |
| 2 | c4 | e6 |
| 3 | ♘c3 | ♗b4 |
| 4 | cxd5 | ♗xc3+ |
| 5 | bxc3 | ♕xd5 |
| 6 | ♗a3 | ♘f6 |
| 7 | ♕b3 | ♘c6 |
| 8 | ♕xd5 | ♘xd5 |
| 9 | ♖c1 | ♗d7 |
| 10 | e4 | ♘b6 |
| 11 | f3 | O-O-O |
| 12 | ♗d3 | a6 |
| 13 | ♘e2 | ♘a5 |
| 14 | O-O | ♘bc4 |
| 15 | ♗b4 | ♘e3 |
| 16 | ♗xa5 | ♘xf1 |
| 17 | ♔xf1 | b6 |
| 18 | ♗b4 | a5 |
| 19 | ♗a3 | ♔b7 |
| 20 | e5 | f6 |
| 21 | f4 | ♗a4 |
| 22 | ♔g1 | h6 |
| 23 | ♗g6 | fxe5 |

| | | |
|---|---|---|
| 24 | fxe5 | ♖hf8 |
| 25 | ♗xf8 | ♖xf8 |
| 26 | ♘g3 | ♗c6 |
| 27 | ♘h5 | ♖g8 |
| 28 | ♖f1 | ♔a6 |
| 29 | ♗f7 | ♖f8 |
| 30 | ♗xe6 | ♖e8 |
| 31 | ♗b3 | a4 |
| 32 | ♗f7 | ♖e7 |
| 33 | ♗g6 | ♗b5 |
| 34 | ♖f7 | ♖e6 |
| 35 | ♖xg7 | ♗e2 |
| 36 | ♘g3 | ♗c4 |
| 37 | ♗b1 | ♖f6 |
| 38 | ♖g4 | h5 |
| 39 | ♖h4 | c5 |
| 40 | ♖xh5 | cxd4 |
| 41 | cxd4 | b5 |
| 42 | exf6 | ♔a5 |
| 43 | a3 | ♔b6 |
| 44 | ♖f5 | ♗e6 |
| 45 | ♖f2 | ♔c6 |
| 46 | f7 | ♗xf7 |

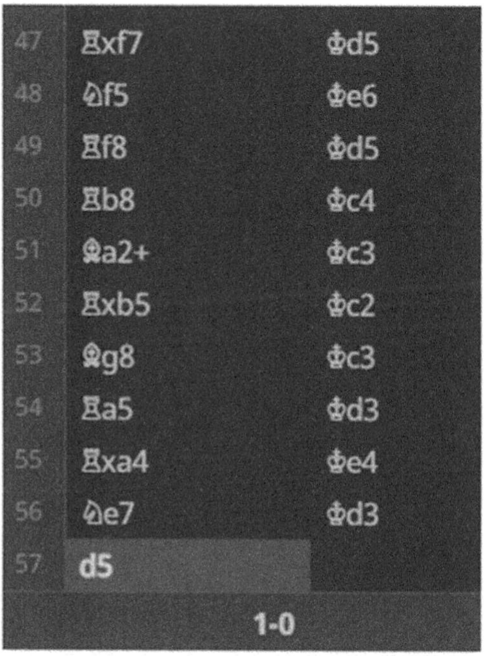
47 ♖xf7 ♔d5
48 ♘f5 ♔e6
49 ♖f8 ♔d5
50 ♖b8 ♔c4
51 ♗a2+ ♔c3
52 ♖xb5 ♔c2
53 ♗g8 ♔c3
54 ♖a5 ♔d3
55 ♖xa4 ♔e4
56 ♘e7 ♔d3
57 d5
1-0

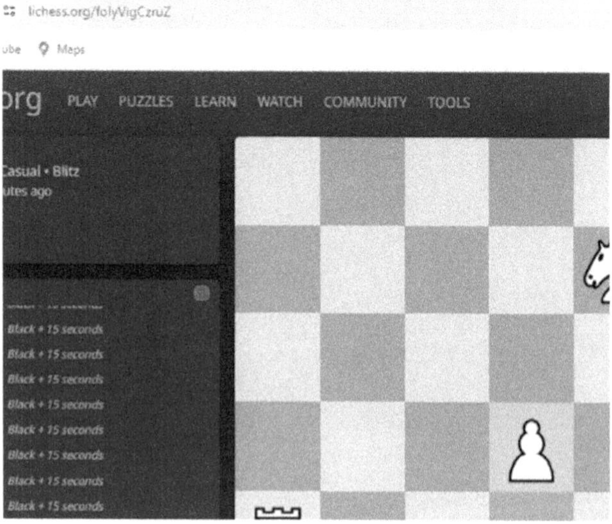
lichess.org/folyVigCzruZ
Maps
PLAY PUZZLES LEARN WATCH COMMUNITY TOOLS
Casual • Blitz
Black + 15 seconds
Black + 15 seconds
Black + 15 seconds
Black + 15 seconds
Black + 15 seconds
Black + 15 seconds
Black + 15 seconds
Black + 15 seconds

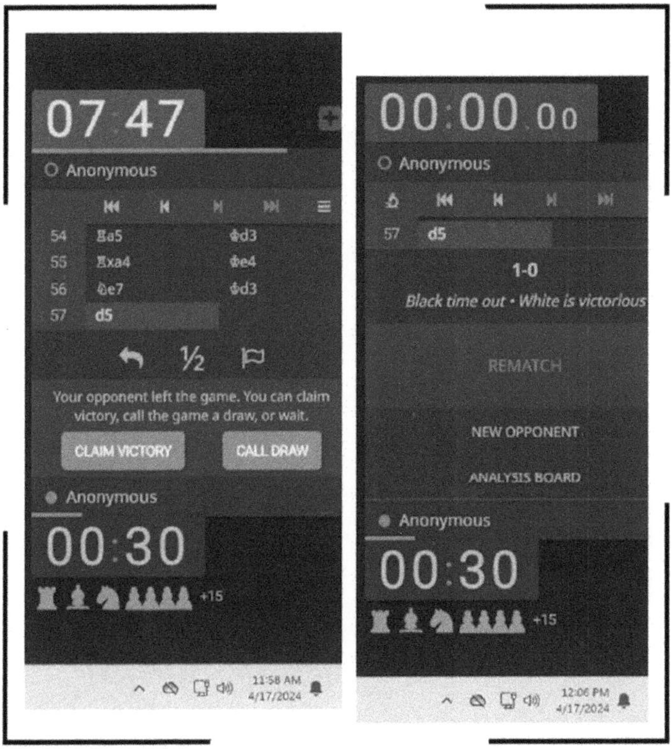


[conclusion of presentation 1 (of 2) in this set]

***   ***   ***   ***   ***   ***   ***

[beginning of presentation 2 (of 2) in this set]

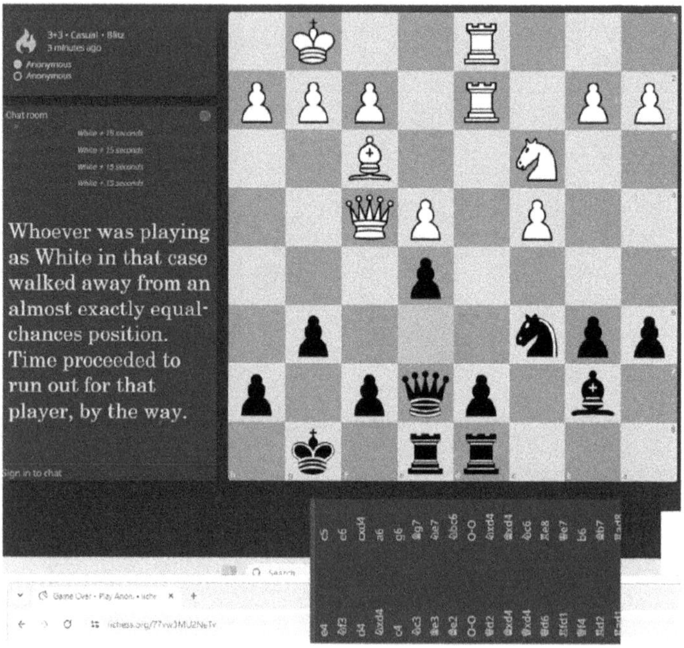

From another perspective, it was not a dead-even type of position; rather, it was a position involving a slight advantage for White per a Stockfish 16 calculation of +0.31 at a depth of 36/45, with 19.Qe3 Nd4 20.Ne2 Nxf3+ 21.Qxf3 Qb4 considered best.

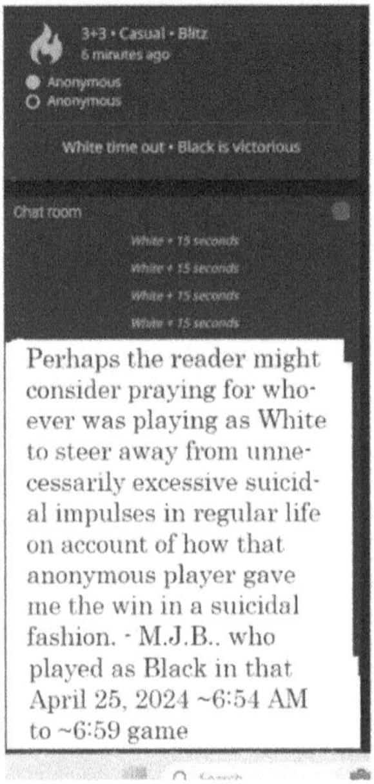


Perhaps the reader might consider praying for whoever was playing as White to steer away from unnecessarily excessive suicidal impulses in regular life on account of how that anonymous player gave me the win in a suicidal fashion. - M.J.B.. who played as Black in that April 25, 2024 ~6:54 AM to ~6:59 game

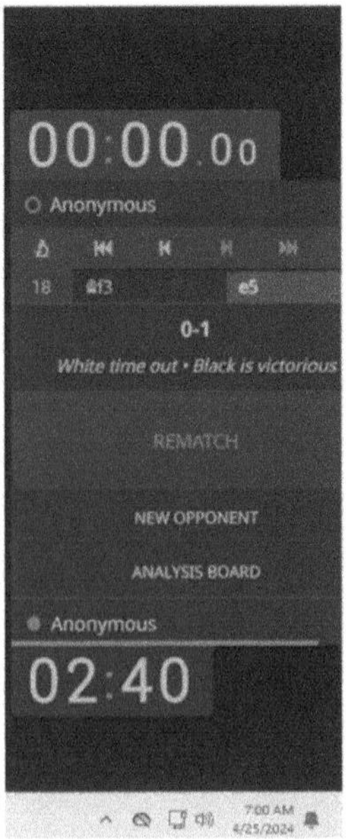

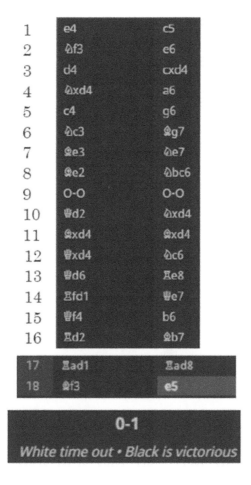

| | | |
|---|---|---|
| 1 | e4 | c5 |
| 2 | ♘f3 | e6 |
| 3 | d4 | cxd4 |
| 4 | ♘xd4 | a6 |
| 5 | c4 | g6 |
| 6 | ♘c3 | ♗g7 |
| 7 | ♗e3 | ♘e7 |
| 8 | ♗e2 | ♘bc6 |
| 9 | O-O | O-O |
| 10 | ♕d2 | ♘xd4 |
| 11 | ♗xd4 | ♗xd4 |
| 12 | ♕xd4 | ♘c6 |
| 13 | ♕d6 | ♖e8 |
| 14 | ♖fd1 | ♕e7 |
| 15 | ♕f4 | b6 |
| 16 | ♖d2 | ♗b7 |
| 17 | ♖ad1 | ♖ad8 |
| 18 | ♗f3 | e5 |

**0-1**

*White time out • Black is victorious*

(conclusion of presentation 2 (of 2) in this set)

Next, consider the move records for two games that happened in Moscow in the year 1968.

**Estrin, Yakov - Bykhovsky, Anatoly A** ½-½
**C67** Ch Moscow Moscow URS 1968

1.e4 e5 2.Nf3 Nc6 3.Bb5 Nf6 4.0-0 Nxe4 5.Re1 Nd6 6.Nxe5 Be7 7.Bd3 Nxe5 8.Rxe5 0-0 9.Nc3 c6 10.Qf3 Ne8 11.b3 d5 12.Bb2 Nf6 13.h3 Be6 14.Rae1 Nd7 15.Rh5 g6 16.Ne2 Bf6 17.Bxf6 Qxf6 18.Qxf6 Nxf6 19.Re5 Rfe8
½-½

**Kholmov, Ratmir D - Estrin, Yakov ½-½**
**C44** Ch Moscow Moscow URS 1968

1.e4 e5 2.Nf3 Nc6 3.Bc4 Nf6 4.d4 exd4 5.e5 d5 6.Bb5 Ne4 7.Nxd4 Bc5 8.Be3 Bd7 9.Bxc6 bxc6 10.0-0 Qe7 11.f3 Nd6 12.Bf2 Nf5 13.Nc3 0-0 14.Re1 Nxd4 15.Bxd4 Rab8 16.Kh1 Rb4 17.Bxc5 Qxc5 18.a3 Rd4 19.Qc1 Rc4 20.Qd2 Bf5 21.Rac1 a5 22.Ne2 Rxc2 23.Rxc2 Qxc2 24.Qxc2 Bxc2 25.Nd4 Ba4 26.Rc1 Rb8 27.Nxc6 Bxc6 28.Rxc6 Rxb2 29.Kg1 Kf8 30.Rxc7 Rb3 31.a4 Rb4 32.Rc5 Rxa4 33.Rxd5 Ke7 34.Rd6 Ra2 35.h4 h5 36.Ra6 a4 37.Kh2 g6
½-½

Part U

# CHAPTER 10, SECTION 5, PART V, WITH V FOR 22 INSTEAD OF V FOR 5 IN THIS CASE; THE 10.5.V HERE COMPLEMENTS THE EARLIER 10.5.E MUCH AKIN TO HOW GLUONS COMPLEMENT QUARKS: A REVISED INTRODUCTION (A REPRISED OVERVIEW AND OUTLOOK)

A mixture of praise and criticism:

1. The United States of America is extraordinary in a great many ways. It has, sometimes through teamwork with other nations/organizations and other times through going on its own, with very mixed results, brought to our world an exquisite variety of ideas, methods, and technologies that have to varying degrees promoted freedom, equity, equality, legitimate differences, diversity, unity, multiplicity, cohesion, division, agony, and ecstasy. It still has the opportunity to become a more perfect nation, yet it can be difficult at times for a sincere citizen to sort through the competing punditry on the various sides of the issues.

2. Antarctica, The Arctic, The Middle East, Each Midwest, Europe, Asia, Africa, and Australia present mixtures of mystery, levity, seriousness, danger, and opportunity to each other and everyone else.

3. Almost every worker and almost every owner in virtually every organization might be subject to theologians and other influencers characterizing each of them as befitting the trite adages, "All fall short of the glory of God" and "We all have room for improvement." However, if we hold on to such idea structures too tightly, then we could be led astray by excessive attachments and aversions instigated by being too uptight. Too uptight, that is, with intentiongs to relate all people and experiences to the idea structures thoroughly pounded into our minds over the eons by theologians and other influencers.

4. Ancestors and descendants can prove extraordinarily beneficial, harmful, or, in some vast array of ways, both. Considering competing perspectives might lead to arriving at wisdom accepting the contradictions and paradoxes of thought, imagination, and experience as making perfect sense.

5. The U.S. Military-Industrial Complex is quite influential, and however much or little anyone might know, evaluating it might prove more meaningful when compared and contrasted with other nations' military-industrial complexes. Taking this further, consider all relevant complexes and all relevant simplexes.

# PART W

## "Yet Another Playlist Idea, With Threats and Opportunities Aimed at Any and All Demographics"

(arranged from the energies blowing in the subtle winds of Mind on May 18, 2024) (performers listed on the by-lines)

1. "The New Timer" by Bruce Springsteen
2. "Nebraska" by Bruce Springsteen
3. "Those Were the Days" by Mary Hopkin
4. "Billy Austin" by Steve Earle
5. "Gaté Gaté" by Olivia Newton-John
6. "War Pigs/Luke's Wall" by Black Sabbath
7. "Here I Go Again on My Own" by Whitesnake
8. "Nights in White Satin" by The Moody Blues
9. "Paint It Black" by The Rolling Stones
10. "Prayer for Peace" by The Dalai Lama

NEXT, SOME SUPPLEMENTAL PHOTOGRAPHY WITH MAY 18, 2024 ADJUSTMENTS, INVOLVING THE SKIES FROM THE EVENING OF MAY 17, 2024:

Although, as reflected by multiple passages in this hypervolume, there are things to sharply criticize about Martin Yate's *Knock 'Em Dead 2003*, there are also several very good things about that book. It provides many genuine, helpful pieces of career advice, including proven techniques that can help people win jobs. Since the time of buying a copy of it early in the twenty-first century I have won many jobs, been fired twice, and quit many times. Some have said, "A quitter never wins, and a winner never quits," but others have said, "You've got to know when to walk away." Another adage is, "Strike while the iron's hot."

As mentioned in my article "Perhaps the Dawning of a New Tarot Deck," I designed a personal set of supplemental cards based on the favorable inspiration that I felt from some of my encounters with some parts of that Yate book.

For the first time ever, near the end of completing this hypervolume I chose to include as part of it a scanned copy of those supplemental cards that I lovingly crafted about two decades earlier by triangulating some of what Martin Yate presented, some of what P.D. Ouspensky presented, and a whole bunch of other stuff.

For added expressiveness, portions parallel closely some of the layouts that tarot readers place in front of those who request readings.

Three of the "cards" are not "regular deck cards," but "placeholders for categories." The "regular deck cards" display the phrase "Patterns Modeling Business" on their backs, whereas the backs of the "placeholders for categories" are blank except for standard parallel lines.

# FIRST PAGE OF LAYOUTS OF THE "PATTERNS MODELING BUSINESS" DECK WITH WHICH M.J. BLAIR RELATED MULTIPLE OUSPENSKY PATTERNS, MULTIPLE YATE PATTERNS, AND MUCH ELSE

Note: The original involved the act in which I wrote in ink on standard 3" x 5" index cards that came from the factory each with a blank side and a side with the print of a series of parallel lines.

The images here are proportional to scale but of a different size. Also, the scanning process introduced a few lining and shadowing effects.

THE PLACEHOLDERS FOR CATEGORIES:

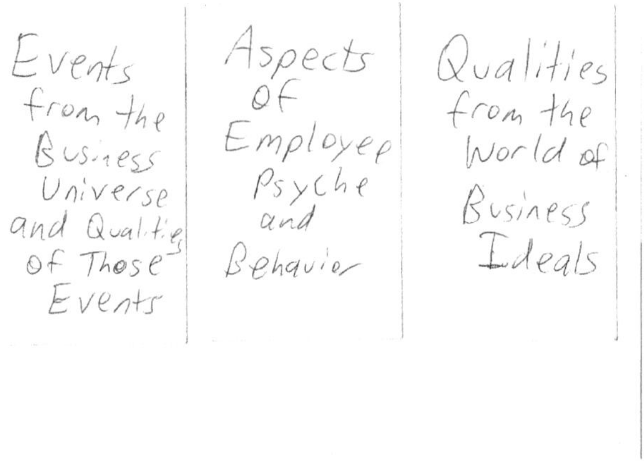

Events from the Business Universe and Qualities of Those Events
Aspects of Employee Psyche and Behavior
Qualities from the World of Business Ideals

# PAGE TWO OF LAYOUTS OF THE "PATTERNS MODELING BUSINESS" DECK

Note: The category "Events from the Business Universe and Qualities of Those Events" had two subcategories:

1. Events from the Business Universe
2. Qualities of Events from the Business Universe

PAGE 3 OF LAYOUTS OF THE "PATTERNS MODELING BUSINESS" DECK

# PAGE 4 OF LAYOUTS OF THE "PATTERNS MODELING BUSINESS" DECK

Honesty/ Integrity
Professional Profile
Qualities from the World of Business Ideals


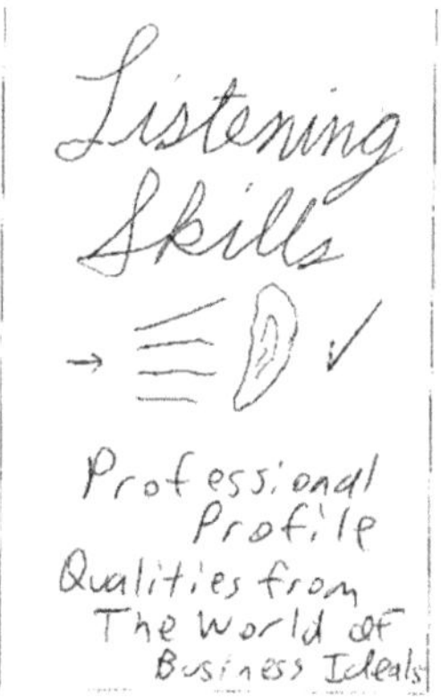

Listening Skills
Professional Profile
Qualities from The World of Business Ideals


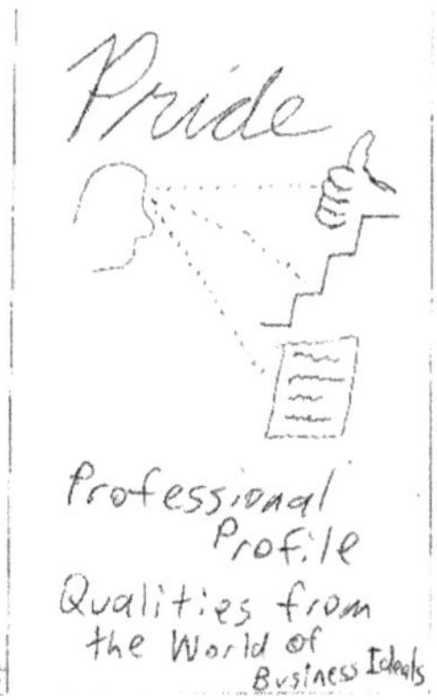

Pride
Professional Profile
Qualities from the World of Business Ideals


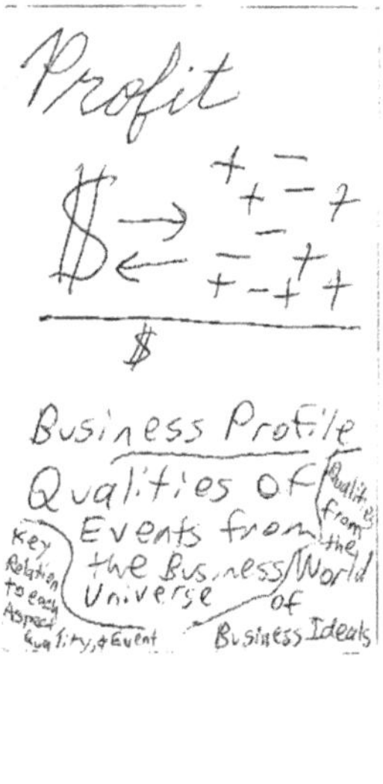

# PAGE 5 OF LAYOUTS OF THE "PATTERNS MODELING BUSINESS" DECK

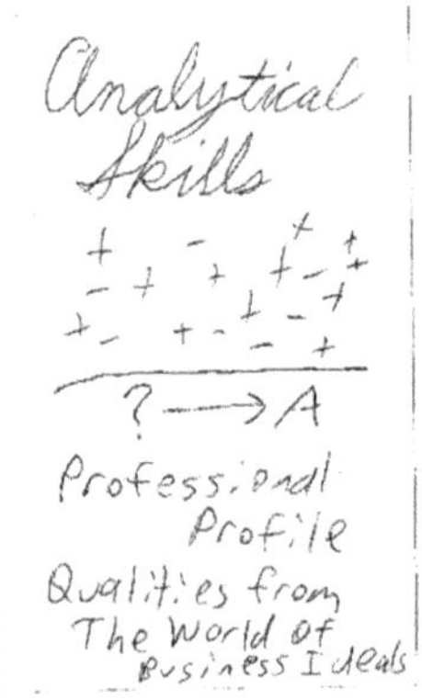

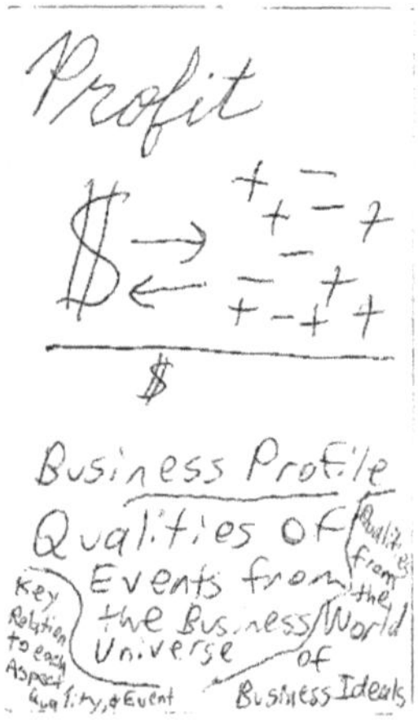

# PAGE 6 OF LAYOUTS OF THE "PATTERNS MODELING BUSINESS" DECK

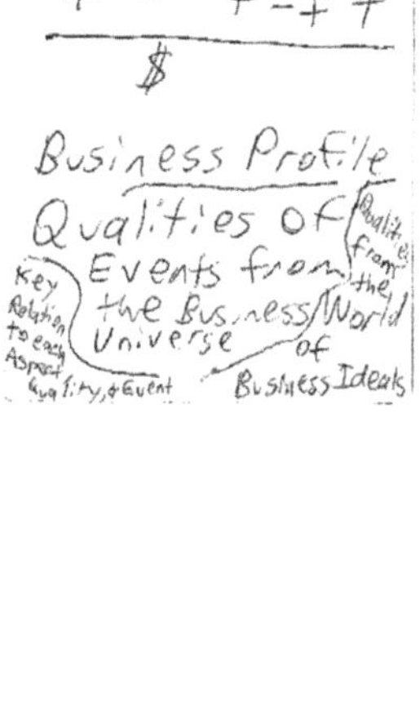

PAGE 7 OF LAYOUTS OF THE "PATTERNS MODELING BUSINESS" DECK

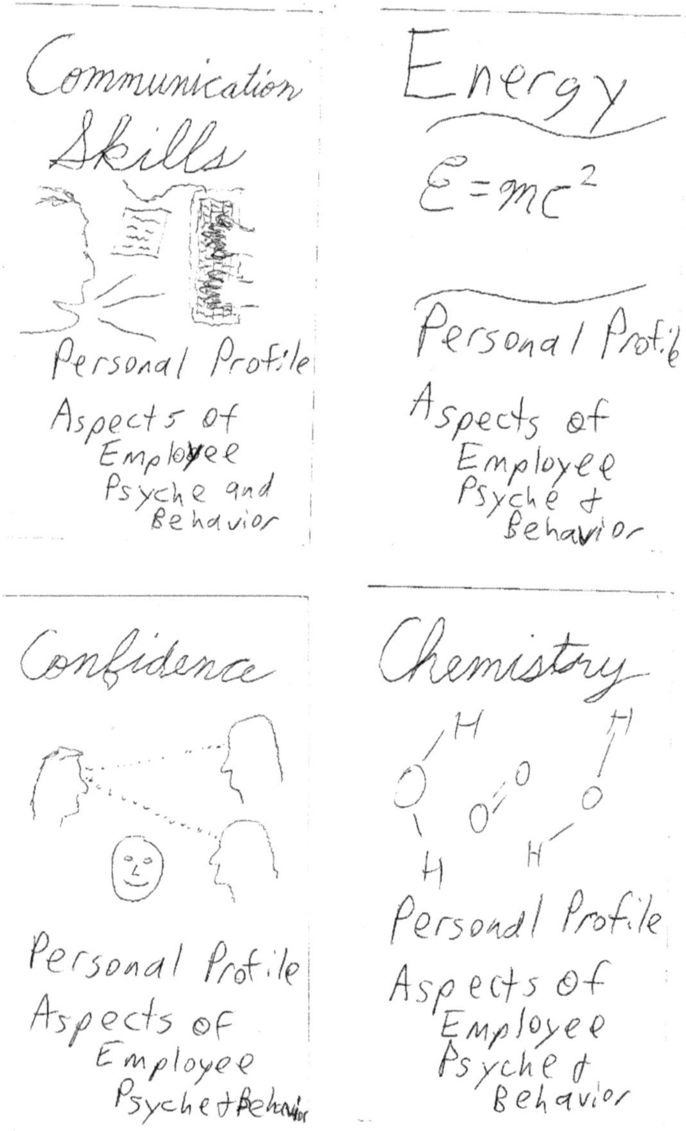

PAGE 8 OF LAYOUTS OF THE "PATTERNS MODELING BUSINESS" DECK

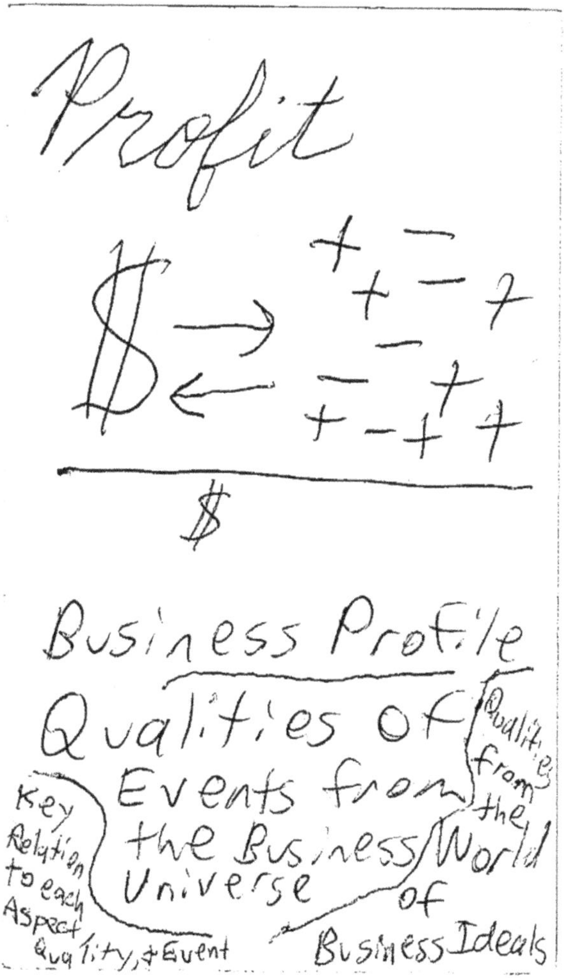

# PAGE 9 OF LAYOUTS OF THE "PATTERNS MODELING BUSINESS" DECK

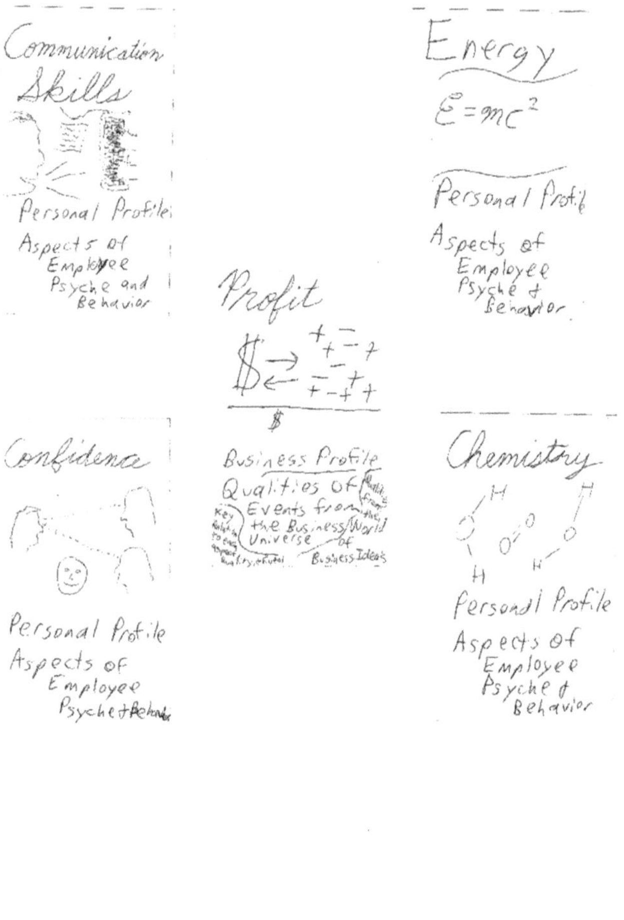

# PAGE 10 OF LAYOUTS OF THE "PATTERNS MODELING BUSINESS" DECK

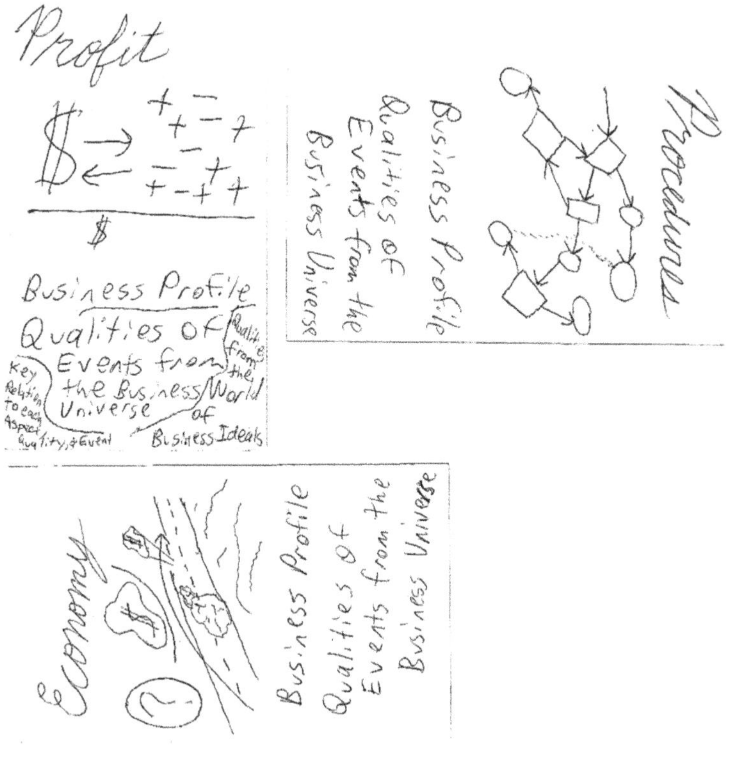

# PAGE 11 OF LAYOUTS OF THE "PATTERNS MODELING BUSINESS" DECK

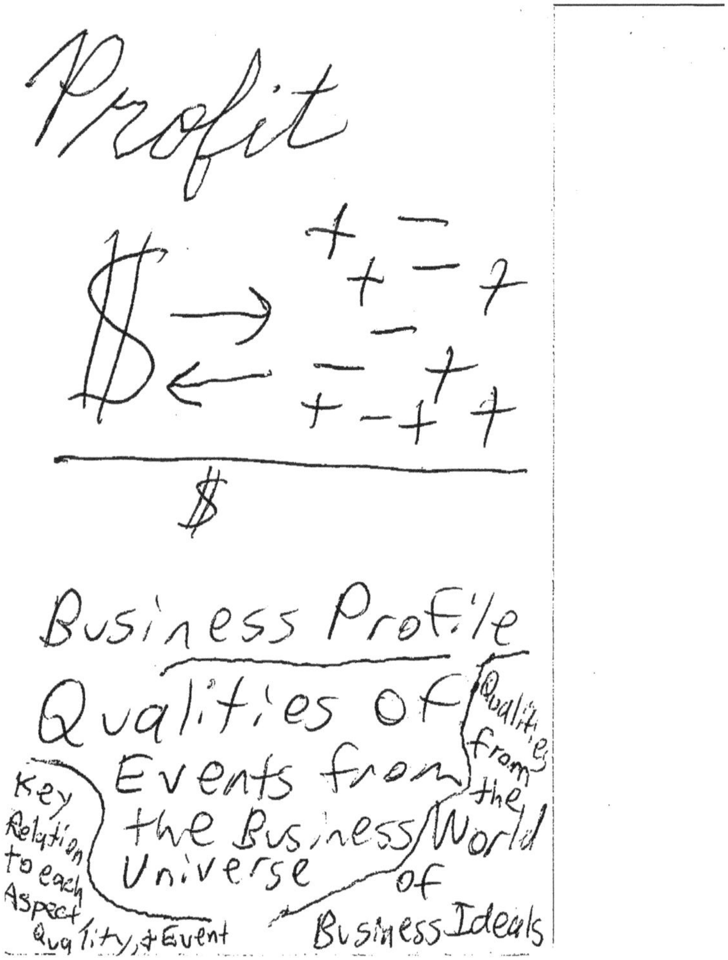

# PAGE 12 OF LAYOUTS OF THE "PATTERNS MODELING BUSINESS" DECK

Additional photography & artwork:

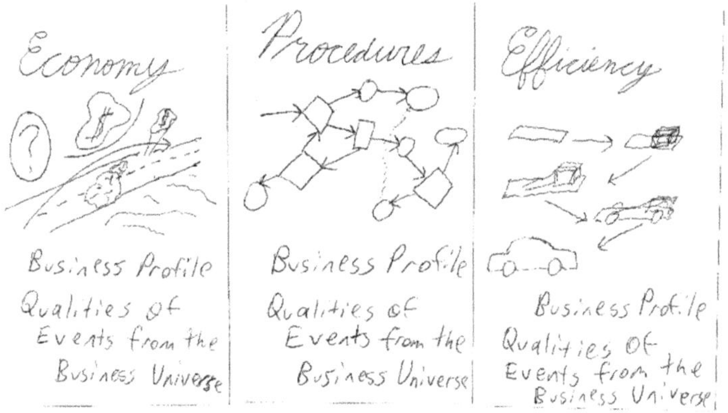
Economy
Procedures
Efficiency
Business Profile
Qualities of
Events from the
Business Universe
Business Profile
Qualities of
Events from the
Business Universe
Business Profile
Qualities Of
Events from the
Business Universe

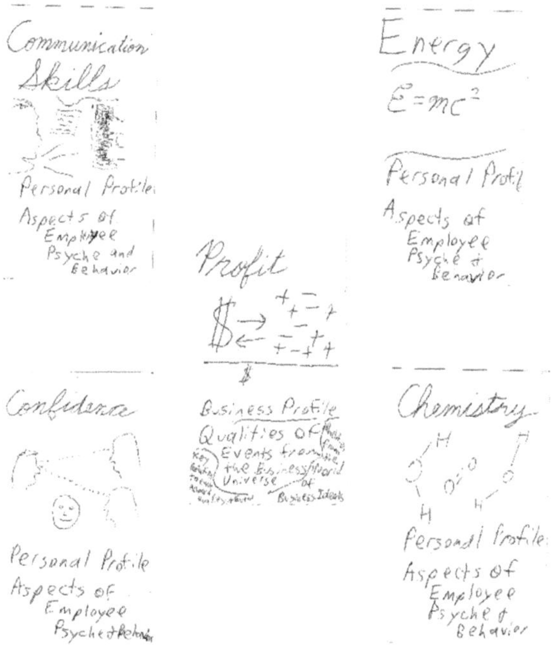
Communication Skills
Personal Profile
Aspects of Employee Psyche and Behavior
Energy
E=mc²
Personal Profil
Aspects of Employee Psyche & Behavior
Profit
Business Profile
Qualities of Events from the Business World Universe of Business Ideals
Confidence
Personal Profile
Aspects of Employee Psyche & Behavior
Chemistry
H
H
O
H
H
Personal Profile
Aspects of Employee Psyche & Behavior

Communication Skills
Personal Profile
Energy
E=mc²
Confidence
Chemistry

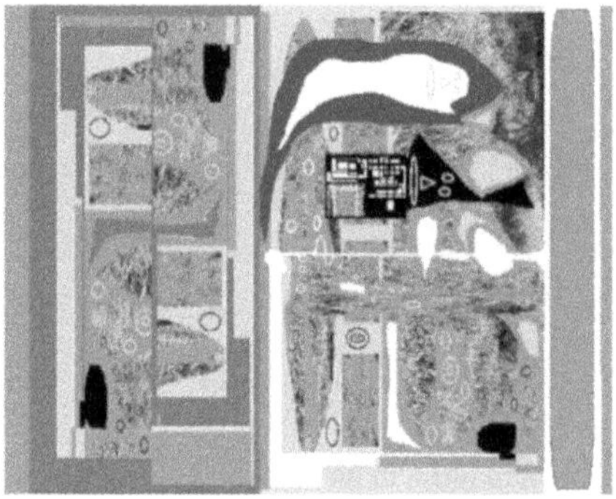

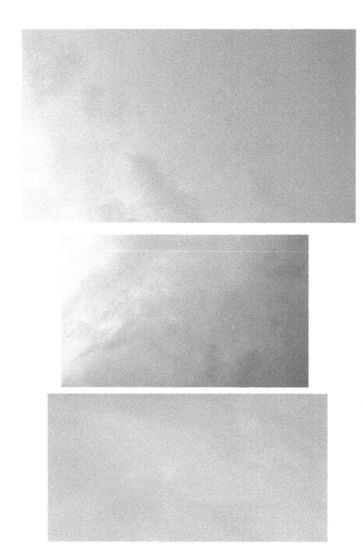

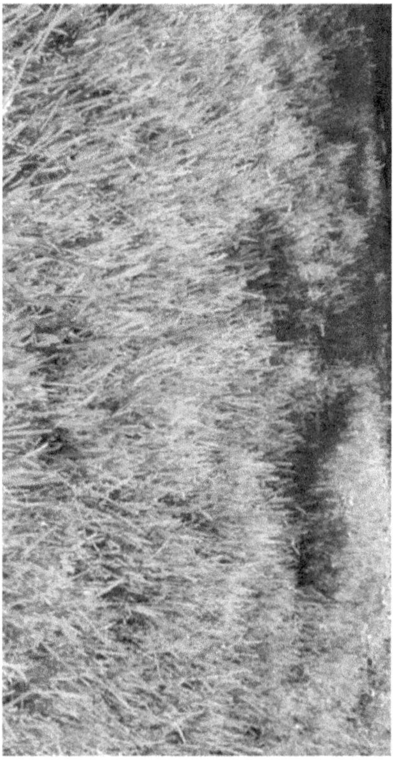

It sure seems that the LinkedIn server(s) sometimes use a time zone East of the U.S. Eastern Time Zone or else there is something else going on to explain that tidbit. --M.J.B.

On a related note, although the nonprofit/educational LinkedIn article "The Forking Paths of the FDIC and the Dodd-Frank Act in Light of Contrasting Comments from Experts" showed on itself, based on whatever the LinkedIn server was doing, as having been published on May 19, 2023 was actually published on May 18, 2023 after 8:35 P.M. CDT but long before 11 P.M. CDT.

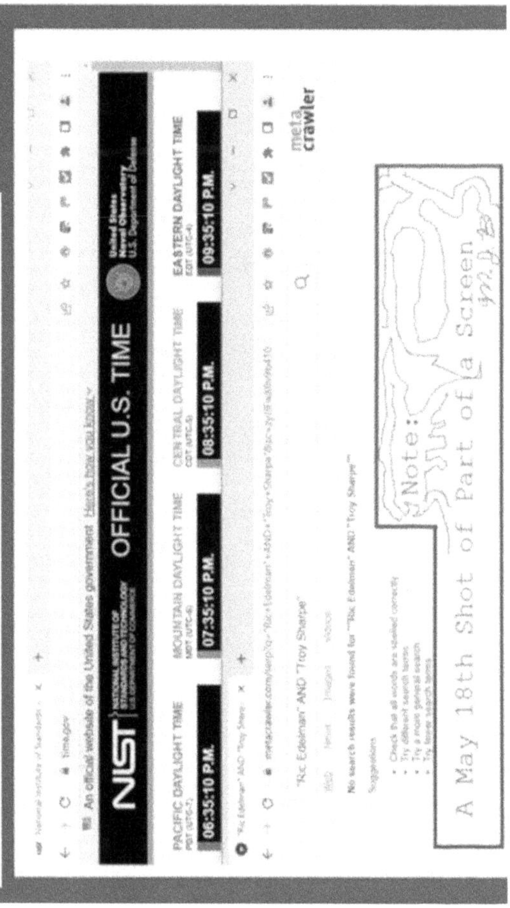


Note: A May 18th Shot of Part of a Screen M.J.B.

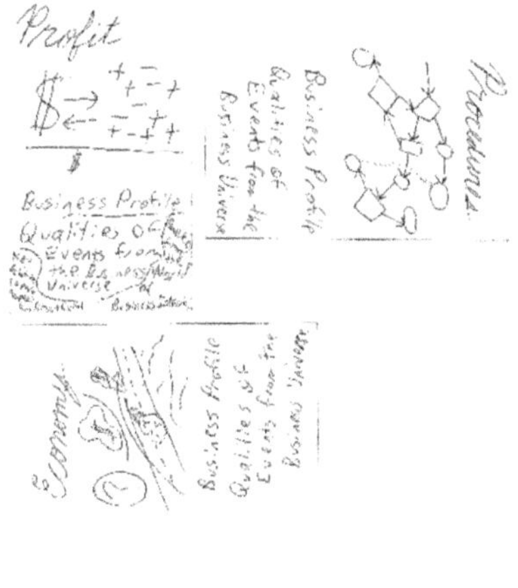
Profit
Business Profile
Qualities of
Events from the
Business Universe
Procedures
Economy

3/23/2021
"execution by tiger in ancient India" - Google Search
"execution by tiger in ancient India"
All
Images
Videos
News
Shopping
More
Settings
Tools
About 0 results (0.34 seconds)
Related searches
types of tigers

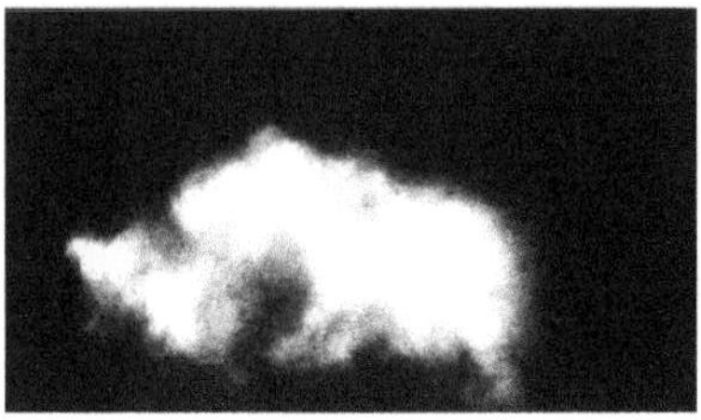

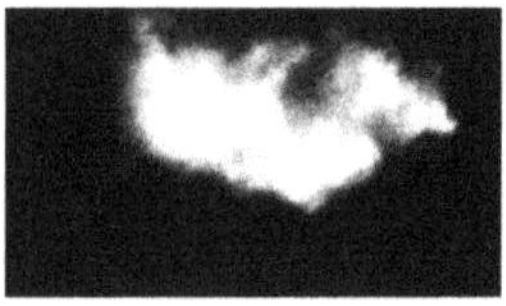

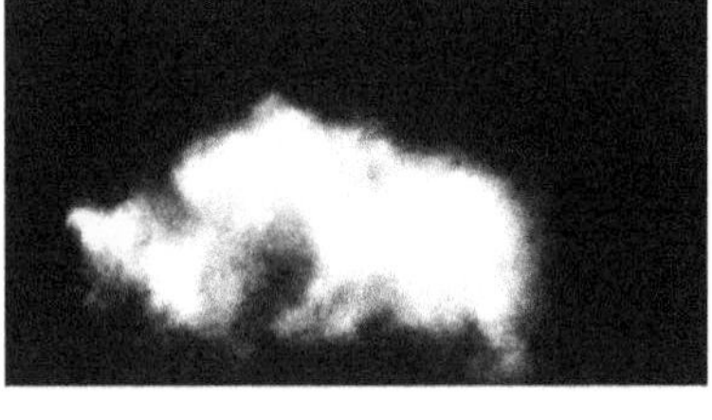

## SECTION SIX

In terms of collateral harm, perhaps the worst thing that anyone ever did to my family—and, by chain reaction, to affected business owners and other business associates of places where I worked in the period from about three-fourths the way into the month of September 2015 through partway into the evening of September 4, 2022—was how some men robbed my family of many possessions and much peace of mind on September 22, 2015. That was while I was at work that day and my mother was at our residence of that time. Although I described that briefly in part of Chapter Nine, let us delve into this from different angles.

I wonder sometimes if the post-September 22, 2015 conflicts that happened between me and some of the people I worked with, including but not limited to John T. Jones, Bill Walker, Natasha McDaniel, Juan Martinez, Steve Estrin, Michael Leng, and Mary Chiang, might not have happened at all had it not been for the occurrence of that brutal robbery. Same goes for romantic conflicts.

Bill Walker and I had a brief, sharp conversation on or about September 23, 2015 about it. He asked me something like, "Do you think about retaliating against the perpetrators if you could find out who they were?"

I answered with something almost identical to, "No. I believe that reality in the long run can take care of that all by itself. Sure, if I get a chance through the court system to help them face justice here and now in this life, then great, that could help, but, *with or without that, in the long run everyone has to face consequences for all actions.*"

Although I expressed that sentiment then and expressed it again in different contexts repeatedly much later, I believe that sometimes we *do* need to actively help bring harsh consequences to those who harm us and our loved ones. Another example of expressing that sentiment was when, in an e-mail I sent on August 5, 2019 directly to then-coworker Natasha McDaniel and cc'd to then-supervisors Juan Martinez and Chris Kolenda, I included the following statement, "Also, I have full faith that whether here or in the beyond, all actions, speech, thoughts, and everything else by everyone everywhere will have fair resolution in the long run, whether any given element takes one month, two hundred years, two billion years, or another length of time."

In some ways we should love everyone, in other ways we should love no one, and in yet other ways still we should utterly transcend the very concepts of loving anyone or not loving anyone. The reality of spiritually mature effectiveness transcends the different concepts of what constitutes love, nonlove, harshness, kindness, comfort, discomfort, spirit, and maturity. (Cf. the totality of all verses of any kind anywhere that point toward awareness that goes beyond.)

As a reminder, here we are considering whether and to what degree to cast a huge amount of blame on the people who robbed my family on 9/22/2015. Indeed, had they simply chosen to refrain from robbing my family, maybe fate would not have led to my ever working for The Financial Advisory Group, which might have been better for many people and organizations, including but not limited to The Financial Advisory Group, True Buddha School, The R.O.C., The P.R.O.C., The Democratic Party, The Republican Party, Holocaust Museum Houston, International Campaign for Tibet, my mother, my cousins, The U.S.A., Juan Martinez, President Donald Trump, President Joe Biden, Russia, Natasha McDaniel, The Ukraine, Steve Estrin, Israel, Amin Nosrat, Iran, the robbers themselves, and me. We could also look at this from all sorts of different angles, after a while growing agnostic as to whether to claim better and/or worse with respect to almost anything almost anyone has done from the beginning of time up until now, regarding the well-being of sentient beings in the context of the entirety of all reality known and unknown. *Think again about those robbers: were they mainly after money, information, artifacts, rare jewelry, documents, rare books, an attempt to intimidate, or something else?*

Nevertheless, their violation of much of my entire family's well-being through their robbery may well have set the spear of destiny or the many spears of trajectories or whatever into a direction conducive toward many repeated instances of subsequent conflicts between my family and people outside of my family and subsequent internal conflicts between different members of my family. Sometimes cruelty begets cruelty, whether directly or obliquely, over and over again, until someone does enough to overcome its repetitive traumatic tendencies.

To reiterate a few details and supplement them, contemplate how, to the best of my mother's combination of short-term and long-term memory, that incident involved several striking details: 1) Those robbers were a group of multiple Hispanic men and multiple Black men, speaking in what seemed a peculiar foreign manner. 2) Based on discussions between her and me, I sometimes perceive a major chance that they had connections with Northern-to-Western portions of Africa and some Western portions of Continental Europe. 3) They wore long white gloves, portions of which went significantly up the way on their forearms.

Thank goodness that those criminals avoided sexually assaulting her in any way, but, goodness gracious, to think of what she must have gone through, being tied up and blindfolded and told that if she would make much movement, then they would immediately kill her! It was one of the most hellacious ordeals that anyone in my family has ever experienced!

Maybe none of the other people referenced in this book might have been nearly as responsible for the at-times intense conflicts from Halloween 2016 to Earth Day 2024 that happened between any of the beings anywhere on Earth. Sometimes when thinking of those wretched robbers who threatened to kill my mother if she would move much at all, tied her up, repeatedly threatened her, ransacked my family's home of that time, and have probably harmed many other people in many ways, I can think of those robbers and whoever their accomplices might have been as who to vote for as the single most expendable organization on Earth, if they are still around as an organization. That includes if it turned out to be a clandestine part of the U.S. government. This is not sedition; if some clandestine part of one's nation-state's government does something unethical and horrific to one's family, and one feels that all sentient beings would best be served by that clandestine part dissolving into extinction, then that is one of the ways of cheering for one's nation state to become a more perfect nation state.

I do not know whether their organization—i.e., whichever organization was behind the robbery—is still around or if karma might have already obliterated it. If it is still around, then I am at peace with if reality obliterates it at any time and by any means. Its destruction is plausibly helpful with the enlightenment of sentient beings, much like the defeat and subjugation of Matam Rudra in some Himalayan legends.

When considering the obliteration of organizations, this is not necessarily involving the deaths of any specific individuals. I know full well from: 1) having signed in April 2001 a contract to start working on a full-time/regular basis for Arthur Andersen LLP starting in September 2002, 2) witnessing the news about Enron collapsing while on its way to later getting obliterated, 3) subsequently getting an update that Arthur Andersen LLP planned to accelerate my start date for the full-time/regular work in its International Tax Department in what was then its Houston office, 4) witnessing that Andersen become more thoroughly devastated, and 5) finally receiving word that there would not be a new full-time/regular position at that firm for me, or much of anyone else, for that matter, in the foreseeable future, as Arthur Andersen LLP became almost wiped off the face of the Earth, fading into a ghost of its former self. None of that obliteration of Enron and none of that near-obliteration of Arthur Andersen entailed necessitating anyone to directly die as a consequence of that, though it was a factor in accelerating some people's deaths compared to when they might have otherwise occurred. Perhaps the total demise of Enron and the devastation of Andersen has been a factor in the mysterious extra conflicts I have had with people in some of the recent years, whether through a lingering effect on my thoughts and behaviors, a lingering effect on the thoughts and behaviors of others, or some "spirit moving in mysterious ways" type of influence on situations.

Returning attention now to the robbers who were the main subject under consideration before that segue into Arthur Andersen-related stuff, there are more angles that people could explore. Think again about what the robbers' motives might have been, and think again about how they conducted that robbery.

Although I did not witness them doing that robbery, due to having been busy with part of a work day in the John T. Jones & Co. office when those robbers struck, my mother described the attack to many relevant people, including members of law enforcement, family members, and a number of relevant insurance professionals.

As far as I know, the Houston Police Department never seemed to get much of anywhere in terms of obtaining new leads on who the hell perpetrated that heinous act. That sometimes makes me wonder whether a) they considered my family too low of a priority to thoroughly take actions against those who harm it, b) the situation simply left things difficult to trace, or c) some U.S. shadow government types operating outside of the laws of the United States might have actually conducted the attack as part of some secret agenda and done that in such a way as to both intimidate HPD into not following up on it and to make it extremely difficult for HPD to obtain much in the way of any tangible leads, etc. That option (c) would seem not very likely at all, though I feel like I cannot consider it entirely outside the realm of possibility, from where I stand. Consider how from my perspective it could seem maybe one chance in a million, one chance in a billion, or another such astronomically remote possibility, maybe even less than one chance in a septillion, whereas from the perspective of the robbers it would probably boil down into either a definite yes or a definite no. For that matter, do we even really have "a shadow government" at all? Some believe it definitely exists. Others believe it definitely does not exist. Also, this would is a case in which many different people disagree with each other about exactly what would constitute a proper definition of "a shadow government." The fact that I could place the Federal Election Commission on the "to" line of an e-mail message that included a Securities and Exchange Commission commissioner on the "cc" line together with many members of the news media also on the "cc" line, while, in contrast, the person I trusted the most among all the recipients was a federal government employee whom I had concealed on the bcc line would cause some people to claim that I acted as somehow being "a member of the shadow government" by engaging in such behavior. However, that is a rather preposterous way of looking at this. If people were to go down that line of thinking, then they might eventually arrive at acting like the woman I observed get a hold of a microphone one day early in the 2010s at a large gathering.

I have only attended a Houston City Council public meeting—in which almost anyone from the general public can attend and, if given the turn to speak, then present something. At that event, from approximately thirteen years before the first publication of this book, things mostly seemed normal except for two very memorable unusual things. One was that they had an exceedingly bright light aimed at the audience, and I kept having to look significantly away from that light and take other steps to try to protect my eyes. The other was that eventually some woman I have probably seen or heard anywhere else suddenly received the microphone and started to spew out a whole bunch of conspiratorial statements, mostly alleging government people of targeting her with many different kinds of surveillance repeatedly. She seemed really over-the-top when she actually alleged people of sometimes following her around with helicopters. I admit that when I finally got around to watching the movie *Goodfellas* (1990) in approximately the February-to-April 2022 period, and a scene in which people in a helicopter *do in fact follow someone around* unfolded on the screen, I thought to myself something like, *That lady back at that city council meeting, who seemed quite bonkers probably was bonkers in many ways, and it seems preposterous that investigators were following her around quite a bit and including at least one helicopter in the process. However, sometimes it really is the case that someone is following some-*

*one else around, at least for a little while, with a helicopter.*

---

## Section Six Part B: An Intermediate Segue That May Help With Understanding Autobiographical and Biographical Extremities

On another note, I think that both Michael Berry and much of his audience did not understand very well what I was getting at with stating that I had believed myself likely to have been targeted in an Alinsky style in the way that Natasha McDaniel, Steve Estrin, Juan Martinez, and Bill Walker had acted toward me. It even seems possible to me that at least 25% of readers who might have read every line of this book up to this juncture might still not understand that very thoroughly at all.

Although I am endeavoring to continue to cast much more thorough blame on the 9/22/2015 robbers plus Saul Alinsky and Paul Churchland, let us let go of them for a little while and focus on getting to a very primary way of understanding why I believe myself to have every right to condemn portions of the behavior exhibited by The Financial Advisory Group, Inc. and Gray Reed & McGraw.

Although I have not witnessed it yet, I heard in approximately 1998 about the existence of a science fiction television episode in which people from a more normal society encounter people on a world where there is a very peculiar criminal justice situation. Specifically, something along the lines of how there was some area considered off-limits, and most of the time, if someone were to trespass there, then the person would not receive any punishment for having done that; however, on some rare occasions, a person would be caught with trespassing there and then be sentenced to death. Sounds rather extreme, doesn't it?!

Well, sometime around the first half of April 2024 I found out from Justin Haynes the probable identity of that very episode: Episode Seven of Season One of *Star Trek: The Next Generation.* Although I have watched some episodes and movies involving The Star Trek Franchise, I have often been somewhat lukewarm toward it, with more attention directed elsewhere, for example religion itself, science itself, *Twilight Zone* stuff, Stanley Kubrick movies, and news. I respect much of what Gene Roddenberry and other people have done with *Star Trek* stuff, but, as with most people aside from Trekkies, I have witnessed only a tiny fraction of the voluminous amount of Star Trek Franchise audiovisual offerings. I do plan to watch that episode between the time of when Synapsid Revelations Press Corporation publishes *Alternative Beginnings and Endings of All Things: Science, Religion, Politics, and Cards, Hypervolume II* and the time of when that same publisher publishes *The Dimetrodons, the Dorians, and the Modern World, Synapsid Critical Edition.*

Early in my life I had a mixture of strengths and weaknesses that led to how, during much of high school, despite outward signs of much academic accomplishment and some athletic accomplishment, I often noticed close correspondence between TV portrayals of nerds and the way that I actually was back then. Eventually, with the help of some of my father's guidance, the help of watching some episodes of *Kung Fu* (1972-1975), the help of watching some episodes of *Kung Fu: The Legend Continues* (1993-1997), and other sources, I was able to adapt enough to being further away from matching the stereotypical nerd, though some changes came at quite a price of curbed enthusiasm toward sex, romance, money, and power. Later, as already described in this book and, from different angles in *Science, Religion, Politics, and Cards*, the April 19, 2001 interview with Amin Nosrat led to a chain reaction in which I radically transformed my life.

On a related note, the Facebook friend who uses the alias "Radically Transformed" is in fact the very woman mentioned in *Science, Religion, Politics, and Cards* as having the name Crystal Brown.

Back now to discussion of how people might come closer to understanding what I presented to the public via calling into *The Michael Berry Show* on August 6, 2021, and some adjacencies.

Many times I had presumed that I would not have to arrive at explaining a bunch of what is next and much of what arrives later in this book, thinking that people would relate well enough to me such as to welcome me with a more consistent benevolence, openness, acceptance, and acknowledgment, but, for better or for worse, that has not turned out to be the case. Therefore, my publisher and I present incendiary facts and truths with much of the remainders. Some might characterize this, metaphorically, as thermonuclear explosions that leave much $^{60}Co$ and $^{90}Sr$ to linger in the atmosphere. Things have happened such that, although many details will almost definitely make some readers cringe, it is seemingly the only way to have a great chance for the percentage of readers who get it to rise to over 85% within the first two years after achieving at least one complete reading.

Before I had even become an adult or anything close to it, there were many times that I treasured accomplishment and the prestige that would go together with accomplishment as the most valuable things in life. Some of that stemmed from a time early in elementary school when, after noticing people honor the most revered of heroes in various fields, I briefly fantasized one day about the idea of what it might be like to be a decorated military general, with lots of medals, lots of praise from society, and plenty of real accomplishments. Also, I often excelled in academia, and on some occasions excelled in some athletic competitions.

Although I do not remember exactly when the next phase happened, I do remember it to have happened in El Paso, at least a few years before the 1994 move from El Paso to Charlotte. It seems to me most likely to have been in the 1985-1990 range, though it might have been slightly earlier or later. What happened was that I entered the realm of mind in which thoughts travel to the idea that could be expressed, *We have to take up such a large amount of time and energy on bodily functions like eating food, defecating feces, drinking water and other beverages, urinating, breathing in air, breathing out our exhaust air, falling asleep, sleeping, and waking up; wouldn't we be able to accomplish so much more if we were simply unencumbered by all those bodily functions! We could use our minds and our energies to accomplish stuff all the time, without having to stop to eat, stop to drink, stop to urinate, stop to defecate, stop to sleep, and we wouldn't have all the breathing in and breathing out to be a drag on putting our full minds and energies to the best possible use of performing useful accomplishments! Especially, to do many of the grandest accomplishments, stuff like advancing science and technology!! Also, stuff like competing in the most praiseworthy of competitions!! Wouldn't it be nice if God or Whatever the Highest Power or Powers That Be Might Be could simply liberate us from having to have these bodies and bodily functions that are such a drag on our ability to accomplish all those truly worthwhile things that go beyond the bodily functions themselves!! Wouldn't that be something!!!*

In contrast, though, I did enjoy the experience of sensory pleasure, and upon leaving that pattern of consciousness treasuring detachment from all sensory pleasures, often I did rejoin the very high percentage of humans at a given time who value the experience of sensory pleasure. *However, I have found myself in many different situations and periods able to return to that detachment from valuing crude sensory pleasures and with that embrace of sublimating intentions in order to aim for something considered more amazing.*

Many times many of my attitudes in those areas shifted, sometimes many times a day. When the Arthur Andersen internship exit interview happened, though, it involved the detonation of a critical mass of ready-for-chain-reaction stuff in just such a way as to cause an extinction event of much of the core essence of having any commitment at all to the value of sensory pleasure for its own sake. Things changed such that I wind up consistently, to whatever degree it might be with a Christian basis, a Noahidist basis, a People-of-the-Book-ist basis, a Buddhist basis, or anything else, or any combination of bases, regarding all present and future interest in sensory pleasure as only earning rights to existence and being when its instances can agree with whatever THE MOST PROFOUND REALITY (read: DIVINITY, ENLIGHTENMENT, GOD, THE

TRUTH, BUDDHA, SALVATION, CONSCIENCE, ETC.) might be. Therefore, (although I sometimes in some ways have probably, from most ways of conceptualizing things, continued to fall short of "The Glory of The Absolute Reality, to Whichever Degree or Degrees That It Manifests as the Enlightenment, Divinity, Salvation or Whatever of Any Way That Correctly Relates to That Absolute Reality, Including Any and All Relativities and Any and All Absolutes and Whatever Else,") at a core level I wind up always aiming for absolute perfection. The various pressures can still be difficult to manage, coordinate, and prioritize at times, but the extinction of anything other than linking all experiences of sensory pleasure to a best attempt at plausible compatibility with proper relation to the ultimate reality has been at the core of my life.

Once in a while I might hear on television and in regular life people bringing up the question, "What is it about you that most completely sets you apart from other people?" Although no one seems to ever bother to ask that question of me lately, in the vast majority of social contexts the best answer I should say aloud would probably be, "That is on a need-to-know basis, and you don't need to know it at this time. If someday a situation happens such that you wind up needing to know that, then maybe you will wind up knowing it then. However, as of this time, I do not believe you to need to know it, and therefore I am refusing to answer that question." The reason why that is probably the best answer in a high percentage of cases involving me is mainly twofold: 1) I believe it best for me to honor an extremely strong duty to maintain an extremely high degree of purity of speech (To explain this reference to "purity of speech," this means to speak accurately to the best of ability when appropriate, and, when not appropriate to speak accurately, to work hard to shut up (i.e., to perform enough omissions such as to avoid contaminating speech with inaccuracies, no matter how many people die as a result of that commitment to purity of speech), because the avoidance of the deaths of people is something I tend to perceive as much less important than the maintenance of an extraordinarily high degree of purity of speech. Insufficient purity of speech can easily sow horrors much worse than physical death. That is largely in connection with how past experiences provide ample evidence that failure to maintain a high degree of purity of speech in my unique situation would have a terrible prospect for what would likely happen as the consequences. Consider this in relation to how it is that many bizarre experiences in my life from 2000 onward probably easily fit into the category of the paranormal, as well as unusual health challenges that I have faced and overcome. I believe it most likely that a failure to maintain pure enough speech would almost undoubtedly result in new rounds of the most hostile versions of paranormal experiences coming back around again, possibly to an even greater extent than ever before. Of course, new rounds of off-the-charts strange experiences in the absence of my doing or saying anything wrong seem probable anyway, yet refraining from provoking unnecessary extra difficulty would seem usually the superior option. Also, it is because I consider purity of speech generally most conducive to helping with the enlightenment of sentient beings, plus other worthy causes that spiritual and religious people aspire to help others with (e.g., what some may call salvation, conscience, justice, equity, honor, goodness, and duty). Also, I admit that different people are on different lifepaths and at different stages of their lives, and, therefore, one person's proper level of purity of speech might differ substantially from another person's proper level of purity of speech. 2) As mentioned earlier, Amin Nosrat's 4/19/2001 criticism of how I had not been acting in as much of a conformist way in the 2/20/2001-4/18/2001 period as needed for Arthur Andersen LLP professional effectiveness, together with all the other factors at that time, led to an extinction event for both intentional orgasm and intentional ejaculation, unless and until I might eventually have a seemingly perfect reason for bringing back intentional orgasm and intentional ejaculation. Reluctance to dare to bring this up in the vast majority of settings stems from several sources, including common sense, True Buddha School guidelines as translated into writing from the words of Grand Master Lu Sheng-yen himself, and observation of the most usual boundaries of interpersonal communication patterns.

*However, the fact that whoever, if anyone, may read this set of passages has actually arrived here is a great indication that such a reader or such readers do actually need to know.*

Here it is, the most direct, intuitive, honest, and simple answer to the question, "What is it about you that most completely sets you apart from other people?" would, in my case as of when composing this book, and as has also been the case for many years, if considered in a voir dire or similar serious setting requiring straightforward clarity, best take the form of the following or something extremely similar: "Although there could be many candidates for what would most set me apart from most other people in general, the one thing that seems most obvious to me as what would generally be most relevant to most of those with a need to know is, in fact, something that would normally be totally taboo to bring up in a public conversation. That thing that seems most obvious as an answer to that question is the fact that after my last-day-of-the-internship interview with Amin Nosrat at Penzoil Place in connection with work for Arthur Andersen, on April 19, 2001, I felt so totally knocked down by life, including how I thought my interpersonal skills had improved so much, and then I'd found out that whatever improvements I'd made didn't count for much of anything as far as Andersen was concerned, with this as a primary driver for the evaluation that I was barely passable to be offered to join them full-time regular. Although I signed a contract to begin a regular position with them, scheduled for September 2002, the way I felt so knocked down by life, with little self-esteem left after that end-of-internship, 4/19/2001 interview, it caused me to join the few who via sexual austerity divorce themselves from the vast majority of the human race, setting themselves apart by choosing extreme restrictions. More specifically, as I felt so knocked down by life and so disappointed about how my interpersonal performance at the time had not been very good, even though I thought I'd made great improvements from early 2000 to early 2001, I lost all interest in physical sensory pleasures in general for a while, and I completely ceased and desisted to experience intentional orgasm and intentional ejaculation. By the way, I mentioned those two separately, even though they are most often concomitant for male reproductive systems, because I later learned of legends of male tantric practitioners sometimes actually experiencing orgasms unaccompanied by ejaculation, and, indeed, sure enough, when taking a Yoga class at what was then the Tanglewilde location of DEFINE Body & Mind (located on San Felipe in Houston; note: that yoga studio location later changed its franchise identification/name), while performing yoga poses and movements in a state of mixing spiritual love, romantic love, and erotic arousal, including having and maintaining a raging erection, I suddenly experienced what would probably best be described as a total body orgasm, and that did not result in any ejaculation happening at the time. (By the way, I did not utter any audible sounds of the types sometimes associated with orgasms, as that would not have fit proper decorum, but I did feel the extraordinary euphoria of well-being often associated with orgasm, and, not only in my erection but, as already mentioned, throughout the entire body, truly loving experiential confirmation that the legends of that are true at least on some rare occasions).

Now you are probably ready to study a mixture of comparison and contrast between the August 23, 2019 EEOC Memo that I composed and the August 23-24, 2019 EEOC Memo that I composed, together with updated commentaries. The format builds on a serialized approach to the 8/23/2019-8/24/2019 text, presenting excerpts of the 8/23/2019 memo at strategic spots between select passages. It also provides supplemental commentary at strategic spots between some of the passages.

A THREE-SIDED AND MANY-SIDED ANALYSIS REGARDING AUGUST 2019, APRIL 2024, MAY 2024, AND ADDITIONAL RELEVANT RANGES

CONTENTS:

3. Additional Commentary

Acronyms:

23-24AUG2019M: The main memo on which this 3-sided-&-Many-sided analysis builds; its full title is, "An August 2019 Memorandum, Concerning The Equal Employment Opportunity Commission and a Related Matter." Beneath the title, it states, "by Maurice James Blair (of Houston, TX)." After that, it displays, "Composed August 23rd-24th, 2019." The original was organized into 12 letter-sized pages, whereas the copy here is organized by serialization into segments.

23AU19M: The original version of the memo, before I adjusted it to have a more civil tone, a more modest approach to communication, and a sequence of presentation more conducive to most readers' ability to comprehend it. That version had the title, "An August 23rd, 2019 Memorandum, Concerning The Equal Employment Opportunity Commission and a Related Matter." After that, it states, "by Maurice James Blair (of Houston, TX)." The original was organized into 12 letter-sized pages, whereas only the most relevant excerpts appear here to supplement 23-24AUG2019M and provide extra springboards with which to jump into performing updated analysis.

TRNSCRS: Transcription Segment

*********************************************

[Start of 23-24AUG2019M TRNSCRS #1]

EXECUTIVE SUMMARY: When I engaged in communications on August 5th, 2019 with other personnel at The Financial Advisory Group regarding reasonable accommodation of my religious practices, they chose to reprimand me on that day and to terminate my employment on the following day, August 6th, 2019. This relates to how they had refused to take steps to carefully seek the truth and clear the air about how one of my coworkers was defaming my character in a manner that strikes at the core of some of my religious practices.

[End of 23-24AUG2019M TRNSCRS #1]

COMMENTARY ON TRNSCRS #1: Prior to going to the EEOC I contacted several attorneys remotely (by e-mail, phone, etc.). Some declined immediately to get involved. One specific attorney offered to get involved, but in a way that I believed would not address what I believed to be the most fundamental aspects of the breakdown in the behaviors by that former employer in relationship with me.

[Start of 23-24AUG2019M TRNSCRS #2]

INTERMEDIATE SUPPLEMENT: There were two related conflicts that were hostile to my practice of religion. One involved defamation of character, the other involved an unjustified threat.

There is strong evidence that one of the main reasons for my recent termination was the employer's mishandling of slanderous statements from a coworker, which at some stage crossed over into libel. Some of the slander was negative enough to meet the legal definition of slander per se. It also contributed to a work environment at times hostile to my well-being, especially to my religious practices of Vajrayana Buddhism, Esoteric Christianity, Zen Buddhism, and other things.

[End of 23-24AUG2019M TRNSCRS #2]

COMMENTARY ON TRNSCRS #2: The intermediate supplement became split into TRNSCRS #2 and TRNSCRS #3. Although one of the coworkers communicated in a way that amounted to slander and libel toward me, including slander per se and libel with major ambiguity, in the main ways that I intuitively relate the facts that I know about to the legal standards, it is clear that what I know about it has some openness to legal gray areas of whether a person's methods of defaming another person's character have enough materiality to fully justify tangible monetary punishment as deemed by a civil court of law. That being said, I am virtually 100% certain that behind my back and hidden from me some terrible types of defamation of my character was committed, greatly exceeding what I directly witnessed.

[Start of 23-24AUG2019M TRNSCRS #3]

When I made a good faith effort on August 5th, 2019 to help the employer resolve the matter internally and eliminate the religious strain that it placed on me, the firm escalated conflict with me repeatedly. Finally, on August 6th, 2019, the firm terminated my employment. When I started to communicate an intention to sue the firm, they appeared surprised. However, I had intended for them to read between the lines previously that if they would choose that course of action, then I would intend to sue them.

I claim that they failed to reasonably accommodate my religious practices. This would mean that they were in noncompliance with the EEOC. However, I am uncertain about whether or not they engaged in other actions in noncompliance with the EEOC.

[End of 23-24AUG2019M TRNSCRS #3]

COMMENTARY ON TRNSCRS #3: As time went by after the composition of that memo, bringing it to the EEOC, filing a charge, obtaining a 90-day right to sue, etc., I eventually came to more fully understand how nebulous it often is regarding who interprets what to actually cross the line into constituting Title VII discrimination.

If I knew then what I know now, I probably would have never even bothered to apply to work for The Financial Advisory Group, Inc. However, if I am to be reasonably objective about the entire situation, then I could ascribe some blame to myself about how, prior to when I did the job search that resulted in working there, I believed it best to wait for maybe another year before doing that search. I had been content to work on a variable schedule for CMCD LLC, to train for and participate in USCF tournaments on the side, and to be involved with various other activities, declining to seek to upgrade career situation until a long while later. When a man named David Tai shared a conversation with me at a temple sometime around May 2018, though, that conversation prodded me into thinking more actively about the possibility of seeking to upgrade again on the employment situation. Sometimes I think back to that and recognize that, perhaps if I had used a more enlightened approach to Zen and everything else, then I might have decided to stick with putting off a next attempt to upgrade on a professional position a while longer. There are almost unlimited numbers of places in my life in which I could second-guess the choices if so choosing, but here it seems best to limit the second-guessing to what would be most constructive to helping the reader, whether or not the reader would happen to be any of the people directly mentioned in this book, any of the people who might work for Gray Reed, any of the people who might work for The Financial Advisory Group, any of the people who have ever heard me talk about some of this stuff on the August 6, 2021 morning edition of *The Michael Berry Show*, any of the people who have ever read *Science, Religion, Politics, and Cards*, etc.

[Start of 23-24AUG2019M TRNSCRS #4]

SELECT INTRODUCTORY ITEMS:

Background Item One: Around September 2018, Juan Martinez, my primary supervisor at that firm, expressed interest in receiving a pdf of the 2005 novel that I registered with the U.S. Copyright Office (yet for which I had declined to register an International Standardized Book Number). I am in some sense the anonymous author of that work, although in another sense I semi-anonymously coauthored that book with The Unknown. It presents the author name on its cover as Shunyata, yet the registration with the U.S. Copyright Office shows the author as Anonymous and the copyright claimant as myself. I provided this to Juan [which we agreed upon ahead of time would be from a personal e-mail address for me to a personal e-mail address for him (in order to keep the book away from the Securities and Exchange Commission-required complete e-mail archiving of The Financial Advisory Group e-mail server)] on November 11$^{th}$, 2018. Giving my supervisor a copy should have made it abundantly clear to him how central my involvement with religious practices of Vajrayana Buddhism, Esoteric Christianity, Zen Buddhism, and other things are to my life. Also, after coworker Jessica Zhang requested a copy of that book around March 2019, I sent her a pdf of the same book on April 20th, 2019, also via personal e-mail away from the FinGroup server. That gave additional ability for coworkers in general to be aware of these elements, supplementing relevant portions of conversations.

Background Item Two: A woman on a bus in Austin in 2001 expressed that she and other passengers were worried that my unusual eye movements might be part of an epileptic fit and they were wondering whether to call an ambulance. The portions of my eye relaxation techniques that involve various linear eye movements alternated with blinking 10-12 times were most likely what disturbed the other passengers.

[End of 23-24AUG2019M TRNSCRS #4]

COMMENTARY ON TRNSCRS #4: As expressed in *Science, Religion, Politics, and Cards* and elsewhere, there are multiple levels of how to conceive of reality as identifying me as the author of the referenced semi-anonymous novel and identifying me as part of a huge team that semi-anonymously wrote that book. In the long run, even though the regularly-observable level of reality would tend to be most conducive to attributing the anonymous authorship to me, it seems more of the primary energy of the situation points toward my teamwork with other beings via the mysteries of the beyond.

Here is an excerpt from *An Encyclopedic Survival Guide for Navigating Normal and Paranormal Experiences* (a collaborative work for which I contributed some portions and performed the composite editing), Encyclopedia Part Three: "A huge part of it involved attempting to create a work co-written by all or nearly all beings... to let the entirety of reality write a book about the entirety of reality."

Here is another excerpt from that: "Significant amounts were conducted on the premise of attempting to remote view across multiple actual universes and to then report the results as purportedly fictional..."

Finally, consider one more such excerpt: "... other sources/resources helpful with co-creating with THE UNKNOWN that mysterious, very channeling-oriented, ultra-collaborative project."

Something that the memo omitted was that the woman on the bus who complained about the eye-movement methods with which to reduce eye strain was that she said out loud on at least one occasion that she practiced Wicca.

[Start of 23-24AUG2019M TRNSCRS #5]

Background Item Three: When I had an internship at KPMG in January to April 2005, there was a rumor that intern Lyle Boudreaux, who had a degree from Tulane University, had been fired from

KPMG on February 21st, 2005 in connection with falling asleep while he was supposed to wait for a manager to speak with him. Whatever really happened behind the surface of the rumor, I remember quite clearly that the last time I ever met him was on February 21st, 2005, to the best of my knowledge. Portions of my eye relaxation techniques involving closing the eyes while rolling the eyes around clockwise 10-12 times and then counterclockwise 10-12 times, or vice-versa, could be open to misinterpretation by some observers to be evidence of being asleep.

[End of 23-24AUG2019M TRNSCRS #5]

COMMENTARY ON TRNSCRS #5: Notice that I omitted the Amy Garland angle on the KPMG and Lyle Boudreaux saga, as well as the Joel Goza angle on that saga.

[Start of 23-24AUG2019M TRNSCRS #6]

Background Item Four: My involvement with The United States Chess Federation (hereafter, "USCF") is closely tied to my religious practices. This is because I often consider my participation in tournaments a test of how well I am integrating the effectiveness of religious practices, cognition, martial arts, philosophy, science, the study and practice of the game of chess, and other things. One of the most important things about my involvement with the USCF is my commitment to ethical chess competition. In my entire time with the USCF, from 2011 to the present, I have avoided cheating and sandbagging. USCF regulations prohibit cheating and sandbagging.

[End of 23-24AUG2019M TRNSCRS #6]

COMMENTARY ON TRNSCRS #6: In the times since I changed in portions of 2000-2004 into becoming consistently much more ethical than I had previously been, I let go of the idea that anyone anywhere is likely to have any privacy relative to the profound spiritual reality in which a given religion, a given combination of religions, and/or whatever else provides that some being or combination of beings of beyond our regular reality can somehow witness and be aware of everything any of us ever does, no matter how concealed it might otherwise seem. Some of why I accept that as an almost-definite given in almost every way conceivable are discussed at length in *Science, Religion, Politics, and Cards* and in the nonfiction supplemental portions of *The Dimetrodons, the Dorians, and the Modern World.* Another helpful thing with that could be *An Encyclopedic Survival Guide for Navigating Normal and Paranormal Experiences.* However, perhaps the best thing to help someone with this has to come from within or from directly experiencing something majestic that emanates from without or from beyond, possibly integrated with what comes from within the soul and/or spirit and/or mind.

[Start of 23-24AUG2019M TRNSCRS #7]

PRIMARY SETS OF EVENTS:

First Main Set:

On Wednesday, November 21st, 2018 I played a practice chess game vs. Thomas Sartor at The Financial Advisory Group (hereafter, "FinGroup"). Either at the time of the game or shortly thereafter, Steve Estrin and I shared a brief conversation. At some point, Steve Estrin said to me that if I would ever beat a FinGroup client in an official chess tournament, then I would soon thereafter be fired. I did not know to what degree he might be joking or to what degree he might be serious, but I became very concerned. This was tantamount to a threat that in some situations I would have a stark choice between violating USCF regulations via sandbagging or losing my job. I knew immediately that in such circumstances I would stick with obeying USCF regulations.

That being said, I had just joined FinGroup on August 6th, 2018. Sometime in November 2018, I tentatively planned for my next USCF-rated tournament to be at The Chess Refinery, likely prior to the end of 2018. At some stages of the Fourth Quarter of 2018 I seriously considered playing on Saturday, December 15th, 2018 at a USCF-rated tournament at The Chess Refinery. However, in connection with losing either most of the night of sleep on November 21st, 2018 or losing the entire night of sleep on that night, worried about how to deal with Steve's threat in relation to other factors, I thought very hard.

[End of 23-24AUG2019M TRNSCRS #7]

COMMENTARY ON TRNSCRS #7: Much of my life from during and after my 2003-2004 Express Tax service experience, I have been extremely concerned about protecting confidential client information. A huge part of why I lost most or all of that night of sleep was that I already knew one of the FinGroup clients years before I ever applied to work at FinGroup, and I had already played that client multiple chess games, including losing to him, drawing versus him, and defeating him. I decline to state here how many games I have played against him, but, do the math, you know from this that I have played at least three chess games against him. Furthermore, I decline to state here whether he has ever joined the USCF, whether or not he has ever played in a USCF tournament, whether or not any of the games between him and me occurred as USCF rated games, what his name is, what his age is, what his wife's name is, etc. However, I will mention that the chess games I played against him occurred prior to when I even applied to work for FinGroup. The idea of a risk that I might have ended up de-feating a FinGroup client in a USCF tournament was not some pie-in-the-sky, hairy-fairy, pixie-dust, hallucinogenic dream kind of notion, it was something I had reason to take completely seriously.

At the time of working for FinGroup, my mother and I were still residents of the apartment unit where we had resided in since a few weeks after Hurricane Ike affected Houston in 2008. When I got home from work on November 21, 2018, I felt in an extraordinary psychological double bind. I had been upset to the core about the threat to my involvement with the USCF, but I did not want to tip off my mother or anyone else outside of a need to know FinGroup confidential information the exact nature of the threat. Therefore, I spoke with her in vague terms about the threat that upset me to such a great degree. We had a conversation that proceeded something very much like the following:

Jim: One of the highest-level supervisors has threatened my involvement with the chess competions.

Ming: What? How did he threaten it?

Jim: I can't tell you now the exact way that he threatened it, but it is *really* a problem.

Ming: Why can't you tell me how he threatened your chess?

Jim: Look, sometimes with these professional things, there are restrictions on what people can say. I should protect confidential information.

To clarify about that conversation, I was thinking it best to block from anyone outside of those working for or otherwise closely-affiliated with FinGroup from being tipped off to even a trace of a clear clue about there having been a client versus whom I had already won a chess game, lost a chess game, and drawn a chess game prior to employment there and to avoid tipping them off to whatever other information they might glean from the ensuing discussions.

On a related note, after attending some number of CPE courses for CPAs, by around 2010 I had become aware that some types of client confidentiality have flexibility in some cases, mainly that there is the ability to present a few salient facts about a real, sample client to outsiders if the communication method reasonably protects the identity of the client. For example, a lecturer or a student in such a continuing professional education class can say something in the manner of, "There was a client who had a rental property, and the client faced XYZ unexpected problem..." if handled appropriately.

At first I had used my independent judgment to not reveal much of anything about the threat to anyone, keeping it totally concealed from virtually everyone, especially USCF players and tournament directors, and providing only the very limited amount of information to my mother reflected by the sample conversational transcript presented earlier in this commentary.

However, stage two in the judgment of how to manage the client confidentiality started the moment on August 6, 2019 when I found out that they were terminating me as an employee of that firm. As mentioned earlier, I had premeditated for a while that I would go after them if they would not handle such a termination in a way with reasonable prospects of refraining from any excessive enabling—or even outright participation in—the defamation of my character. After I noticed that not only had they terminated my employment with them, they had done so in a manner that flew in the face of taking any reasonable measures toward properly mitigating the likelihood of massive and hideous defamation of my character. Therefore, I started to feel at liberty to reveal to people in general the nature of Steve Estrin's threat to my involvement with the U.S. Chess Federation. However, I have still concealed from other people—even my mother—the fact that both Steve Estrin and I—and, for that matter, several of the other 2018-2019 employees of FinGroup—knew that I had played against and defeated, been defeated by, and drawn against one of its clients before I had ever started working at that ensemble registered investment advisory firm. This is one of those kinds of things in which, with the diverse scenarios of how life, I had decided to keep in reserve for if and when the time would be right to reveal it, and, with this very book here the idea of possibly revealing it to the general public someday comes to fruition.

Sometime *after* this book gets published, I plan to read this part of the book out loud to my mother, though she might only understand a tiny fraction of it upon my first attempt to read it out loud to her and deal with the ensuing discussion. Also, if you the reader know people at Gray Reed or FinGroup and would like to discuss it with them, or to buy them a copy or twenty, go for it, be my guest!!!!!

[Start of 23-24AUG2019M TRNSCRS #8]

Much of my chess psychology is rooted in energizing perspectives such as "Death Before Dishonor," "Ask No Quarter, Give No Quarter," and similar things. Sometimes this involves meditating on activities of The U.S. Armed Forces, especially since my late father served in The U.S. Army in combat in both Korea and Vietnam. Sometimes this involves listening to and meditating on related songs, for example, Led Zeppelin's "No Quarter."

[End of 23-24AUG2019M TRNSCRS #8]

[Start of 23-24AUG2019M TRNSCRS #9]

Although other personnel at The Financial Advisory Group communicated favorably toward my commitment to ethical participation in USCF tournaments, Steve Estrin's statement of a threat was the first instance of a material conflict between firm activities and my religious practices. I personally decided on a compromise solution of skipping tournaments at The Chess Refinery until sometime after April 15th, 2019, and to play in a December 14th, 2018 USCF tournament held by Houston Scholastic Chess Association. This was based on knowledge of factors making it much less likely to face off against any FinGroup clients at Houston Chess Association tournaments than at Chess Refinery tournaments. The exact identity or identities of FinGroup clients involved with the Houston chess scene should remain unidentified in connection with this EEOC investigation, on account of FinGroup client confidentiality.

[End of 23-24AUG2019M TRNSCRS #9]

COMMENTARY ON TRNSCRS #9: To reiterate from another angle, when I wrote that I believed it best to hold myself to a stricter standard of how restrictive to be about the information than I am now. However, what little I reveal in this book about that client, who is in some ways at ground zero of the entire conflict, and with whom I have still never directly brought up this issue (as of the time of this book going to print), does not give the general public much of a clue at all about his identity.

[Start of 23-24AUG2019M TRNSCRS #10]

For clarification, part of the related dialogue was along the lines of:

Maurice: "I am not going to intentionally avoid winning a USCF chess game in that situation! It is unethical within the USCF rules to intentionally sabotage one's chess results! Two of the biggest things with the chess ethics are: Do not cheat. Do not sandbag."

Steve [with a coy look on his face]: "Beat a FinGroup client, lose your job."

[End of 23-24AUG2019M TRNSCRS #10]

A Commentary on TRNSCRS #10: If Steve Estrin thought that coddling the client whom I had already defeated, lost to, and drawn against in chess games prior to ever joining FinGroup would be in that client's best interests, connecting that in his mind with a registered investment advisory duty to serve the client's best interests as a rationale under the surface of issuing that threat, then he, in that instance, clearly disagreed with the idea that FIDE Grandmaster Roman Dzindzichashvili and other highly respected instructors have expressed (either by the words or by words to the effect) as, "When you beat your opponent with good play, it is good for them, and it is good for you."

Those who need coddling in a competitive activity should probably steer clear of federation chess until they might change to having the resilience it would take to handle it, unless deliberately choosing to step out of their comfort zones for a self-improvement process or at least one other legitimate reason.

If you are a client of a registered investment advisory firm and psychologically feel the need to avoid experiencing a senior tax associate employed by that RIA beating you in a federation chess competition, then federation chess is probably one of the worst hobbies you could choose for your life. Perhaps you should consider something more like Bingo competitions.

I believe that Steve probably intended well, but as we are well aware, good intentions are not always linked to good results.

However, let us consider this from a radically different perspective which I probably started to contemplate in something like the year 2021 or the year 2022: Steve's way of prodding me in the direction away from having federation chess as a hobby can be thought to parallel the tradition in Sufi Islam in which a religious person can let go of whatever that person's fondest activity would be, thereby acquiring the spiritual and soulful benefits concomitant with that change.

Indeed, in the long run I have let go of all interest in competing in federation chess; such interest has completely and totally disappeared from my life, whereas at the time when Steve issued the aforementioned threat such competition was my fondest hobby.

We could replay these events and analyze them from all sorts of different angles, thinking about how much we might want to blame the game of chess, the investment advisory industry, Steve, the original Adam of the Abrahamic religious lore, the original Eve of the Abrahamic religious lore, thee, thy family members, some theologian from the second millennium, a politician from the thirteenth century, a demonic presence of yestermillennium, some philosopher from centuries ago, me, my family members, the director of some 1930s movie, twenty-eight nineteenth century criminals, the Democratic Party, the Republican Party, the founders of a given movement, the founders of another given movement, or anyone else. In the end, though, the facts remain about whatever has actually happened anywhere, and, whether any given being likes what has happened or not, many beings face choices about what to do next.

(Thus concludes a commentary on transcription segment #10.)

[Start of 23-24AUG2019M TRNSCRS #11]

Sometime around late 2018 or early 2019 I asked Thomas Sartor, in his room, whether he thought Steve Estrin meant that to be serious or a joke, and Thomas said that he believed Steve to most likely intend a mixture of both seriousness and jest.

[End of 23-24AUG2019M TRNSCRS #11]

[Start of 23-24AUG2019M TRNSCRS #12]

In the remainder of the time I worked at FinGroup, after Steve's unethical threat on this subject, he never rescinded the threat. Also, my employment happened to be terminated just three days after the first and only Chess Refinery USCF-rated chess tournament that I participated in. On my last day at FinGroup, August 6th, 2019, I said hello to Steve a couple of times, and the best that I could tell, he actively went out of his way to avoid saying anything back or looking me in the eye.

[End of 23-24AUG2019M TRNSCRS #12]

In that segment I characterized as unethical the essence of Steve's threat to what was then my involvement with the U.S. Chess Federation. As mentioned a little while ago in this work, we could analyze incessantly about whether that threat from him was for the best, for the worst, for a mixed bag, ethical, unethical, a mixture of ethical and unethical, or whatever else.

I did play in one more USCF rated tournament after The Financial Advisory Group fired me from being an employee of that firm, and it was interesting to participate in that January 2022 competition in St. Louis, Missouri. At a core level, as of the time of this book initially going to print in May 2024, I feel absolutely no interest in playing in future federation chess competitions, though I am not absolutely certain about whether or not things will stay that way all the way to the instant of my death. In case James Liptrap or anyone else might worry at the time of this book going to print about the possibility of my participating in future federation chess competitions, such a worry is probably rather ridiculous as of May 2024 and times soon thereafter, because, as of May 2024 I forecast a range of about zero percent to about one one-thousandth of a percent that I will ever again feel interested again in playing in federation chess competitions. A huge part of this is that I perceive that the spiritual windfalls acquired by sacrificing participation in federation chess competitions since early 2022 and sacrificing the CPA license (i.e., the certified public accountancy license that I had held for a little over thirteen years) later in 2022 to have demonstrated themselves to be exemplary spiritual rewards in exchange for the willingness to make those sacrifices. Although I practice Buddhism as a primary religion and Steve Estrin, to the best of my knowledge, practices Judaism as a primary religion, it seems that part of the mystery of the interaction between him and me has led to both him and me energizing some of the mysteries of Sufi Islam as shining upon us in ways beneficial to many Christians, Muslims, Jews, Buddhists, and others.

[Start of 23-24AUG2019M TRNSCRS #13]

However, the termination appears to have been primarily related to the second and third main sets of events.

[End of 23-24AUG2019M TRNSCRS #13]

[Start of 23-24AUG2019M TRNSCRS #14]

Second Main Set:

Natasha McDaniel was my roommate at FinGroup from when I started on August 6th, 2018 until the time of a conflict on or about December 12th, 2018. The origin of the conflict involved my doing activities that would be ethical and legal in the office with or without the lights on and with or without the door closed, yet, choosing to, in the words of Led Zeppelin, "Close the door, put out the light."

[From the beginning of the song "No Quarter," written by Jimmy Page, Robert Plant & John Paul Jones. Lyrics included here as a fair use of copyrighted material.]

[End of 23-24AUG2019M TRNSCRS #14]

COMMENTARY ON TRNSCRS #14: My conscious mind, with the use of logic and sequences of other events from that time, plus other factors, is in some ways completely certain that the conflict referenced occurred on December 12, 2018, but there is something so surreal about the entire set of it, that I best show extra caution about the date number. This way I can focus certainty and clarity on other aspects of what happened, and to hermetically seal some portions of the purity of speech of this process.

On a related note, if I had in the last instant with a chance to either turn off that light or not turn off that light known then what I know now, then one course of action then something I believe I might have done, perhaps with better results, though we will probably never know for sure, would have been to think to myself, *You know what, the way that Estrin blew to smithereens the unity of loyalty between my loyalty to the entirety of reality and my loyalty to The Financial Advisory Group, the best thing to do is to say to hell with working here any longer. Except maybe for two weeks' notice, that is. Before any more time goes by, I'll sit down and compose an e-mail to go to the entire firm, presenting in it a combination of giving my two weeks' notice and explaining how wrong I believe the threat from Steve to my involvement with the USCF is.*

After that, the body of such an e-mail might have taken the form, "With this message I hereby give two weeks' notice of my resignation from FinGroup. We could part ways sooner if you wish to accelerate this end of my employment relationship with you. Steve destroyed the main core of unity between my loyalty to FinGroup and my loyalty to The Totality of Reality. It has been nice knowing you."

Also, as part of that, there would not have been much reason to later turn out the lights, but, as we know, events did not transpire that way. Although my conscious mind did not strategize with precision toward arranging for it to happen, as fate would have it, the act of turning out the lights and thereby alienating Natasha McDaniel to a much greater degree than I had previously alienated her was part of enlightening Steve Estrin, Natasha McDaniel, FinGroup, myself, and others about how much of a watershed event it was when Steve Estrin chose to threaten my involvement with the USCF. In many respects, I can look back on all of that now with a mindset of, "All's well that ends well."

---

Back then I would have found it unbelievable and unfathomable the degree of hostility that the firm ended up showing toward me.

Looking at things from their perspective, though, they probably would have found it unbelievable and unfathomable that I would fight back against their hostility with the amount of ferocity, strategic discipline, righteous indignation, and vigor that I unleashed in self-defense, defense of the First Amendment to the U.S. Constitution, a way of bearing true witness with which to defuse the problems caused by false witness borne by others against me, the accomplishment of Vajrayana Buddhist activities, the accomplishment of Esoteric Christian activities, the accomplishment of Noahidist activities, a set of beyond-any-physical-contact Jeet Kune Do demonstrations, and more.

All right, back then I had no idea that so many people in FinGroup and so many people outside of FinGroup would on so many occasions think about the balance of force between uncertainties about to whom, if anyone, to give the benefit of the doubt, then choose to go hard in the direction of giving me none or virtually none of the benefit of the doubt and to give my detractors a huge amount of the benefit of the doubt, but I have adjusted. Now that I am deeply aware of that, there are many cases in which I simply preemptively kill many paths of possible mutual benefit before otherwise even starting them, as part of risk management, fully cognizant of how people have tended toward much less favorability toward me and much more hostility toward me than I previously thought people would tend to trend toward demonstrating. Some of this I have been able to ascertain through paltry book sales, some of it from how Michael Berry himself demonstrated only a small fraction of the understanding I might have otherwise assumed him to have arrived at by the end of my February 22, 2024 phone call with him (reminder: portions of it aired on his March 15, 2024 morning show), some of it from the general trends of what happened at Goodwill Houston in portions of the third quarter of 2023, and some of it from various other experiences.

Many such cases of being less open to initiating what I might otherwise have imagined possibilities with a good chance for mutual benefit—that is, to be more judicious in making such attempts—have been based on hard-won, tough experience.

This could be thought of as analogous to someone who figures out a variety of poker hands to tend not to work very well when enough of the intangible and tangible context going with them wind up going in certain ways, then decides in a great many such cases to use the "fold early and fold often" approach to unfavorable circumstances.

There have also been many situations in which I have continued to be willing to take the extra risk and go the extra mile to open the door to reasonable chances of high-risk, high-reward paths, whether of mutual benefit or of competitive advantage or both, along the lines of a "hold and check or hold and raise when factors are sufficiently auspicious" approach.

(Thus concludes COMMENTARY ON TRNSCRS #14.)

[Start of 23-24AUG2019M TRNSCRS #15]

I believe that my subconscious and semiconscious levels of mind encouraged me to coordinate this as an attempt to supercharge psychological preparation for the December 14th, 2018 chess tournament. Meanwhile, my conscious mind included a flashback to a desert cave tour from when I was a child. In that tour, the tour guide briefly turned off all lights in part of the cavern, presenting an environment of absolute darkness to the tourists, which included myself. In contrast, although the FinGroup room had no windows, I found that the electronics in the room left it with very noticeable background light.

[End of 23-24AUG2019M TRNSCRS #15]

COMMENTARY ON TRNSCRS #15: Those of you who have ever heard my August 6, 2021 call with Michael Berry probably remember how I mentioned this during that call, as well as many of the other details in the transcribed memo, though there were many things in the call but omitted from the memo and many things in the memo but omitted from the call.

To the best of my knowledge and memory, the only inaccuracies in what I stated during that call, relative to all that transpired up to the time of that call, were de minimis things like whether accidentally adding one or subtracting one from quoting a given year number & intending to say "Sonora" when saying "Sonoma."

Also consider for a little while a so-similar-and-yet-so-very-different detail from a book which has been in my household for years, although I have seldom looked at it: I remember that sometime circa September 2019 I picked it up and happened to open to a passage that describes how one of Richard Eyre's friends would calm himself down and brace himself for the unknown at home after a difficult work day by sitting in a closed garage, lights off, "there in a dark car, imagining the worst scenario..." (*Teaching Your Children Values* by

Linda Eyre and Richard Eyre; 1993, Fireside; New York, NY; p. 80; ISBN: 0-671-76966-9 paperback).

[Start of 23-24AUG2019M TRNSCRS #16]

Although my choice of how to manage the room in that situation had unusual elements, everything I did was well within the boundaries of the law, general ethics, and basic common decency, even if some might question the etiquette of choosing to close the door and turn off the lights in a shared business office room when alone there.

At some point I found myself with the eye relaxation at or near completion, still maintaining behavior perfectly acceptable within a business office environment with lights on and people around. Assuming, that is, that they do not jump to the conclusion of an epileptic fit happening or become enraged about someone falling asleep on the job.

[End of 23-24AUG2019M TRNSCRS #16]

Something obliquely reminiscent of this, besides the rumored KPMG act of firing Lyle Boudreaux for falling asleep on the job, was that sometime approximately in the September 1995 to April 1996 range, fraternity brother Henry Lin, who had a habit of staring into people's eyes much longer and more intensely than most people would find appropriate, stared at me while I used a study method of closing my eyes to help with the concentration on the coursework. I was completely wide awake, sitting there in a room, and Henry said to me, "You're asleep, aren't you?" or words to that effect. (The conversation proceeded essentially the same as what shows here, to the best of my memory.)

I answered him, "No, I'm not asleep. I was studying with my eyes closed."

He said, "No, you weren't. You were asleep." His tone indicated ambiguity of whether he was teasing or actually thinking what he was saying to be true.

I fired back, "No! I really was awake, using a different way to study the stuff."

He argued further, "You were asleep!"

I again fired back, "Look, I was actually awake. I know what actually happened."

Although I never knew for sure if he was teasing or actually believing me to have been asleep, I know that I was wide awake, with my eyes closed while concentrating on extra ways of engaging with the course information.

Many years later, I received word from fraternity brother Michael Swinson that Henry Lin had eventually turned up missing. That gave me extra pause, because it was within a couple of years or so after *Avengers: Infinity War* (2018) and *Avengers: Endgame* (2019) had been out to the public, and I remembered from seeing those films that they were largely filmed in Georgia, USA, and I remembered Henry to have had some prior personal connection with spending much time in Atlanta, GA. Something to do with that sense that there are many patterns suggestive of many terrible things between the patterns in the mysterious areas of causation, two amazingly popular box office movies that included the portrayal of strange disappearances, a nexus of Georgia, a fraternity brother who acted in ways that might rub some people a little extra the wrong way, and that fellow turned up missing. That seemed a bit much for me to sort through and process, yet I eventually came to accept it: Henry Lin disappeared, and we might not ever get any closure in this lifetime of what happened to him to cause him to be missing.

If I let go of fretting about that, though, and look at what Michael Swinson actually sent me in context, then it might not seem so menacing at all about the mystery of what happened to Henry Lin. Here is part of the actual March 20-25, 2021 correspondence, assigning dates the best I can tell from examining the Facebook messenger display, in some cases with clear date stamps and in other cases appearing to omit the date. This transcript adjusts punctuation, word usage, etc. issues via the bracket [recommended standard grammar, punctuation, &c.] method rather than the added [sic] labeling-for-unconventional method:

March 20, 2021: Swinson: Anyway, I asked a couple of [H]enry's friends via text if they have his contact info. I'll let you know if I hear anything.

March 20, 2021: Blair: Great. Either way, thank you for this dialogue.

March 25, 2021: Michael Swinson: His friends [got] back to me. Unfortunately[,] they said[,] '[H]e has disappeared[.]' They don't know where [he] is now or how to contact him[.]

[Start of 23-24AUG2019M TRNSCRS #17]

I was sitting at my desk. Natasha started to open the door. She said, "Are you asleep?" Then I got up to talk to her, but she rushed off down the hall, apparently in the direction of Juan's office. Chris Kolenda arrived almost immediately at my room, and he started to talk with me about some client work. I tried to focus the best I could on what Chris was discussing with me, yet I felt a degree of concern about what Natasha might be saying to Juan.

[End of 23-24AUG2019M TRNSCRS #17]

In some ways I believe that a valid way to blame me, from a Buddhist perspective, a Christian perspective, or a similarly religious and/or philosophical perspective, is to say that I was too attached to money and social status in wanting very badly to keep things going smoothly with the job. That was in the hopes that it could play into a narrative of my being a legitimate white-collar professional and that I could make much more lifetime income via it. This caused me to worry too much about not rocking the boat after things started to hit the fan, excessively trusting management, and other things. After the way things eventually snowballed, I reflected on it and realized that for future scenarios that would start to veer even a little bit in the direction of significant risk of defamation of character, I would fight hard for my reputation early and vociferously, considering every job to be totally expendable at any instant of time in such scenarios. When I worked at Goodwill Houston in 2023, I planned that approach going in, and I executed speech and actions according to that plan.

Although part of that was conveyed in a small amount of Chapter 5, here is another exhibit that is illustrative:

After a Human Resources Goodwill Houston employee named Shannon sent me a September 6, 2023 message that included, in part, “We have received several emails from you regarding your inability to report to work that were sent to management.” It also asked, “Can you provide me with the details of your inability to work after you submitted your notice and interest to self-demote?”

I answered that GWH HR Shannon on September 10, 2023 with a message that was lengthy. Here are a few highlights:

[Start of Highlight #1 of the 10 SEP 2023 Email]

It is not inability to work, and it was not inability to work. I am still able to work in general and am choosing not to work for Goodwill Houston.

[End of Highlight #1 of the 10 SEP 2023 Email]

[Start of Highlight #2 of the 10 SEP 2023 Email]

There could be arguments made on each side of whether or not Steve Estrin (who was one of FinGroup's three highest-ranking persons at that time) should have or should not have issued the threat that he did against me on the day before Thanksgiving in the year 2018 (i.e., the threat that I would lose the FinGroup job soon after defeating a FinGroup client in a serious chess competition if that were to occur while employed by that firm).

However, what almost no one knew at the time, and still probably extremely few know today, was that my main employment model at the time included sequestering commitments to degrees of acting out Vajrayana-based holy war, Tetragrammaton-based holy war, and other types of holy war mostly to the U.S. Chess Federation activities that I was involved with (with USCF competitors serving as proxies for energies to sort themselves out within the deeper realities). When he breached that sequestration, it started to reopen the door to bringing back those types of holy war into the open of a major presence outside of USCF activities, especially with FinGroup as, for a while, the potential main target, until those could shift elsewhere (which they eventually did).

In contrast, at some stage in mid-2019 Darryl Nelson, who was also one of the three highest-ranking persons of FinGroup in much of the 2018-2021 period, indicated to me that he believed that Steve Estrin was wrong to issue the aforementioned 11/21/2018 threat, and that the nature of my commitment to the USCF activities was on the right track.

There are several extra levels to this, and there were multiple chain reactions that unfolded.

[End of Highlight #2 of the 10 SEP 2023 Email]

[Start of Highlight #3 of the 10 SEP 2023 Email]

Eventually, I reached stages in life in which I decided that in all future employment relations, unless and until I were to change methods of operation, I would presume that most of American society would likely be deficient enough or potentially deficient enough in actually, truthfully, and fairly using a combination of Truth, The First Amendment, and The Civil Rights Act of 1964 to be compatible with my continuing many of the old ways that I used to approach interactions with coworkers and supervisors.

Prior to the conflicts with FinGroup and the revelation that the attorney I met with on October 18th, 2019 believed that a judge would have most likely ruled summary judgment in favor of the employer in the case of my EEOC charge against Fin-

Group, and some related events, I believed in giving plenty of leeway/tolerance to supervisors and coworkers in terms of disrespectful behavior, questionable behavior, and unwarranted condescension toward me. That was part of not rocking the boat and allowing myself a better chance to fit into a reasonable chance for stable employment relationships in the long run, trusting that if supervisors and/or coworkers and/or entire employers would act with disrespect, excessive questionability, and excessive condescension in ways that would very possibly snowball into huge problems, then methodically dealing with it properly later would almost definitely resolve things reasonably well and reasonably smoothly.

HOWEVER, after many of those things happened, including how those and other factors nearly destroyed my life as of mid-2021 and how I subsequently recovered most of my life force the instant that I posted to Facebook on July 12th, 2021 a memorial to my 2011-2019 USCF activities, I have tended to have a different approach to employers.

Specifically, as there is no likelihood of a safety net of using attorneys and the legal system to fully fight back against most possible forms of harmful treatment from coworkers and supervisors, especially the bearing of false witness against me in significant ways, in that the combination of all factors of my life, background, and affiliations do not seem compatible with reasonable protection in those ways via the courts and threatening to sue employers and/or former employers via civil actions, there is a new approach: Once anyone starts to significantly veer in the direction of the types of bearing false witness against me that could snowball into huge problems later, I simply directly and swiftly push back with bearing true witness, fighting back directly and quickly against anyone I believe I should, including intentionally going many levels beyond what some of them might believe to be within proper bounds of intensity of forcefully pushing back and/or pushing back much more instantaneously than they would believe proper.

That includes, when in employment relationships in which I am not in charge of the organization, being ready from the first instant I start a new job to defend the truth in ways such that I am ready to be fired at any time and ready to quit or give two weeks notice at any time. Better to get fired while already sufficiently defending the truth about my life, my actions, my reputation, and each being's life and everyone's reality in general such as to have no need to resort to EEOC charges, attempting to do lawsuits, etc. Also, on the other side, better to quit while using the quitting as part of sufficiently defending the truth about life, actions, reputations, and realities without having any need to resort to EEOC charges, attempts at lawsuits, etc.

A huge part of this idea is that, although the experiences of 11/21/2018 to February 2022 were great learning and strengthening experiences in many ways for me, seasons have changed in my life such that I should not return to the way I was before going through those experiences, as I, in many ways, cannot afford to go through much of that kind of pattern again now that those experiences have happened and showed that the old mindset was oblivious to how large percentages of the workings of American society would not likely have my back.

Since I no longer have much expectation for the attorneys, judges, and courts to ever fully or anywhere near fully have my back very much at all in those November 2018 to February 2022 types of patterns, and since I found that using the vigorous communication of truth to be effective, I in recent times have usually defended myself almost instantaneously with whichever means I would believe correct, often with little or no regard for if some people think I am going outside the normal boundaries of how intensely and viciously defend oneself and the truth through interpersonal communications.

[End of Highlight #3 of 10 SEP 2023 Email]

[Start of Highlight #4 of 10 SEP 2023 Email]

When I chose to change from being a Merchandising Specialist / Pricer to being a Donation Specialist, that was what I believed to be the best means of justifiably retaliating against Liz for what I believed to be overstepping a bound with using her position to impose on me from the instant of a previously-described-to-you-by-e-mail August 17th, 2023 conversation onward a restriction against what previously seemed the normal Merchandising Specialist / Pricer autonomy to self-determine if an appearing-significantly-more-special-than-normal-range chair of typical dining/office chair size should be granted a price over $9.99. (As mentioned previously, she indicated that from that moment onward, if I were to ever again dare to have such an idea about any such chair, then I should, in accordance with her stipulation, get a supervisor to provide a second opinion with which to either confirm or reject eligibility for such a price.) Although I decided to sidestep explaining this to Melanie at the time of changing from Pricer to Donation Specialist, in the interests of team cohesion and not escalating problems at the time, as you may recall, I later mentioned some information about it to you be e-mail. Also, I used the spoken word to communicate this to Crystal and Alex on August 18th, 2023, the same day that I requested the change. I believed it at the time best to refrain from speaking of it to either Melanie or Liz, though I also believed it best at the time upon inquiry from Crystal and Alex to answer them very directly about it. Later, as part of explaining the giving of two weeks notice, I chose to mention it to Melanie by the spoken word.

[End of Highlight #4 of 10 SEP 2023 Email]

[REMINDER: THE PRECEEDING CONTINUED COMMENTARY ON 23-24AUG2019M TRNSCRS #17]

[Start of Highlight #5 of 10 SEP 2023 Email]

I am still very capable of working in general, and I still respect Goodwill Houston, yet I believe that I will almost definitely not look to rejoin Goodwill Houston as an employee in the future. The main core essence of why I resigned from working for your organization was that the combination of how Melanie was attempting to manage the conversation that led to the resignation (although involving Melanie acting based on good intentions and very limited information) was such that the best way fight back against all false and harmful patterns everywhere and to fight in favor of all true and helpful patterns everywhere would be to provide the two weeks notice of resignation then and there.

Already, back on August 18th, 2023, I had come very close to giving two weeks notice as what I believed then to be justifiable retaliation against a combination of Liz's stipulation of extreme restriction on my autonomy as a Pricer and many specifics of other interactions with several Goodwill Houston employees, yet I had decided on that day to instead of going straight into resignation to try to get working for Goodwill Houston to still work in the long run with a shift away from the Pricer issues (especially, pricing autonomy, quotas, criticism for if carts would be insufficiently full, criticism for if carts would be too full of glass items in ways deemed precarious, and perceived differences of treatment toward different pricers).

By the time I became a Donation Specialist on August 20th, 2023, I was both very open to the possibility of working as a Goodwill Houston employee for many years and the possibility of resigning very soon at any time, including in some ways being only a few millimeters away from giving two weeks notice.

Of course, I still recognize that every employment role and every employer can involve mixtures of unique challenges and opportunities, and I am prepared to make additional adjustments as things continue to happen.

[End of Highlight #5 of 10 SEP 2023 Email]

[Start of Highlight #6 of 10 SEP 2023 Email]

I believe that my 3/24/2023-9/4/2023 employment relationship with Goodwill Houston was a mutually beneficial season for both that employer and myself, and I believe that seasons changed such that my departure made sense.

[End of Highlight #6 of 10 SEP 2023 Email]

[Start of 23-24AUG2019M TRNSCRS #18]

Next, Chris and I were still in the middle of talking about the client project, and Natasha stepped inside the door for a moment in a highly agitated state. Chris said something like, "Natasha, what's wrong?" Natasha said something like, "He know! He know! [sic]." I started to wonder what in the world was going on with Natasha's perception of things. I wanted to go talk with Juan about things and try to immediately clear things up, yet Chris was busy discussing some client work with me, and Chris was also to some degree a supervisor for me. Therefore, I continued staying with Chris, still uncertain what in the world Natasha might possibly be saying to Juan, and what Juan might be saying to Natasha.

A little later, Chris exited the room. After that, Natasha entered the room. She then took out a can of Lysol and started spraying it on portions of her desk area. I said with shock, "What the hell?! I was only doing eye relaxation." She said, "I don't want to hear it! I don't want to hear it!"

[End of 23-24AUG2019M TRNSCRS #18]

[Start of 23-24AUG2019M TRNSCRS #19]

I became very concerned that the entire situation was spiraling out of control. Therefore, I walked down the hall to talk to Juan. He was reasonably friendly. He said something like, "I don't believe you did anything wrong with your meditation." I said, "It was eye relaxation, not meditation." He then proceeded to say things about how while he believed I had avoided any wrongdoing, it is natural for people working closely together to have conflict, and that Natasha and I have very opposite personalities. Therefore, he was making arrangements for Natasha to get reassigned to sit somewhere else, and he asked me to avoid talking with Natasha on the subject further, and to generally avoid Natasha for a while to give her space while the situation would cool off.

This put me under extra strain. I knew quite clearly that I had avoided wrongdoing and that Natasha was acting in a hell-bent way of extreme hostility toward me. The way that Juan communicated with me on the subject, though, I was concerned and in a psychological double-bind. Any time I might go to human resources, high ranking personnel, or just about anyone else and explain the truth, from that moment forward, I sensed that each time would involve a degree of risk that my employment could soon be terminated. However, each time I might choose not to go to someone to talk about it, there would be an increased risk of people spreading a very harmful form of slander against me.

After the incident I made a concerted effort for my primary set-up for these eye relaxation techniques at FinGroup to involve having the lights on, the door open, and facing directly or almost directly away from the door.

[End of 23-24AUG2019M TRNSCRS #19]

[Start of 23-24AUG2019M TRNSCRS #20]

Also, Erin Hudson, the main IT person, collected the password for my company e-mail and server access on Friday, December 14th, 2018, although it is unknown to me whether or not this was connected with company reaction to communications between Natasha and Juan.

After Erin collected my password, I spoke with Juan and he corroborated Erin's description of collecting passwords from everyone in order to help make sure that some software updates would go smoothly. Although I felt uncertain about whether there was any accuracy in the notion that they presented, I decided to go along with things, making a mental mark in case later on it would be best to relate this to someone.

On Monday, December 17th, 2018, I changed my password, though with some difficulty. Erin characterized this difficulty as related to my changing the password too often in the time leading up to that morning.

[End of 23-24AUG2019M TRNSCRS #20]

{START OF COMMENTARY ON TRNSCRS #20}

Although Klynveld Peat Marwick Goerdeler Limited Liability Partnership, better known to the public as KPMG LLP, KPMG International Limited, or KPMG, is what I generally consider to have been the most consistently ethical and effective of the former, primarily-white-collar-work employers for which that I have had the privilege to work, this may have been a case in which I placed too much emphasis on my impression of valuable takeaways from my January-April 2005 KPMG internship experience.

One of the other interns of that period was of the name John Martinez; bear with this text, believe it or not, the FinGroup experience included a supervisor of the name Juan Martinez, the KPMG experience included a peer-level coworker named John Martinez, and they were two completely different people, and their names could be easy for a casual reader to mix up. Let go of all the FinGroup controversies for at least a little while to imagine back to one of the scenes from KPMG, circa the February-to-March 2005 period, involving a female supervisor of the name Evgenia Karpenko.

There it was, somewhere approximately in the range from about a quarter of the way into that internship to about three-quarters of the way into that internship. I was seated at a computer that was in a state such that password entry would be needed in order to get back to normal usage, and the password needed was my KPMG password of that time, something that, if compromised, could grant another person unfettered access to impersonating me by electronic mail and other highly problematic things that could wreak havoc on my professional reputation. Evgenia instructed me to go ahead and log in. Both John and Evgenia were somewhat nearby, close enough that I was concerned that my password might become compromised, whether by an intentional or unintentional act of the combination of witnessing and memorizing by either one of them. Also, I remembered that when Psi Upsilon Fraternity Brother Roger Wistar was my roommate during what was both his and my sophomore year at Duke University, he was extra careful with everyone, it seemed, whether me or another fraternity brother or anyone else, to guard at least one of his passwords as if his life would depend on it. I felt a similar way to Roger about that type of protection in general at that time. As of May 2024, I still do, though what transpired in the conversation between Evgenia and me in early 2005 has caused me to on some occasion be willing to concede a modest degree of password vulnerability.

The circa-February-March 2005 conversation under scrutiny proceeded essentially identically to the following:

Evgenia Karpenko (with John Martinez standing very near to Maurice and easily able to look at the keyboard onto which Maurice is set to type): Go ahead and log in.

Maurice Blair (concerned about the risk that this might lead to either John or Evgenia accidentally learning of the password and the astronomically-remote risk that at least one of them might actually intentionally learn that password): Maybe you and John should step aside so that I make sure to keep my password secure.

Evgenia: Oh, come on! It's not like you really have to worry about John or me daring to try to steal your password. Oh, please!!

Maurice (feeling caught between a rock and a hard place, yet recognizing that there needs to be some way to navigate through it; also recognizing that things such as the February 1973 *Kung Fu* episode "The Tide" indicate the prime importance of being able to trust at least some of the time): OK. I'll go ahead and log in right now. If something truly terrible later happens because of this, then I have faith that there will be sufficient recourse.

(Maurice then logs in to the KPMG computer with the relevant password of that time.)

Evgenia: There, that wasn't so bad, now was it?

Maurice: Yes, and if something happens later, then we can cross that bridge when we get there.

---

There were a few times when working at FinGroup that the experience of that interaction with one of the 2005 white-collar-work supervisors, specifically Evgenia Karpenko, pointed toward the need to sometimes demonstrate to other professionals in a work setting the kind of trust that leaves oneself vulnerable to someone else there accessing a password that might leave oneself wide open to someone else impersonating oneself and wreaking havoc on one's reputation.

Therefore, even though Erin Hudson's request on Friday, December 14, 2018 to obtain my main FinGroup password of the time seemed to me to stink to high heaven, I chose to honor it anyway. Also, I thought that speaking with Juan Martinez about it would allow me to better gauge the situation. The main sense I got from that follow-up inquiry with Juan was that I could not fully read with absolute certainty whether he and Erin were telling me the truth about the password situation or if they were feeding me lies based on the company having become suspicious in the wake of the circa-February 12, 2018 incident of my choosing to close the door, put out the light, and subsequently deal carefully with all manner of interactions with other FinGroup personnel. Also, after those two interactions, one with Erin and one with Juan, I considered asking around to find what people might say about whether Erin had actually taken the extraordinary measure of obtaining everyone's main passwords in some peculiar situation of tending to the main computer server's processes or not. However, I thought better of it. Looking at it in several ways: 1) If it was actually a fully legitimate request made of all of the employees with accounts tied to the server, then I would look extra stupid, suspicious, and paranoid to the other workers for daring to inquire about such a thing, especially having this placed on top of the hostilities toward me that Natasha had been expressing, potentially swaying multiple co-workers even further against me than they might already have been. 2) If it was actually a black ops type of activity in which they would place my use of the server under deep scrutiny, then they would discover several oddities that might give them some pause about the idea of trying to mess with me. Namely, a little while before I closed the door and turned off the lights, on the legal, paid-for, Napster music streaming service, I had used my work computer station to listen to the Platters' songs "Only You" and "Twilight Time," and after all hell seemed to break loose between Natasha and me, using that same service on the same work station I chose to listen to the Led Zeppelin song "No Quarter" and the Simon and Garfunkel song "The Sound of Silence." 3) Although it seemed astronomically remote then and still seems astronomically-remote now as a far-fetched possibility from where I stand, if they were to have actually had the nerve and lack of ethics to dare to impersonate me from within my account, then the full force of the REALITY BEYOND ANY AND ALL OF THE REGULARLY-OBSERVABLE HUMANS—THE REALITY THAT RELIGIOUS PEOPLE, SCIENTIFIC PEOPLE, AND OTHERS REGARD AS THE

REALM OF THE SUBLIME would be thoroughly on my side in the long run in fighting back.

Even in the absence of the type of server management malfeasance described as a far-fetched thing for me to have a degree of pause over in connection with item #3 in that list, I still had then and still have now an awareness of the basic readiness-to-fight-back dynamic referenced in that item. That also can apply to anyone anywhere facing major challenges. Although I have only read a tiny fraction of the available literature from Jocko Willink, I am very aware that he has repeatedly expressed in a variety of ways how when the going gets very tough, we, in many ranges of cases, had best fight back with much of what we have got, and, if it gets extremely life-and-death, then we might have to fight with everything we have got.

Therefore, all of us, when facing extreme challenges, to whatever degrees brought on by women, men, children, extraterrestrials, animals, plants, weather patterns, seismic events, events that emanate from the astrophysics of comsic scales, or anything else, can consider carefully and team up with THE REALITY BEYOND ANY AND ALL OF THE REGULARLY-OBSERVABLE HUMANS—THE REALITY THAT RELIGIOUS PEOPLE, SCIENTIFIC PEOPLE, AND OTHERS REGARD AS THE REALM OF THE SUBLIME.

[Start of 23-24AUG2019M TRNSCRS #21]

Third Main Set of Events:

I noticed greatly heightened hostility toward me starting around the early afternoon of August 2nd, 2019. Also, on Monday, August 5th, 2019, I found a weekend e-mail from Natasha regarding her review of a tax return I had worked on. After normal review notes, she added an extra comment along the lines of, "Maurice, stop trying to get other people to do your work for you." I explained that I considered the two items she pointed out to have been procedurally incidental, yet I now revised my view of them to being things that should not have gone to review without resolution.

Sensing a combination of multiple forms of intense coworker hostility from recent days, I chose in the morning of August 5th, 2019 to offer in a spirit of teamwork and harmony a chance to internally get the slander issue behind us, without even having to say the word slander out loud. I composed and sent an e-mail to Natasha, adding Juan Martinez and Chris Kolenda on the cc line, including a very clear explanation of a number of facts that refute the centerpiece of her likely slander per se without making any specific reference to the contents of that slander. In addition to that, I mentioned in the e-mail that I would gladly volunteer for a polygraph, bearing in mind the high percentages of accuracy with polygraphs, and that I would gladly volunteer for video-recorded cross examination. Part of my reason for doing this was that ever since

Juan forced me into a psychological double-bind on this issue, it would from time to time drag down my job performance. I knew all along that I avoided anything of moral turpitude at the FinGroup office, yet I would every once in a while hear or overhear statements suggestive of people believing otherwise.

Natasha responded by e-mailing me, with Juan and Chris on the cc line, that she did not know why I was choosing this time to bring up this issue, and that she considered my e-mail to be gibberish and a waste of time. She also stated that she would never want to hear from me again about the subject. I answered that there was evidence of repeated slander by her against me, that there should not be major slander in the workplace, and that I neither appreciate nor approve of the slander. I also added that my e-mail was not gibberish, and now that she had put things into writing, she had crossed over into libel, and that I neither appreciate nor approve of the libel. I added Tina Nava, the main human resources person to the cc line, which also had Juan and Chris.

That being said, because multiple people at the firm had criticized me for making e-mails too long, and sometimes rather harshly, I included only a very small excerpt of the previous e-mail thread. The resulting e-mail was reasonably compact.

Sometime went by, possibly an hour, and Juan came over to speak with me, attempting to reprimand me. I told him that I believe in the value of addressing this issue and that not clearing this up had been dragging down my work performance. We had a very long conversation in which he expressed major skepticism about whether or not he could have confidence in keeping me as a team member. He also said that Tina said that my e-mails on this issue would need to stop. I related to him a variety of some autobiographical details, which I hoped would help him understand the situation better. He continued to express criticism toward my choice of actions. I continued to stand up for the value of my choice of actions.

Time went by, and Natasha gave no e-mail response to the message in which I stated clearly that she had committed slander and libel against me.

On August 6th, 2019, at about 5 PM, Tina and Juan met with me to issue the termination of my employment with The Financial Advisory Group. It left completely blank the area that would otherwise include words to describe the "reason for separation." When I asked for the reason, they simply answered that it was "an executive decision."

During the meeting Tina made reference to my

being able to keep the employer-provided health insurance to the end of August if there could be a "peaceful exit." Around that time, I asked about if a peaceful exit would be compatible with attorneys contacting them prior to the end of August or if attorneys would need to wait until after August. They seemed very surprised, possibly blindsided by the idea. However, they later explained that the reference to a "peaceful exit" involved exiting the building without incident.

The termination agreement referred to my pay lasting through August 14th, 2019. However, the related payment was for August 1st to 15th, 2019. The pay statement corroborated showing all the way to the 15th. I do not know whether this was due to an administrative simplification or if something else happened.

---

Footnote 1:

Although I never heard from people a direct statement of exactly what Natasha falsely represented as happening, there was ample evidence that it involved an allegation of sexual misconduct. However, under practically any interpretation of sexual ethics and the law, I completely avoided sexual misconduct while on the premises of the building at 5599 San Felipe, Houston, TX 77056, which includes The Financial Advisory Group in portions of the 9th Floor.

[End of 23-24AUG2019M TRNSCRS #21]

[Start of 23-24AUG2019M TRNSCRS #22]

Footnote 2:

Due to the overwhelming evidence that Natasha's slander against me included slander per se of a sexual nature, some of the footnotes will address some issues often left unspoken in many social settings.

I have never exposed my genitals in the working areas of any of the employers at which I have worked during my entire professional career, with the exception of restrooms. This includes factoring in the rare occasions of forgetting to zip my pants in a business office where I worked. In those cases, there was either absolutely no genital exposure or there was no material genital exposure of any kind, on account of the underwear providing an extra layer of protection against that. Within those work places, any and all material amounts of genital exposure took place in the restroom areas.

That being said, there was a May 2005 job interview in the Dallas/Fort Worth area, in which I had no idea that I left my zipper down and I happened to be wearing the type of underwear that can flop somewhat open. I was oblivious of the issue during that interview until the following dialogue. Someone asked me, "Would you like to go to the restroom?" I said, "No thank you." The other person said, "Your zipper is down!" And I was mortified.

Not long after that I left the interview site, and I called up the employment agency recruiter who had set up the interview. I told him that I was very sorry about the job interview and how it went. He told me that I did not need to be sorry about the interview.

On a related note, the only physical contact between my hands and the genital region of my pants in the business office work environment, when away from the restroom, involved brushing off lint, straightening out the positioning of the pants, and similar activities of a primarily nonsexual nature. That being said, there were some times when at places of work there was adjusting the positioning of the pants via touching the outer thigh or belt area or other areas while avoiding any direct stimulation-oriented contact, while at the same time maintaining an erection. This I believe to still be within the range of reasonable etiquette, although it is often most appropriate in some of those business contexts to adjust the mind to get the biofeedback system to calm down to return to including a flaccid state.

[End of 23-24AUG2019M TRNSCRS #22]

COMMENTARY: Consider the following information that appeared in 23AU19M, but which I chose to withhold from 23-24AUG2019M:

[Start of Paragraph Straddling End of Page 9 and Beginning of Page 10 of 23AU19M]

On a related note, sometime around the First Quarter of 2019 or thereabouts, one day I heard from some male coworkers that they saw on an elevator an obscene sentence and diagram involving the name, "Chris." Later on that day, I saw Chris in my room, and I said to him something like, "Chris, I heard a rumor about something people were saying was in the parking garage elevator, written on the condensation. I don't know if maybe I were you I might consider talking with HR about it." Chris then said, "Maurice, I want you to take the idea of talking to HR completely out of your vocabulary!!" I did not say it out loud, but that made me wonder to myself, "What the hell is going on with Chris saying this? I guess things here are wide open and wild like the Wild West to the point that we need to avoid talking to HR except in the most over-the-top extreme kinds of situations. This is kind of strange. However, it does mean that I can relax somewhat more about joining others in pushing the envelope with things like saucy talk." In hindsight, it looks like Chris saw the likelihood of some of the later FinGroup problems coming from a mile away, metaphorically speaking.

[End of Paragraph Straddling End of Page 9 and Beginning of Page 10 of 23AU19M]

[Start of 23-24AUG2019M TRNSCRS #23]

Footnote 3: My religious practices have changed many times in my life. There were some idealistic times when young, and there were some bleak times. Some of the bleakest forms of atheism were among my primary beliefs around mid-1998 to mid-December 1999. However, from December 1999 to April 2000 there was a transition to being more open to faith in religion. A major amount of my involvement with my current religious beliefs and practices dates to various phases during the early 21st Century.

Footnote 4: On April 19th, 2001, I had an exit interview for my Arthur Andersen internship. My role had been as a Tax Intern, specifically in the International Tax portion of the Houston office of that firm. During the interview, Amin Nosrat informed me that the firm would like for me to join them full-time starting September 2002, a few months after my scheduled graduation from the Master of Professional Accounting program with The McCombs School of Business at The University of Texas at Austin.

However, Amin Nosrat told me that the firm would be taking a major risk with bringing me on board full-time.

[End of 23-24AUG2019M TRNSCRS #23]

COMMENT: Consider the following:

[Start of the occupying-portions-of-pages-11&12-of-its-memo Footnote 6 of 23AU19M]

Footnote 6: When Erin Hudson collected my password on Friday, December $14^{th}$, 2018, I became very concerned that the company might be attempting to coordinate a falsified character assassination campaign against me behind my back using the access to the password, yet I knew that it would be very bad etiquette to mention any of this suspicion out loud. Therefore, I resolved to trust that the company was most likely not doing anything nefarious, and that I would completely avoid logging in over the weekend, as part of providing a greater degree of clarity during a potential future conflict. Clarity regarding whether or not the company might have attempted to impersonate me via e-mail, that is.

Also, on this entire subject more generally, that weekend I started making tentative plans that, should the issue of Natasha's major slander against me ever to come to a head, with the company acting with extreme hostility toward a combination of multiple religions, my reputation, and the truth, then I would intend to attempt to use a lawsuit as an instrument of annihilation against the firm, in self-defense and in defense of Vajrayana Buddhism, Esoteric Christianity, Zen Buddhism, Jeet Kune Do, The First Amendment to the United States Constitution, and more.

Or, if the firm might somehow survive, it could fall into the category of "what does not kill you makes you stronger."

This brings to mind *Ecclesiastes* 7:5, "*It* is better to hear the rebuke of the wise, than for a man to hear the song of fools." [Quoting the King James Version of *The Holy Bible* here.] In an extreme conflict situation, we could expect all parties involved to hear significant rebuke from quite a variety of sources.

According to plan, that potential lawsuit would be in defense of truth, common decency, religious practices, my reputation, and many other things. Of course, I knew that it would not be polite to say this kind of idea out loud or to overtly put it into writing at work, unless and until such a time would come for it. And that would most likely involve FinGroup crossing some redline. Occasionally doing or saying things to signal them to read between the lines still seemed fair game, though, within the normal boundaries of business etiquette.

Then, from August 5th-6th, 2019, I felt that the situation became right to give them a choice repeatedly, to reasonably accommodate my religious practices and the truth or to escalate a conflict. They repeatedly chose to escalate conflict, although I preferred at each turn for them to decline escalation and set out on some appropriate way to harmonize.

Finally, the nature of the termination of my employment, given the overall context of facts and circumstances, was a clear act of FinGroup crossing the related spiritual redline. Therefore, I brought up the idea of a lawsuit against FinGroup during that August 6th, 2019 meeting. This was in accordance with how I had already planned ahead for this contingency, approximately sometime between 11 PM Central Standard Time in the evening of December 14th, 2018 and 5 AM Central Standard Time in the morning of December 15th, 2018.

[End of the occupying-portions-of-pages-11&12-of-its-memo Footnote 6 of 23AU19M]

Many times in my life after I joined what could be termed Sexuality's Ejaculatory-Restriction Team Austerity early this century, I felt that the only extremely solid basis for defending myself in a simulated trial by almost-omniscient beings as described in Part R of Section Five (in which one's religious identity group(s) cannot be leaned upon as a defense, yet all facts of behavior and telepathic into the total experiences of the person on trial are known by both the defense and the prosecution) would be my many years of sustained high-quality performance as a member of that team.

[Start of 23-24AUG2019M TRNSCRS #24]

He mentioned that much of my behavior was "goofy." For example, I had joined the group of coworkers who took the first limousine from Chicago O'Hare Airport, whereas I should have waited for the second limousine or later. As another example, during one of the lunch conversations, people perceived one of my comments to stoke the fires of Texas Longhorns versus Texas A&M Aggies rivalry feelings in a context in which it was most inappropriate to stoke such fires.

(Technically, the incident in question began with someone asking why I chose UT for the master's program, after having been accepted by both UT and A&M. In an under-slept, exhausted condition I managed to say, "Because it's the best school." However, I did not intend to put Texas A&M down or to say that Texas is all-around superior; rather, I was attempting to say that I recalled seeing accounting graduate program rankings that listed McCombs School of Business at The University of Texas at Austin as having the top-ranked accounting program nationwide. People there, including several graduates of Texas A&M, however, took it to be an emphatic school rivalry statement.)

He told me that in order to be less goofy, and in order to have better interpersonal skills, there were some things I should do, and he listed about half a dozen of them.

However, from around December 1999 to the time of the April 2001 interview I felt that my interpersonal skills had improved dramatically compared to my life from previous times. I felt extraordinarily disappointed in myself for not demonstrating nearly as much improvement as I had perceived myself to have achieved.

The degree of disappointment in myself that I felt at that time was at such an unspeakable level, that although I signed on to join full-time with Andersen, planned for September 2002, I felt little-to-no-joy about the situation. There were many effects. One of them was that for a while I completely lost interest in the physical experience of orgasm. Then, as some time went by, I found extra levels of clarity of mind and what I perceived to be a boost to consciousness of deeply spiritual elements of things. As time went by, I started to decide to completely avoid intentional orgasm, until such a time as I might someday get married. I also studied various areas of religion, and found some things in various areas that encouraged this type of approach. Indeed, in the years since then, all the way until now, I have completely avoided intentional orgasm, even on the rare occasions of having sex with women, in keeping with some spiritual practices involving this nature of regulating sexuality. A degree of stimulation at times would be appropriate, in some contexts, within how I coordinate these spiritual choices, though aimed at avoiding a climax.

One of the areas of emphasis in some of the related religious practices involves the male body avoiding ejaculation. Some of these spiritual traditions also present possibilities of the male system experiencing orgasm, even sometimes whole-body orgasm, while avoiding ejaculation.

On a related note, there have been a number of calendar years in which I completely avoided accidental ejaculation except for those triggered by the sleeping state of the body [i.e., nocturnal emissions, including rare occasions when I suddenly woke up in the brief window of time between the sleeping state triggering and the emission happening]. Specifically, those were the calendar years of 2006, 2008, 2009, 2011, 2016, 2017, and 2018. On a related note, 2011 and 2016 were at an extra level of the spiritual practice, as they included sex with women while successfully intentionally avoiding orgasm. I do not keep written records on this sensitive subject of human activity, and I rarely speak about it, in keeping with etiquette guidelines to generally stay quiet about this type of thing.

[End of 23-24AUG2019M TRNSCRS #24]

COMMENTARY: With the 2011 extra-level perfection of that practice the partner seemed definitely a cisgender woman and was probably about 27 years old at the time. In contrast, with the 2016 extra-level perfection of that practice the partner expressed femininity through clothing and portions of behavior, and appeared to lack an Adam's Appple, but she had some very unusual aspects of appearance, and I am highly uncertain about her precise gender classification. If law enforcement—whether the portions receiving complimentary copies of this book or any other portions—wishes to interview me thoroughly about this or anything else, then go for it. *Not only do I feel fine about dealing with any and all risks of interactions with law enforcement, I feel fine about dealing with any and all possible risks of instant human extinction by any method(s) known or unknown to anyone.*

[Start of 23-24AUG2019M TRNSCRS #25]

Also, in 2019 thus far I have completely avoided accidental ejaculation except for those triggered by the sleeping state of the body. However, when I participated in a yoga class on June 1st, 2019, I experienced what I would characterize, in retro-spect, as a degree of unintentional, sustained whole-body orgasm, while avoiding ejaculation. I admit that some would characterize that experience as simply an extreme euphoria of well-being, without quite reaching the definition of orgasm; however, semantics, aside, whichever way we may look at this, I believe that my religion-based extreme sexual regulation is closely related to how well that yoga session went.

[End of 23-24AUG2019M TRNSCRS #25]

COMMENTARY: Many people can get caught up in the semantics and how to twist and contort definitions (e.g., the infamous controversy around how President Bill Clinton deflected questions about whether Monica Lewinsky had performed fellatio on him in the oval office as part of an extramarital affair; also, e.g., the gospel expressions of Christ criticizing the Pharisees), and, in relationship with that, 23AU19M included more directly how I think and feel and remember the nonejaculatory total-body orgasm experience from the June 1, 2019 yoga session, whereas 23-24AUG2019M included how I filtered my writing about it to attempt to have it more agreeable to many readers who might have felt their sexual paradigms excessively under siege by what I wrote.

Here is how 23AU19M expressed it:

However, when I participated in a yoga class on June 1st, 2019, part of the time I experienced unintentional, sustained whole-body orgasm to a degree, while avoiding ejaculation.

Back to Some March-to-May 2024 Discussions:

As an update to the time of the publication of this book, I shall omit the exact performance record of my continued activity on Team Sexual Austerity, but, suffice it to say, I have continued to perform extremely well in terms of severely restricting my biological system's rare occurrences of ejaculation, almost all of which for over two decades now have been limited to those triggered by wet dreams. This has included continued the over-23-years-straight streak of practicing the complete and utter extinct-tion of intentional orgasm.

If I someday get married, then that could present a time in which part of the Esoteric Christian practice and the intermediate-level Vajrayana Buddhist practice might diverge on this austere sexual regulation.

Part of the way I presently (of the marital status of being single) practice Esoteric Christianity involves continuously successful adherence to the guidance found on the Internet many years ago that stipulates that total extinction of intentional orgasm should be practiced by all human beings at all times, whether single or married, lest they fall prey to one or more form of the sin of fornication. In that conceptualization, it is such that a married couple can only avoid the sin of fornication if they meet both the condition of honoring marital fidelity *and* the condition of avoiding intentional orgasm when having sex with each other.

Part of the way I presently (of the marital status of being single) practice Vajrayana Buddhism involves continuously successful adherence to the intermediate-level guideline to completely avoid any instances of intentional ejaculation (if a male; bear in mind that some have stated that the related such guideline should function differently for the females).

Although I decline at this time to forecast any specific probabilities about the chances of my ever someday getting married to anyone, there is, as is clear from this discussion, a potential contradiction in those two types of guidance. Yes, bear in mind that there are many different ideas of what people should do as part of practicing Esoteric Christianity and many different ideas of what people should do as part of practicing Vajrayana Buddhism, but I have found some of what has worked very well for me for many years consistent with both of them. The possible future issue to have to navigate, with no clearly-chartered path seeming to be available for an ideal, premeditated resolution, is whether to be open to intentionally experiencing orgasm while having sex with the wife in that marriage or to remain completely closed to intentionally experiencing orgasm. The intermediate-level practices of Vajrayana Buddhism (in this version of interpreting them) would be compatible with it as one of the spiritually-viable changes available, whereas the practices of Esoteric Christianity (in this version of interpreting them) would label it as one of the manifestations of the sin of fornication. In contrast, most mainstream versions of Christianity would consider intentional orgasm during sex between a husband and a wife while married to each other to not inherently be a type of fornication, per a very large numbers of fragments of sermons from a very large number of Christian preachers and other Christian clergy members from diverse denominations, as well as some who consider themselves to be nondenominational. That is also an often-unspoken implication among much of the Christian laity a high percentage of the time, as we can know without having to perform some total mind-melding exercise; rather from taking cues from huge numbers of conversations and other presentations.

To whatever degree anyone reading this might find the discussion ridiculous, and to whatever degree anyone reading this might find the entire discussion serious and enlightening, as well as to whatever degrees, if any, a given reader might wind up vacillating between those alternate perceptions of it, here is a takeaway that might prove a breath of fresh air to many members of any of those three camps: *There can be advantages to various practices that can assure one that one is on the correct path of maintaining a kind of moral high ground over the vast majority of the human race, but sometimes utilizing a seam that allows accord between different competing versions (of judging on what criteria that moral high ground consists) can only last for as long as some crucial condition avoids changing.*

* * * * *

Also, in case there was any doubt about it before stating it point blank, I have often thought about streaks of perfect records of limiting every experience of that to the wet dream category as paralleling statistics reflecting sports performances, such as a baseball player's fielding percentages (i.e., instances of avoiding errors to succeed in fielding divided by the total opportunities to succeed at that), a football team shutting out an opposing football team from scoring over an extended portion of a game or even over an entire game, etc.

*Previously, for many years prior to the developments of mid-December 2018, I thought I would never inform many people of this very much at all, based on the premise that no one would be likely to ever dare assault my character on what, from the kind of trial orientation from Part R of Section 5 of Chapter 10, would be, quite possibly, the only very solid thing I have going for myself as a total defense.* The fact of being on Team Austerity for a long time is, from that perspective, in some ways the only thing I have going for me that can prove beyond virtually any 10:R:5 trial-by-beings-of-the-beyond attack, and, in other ways, one of the few things that I definitely have going for me thus far in this life.

How dare Natasha McDaniel or anyone else present things in such a way as to be strongly suggestive of stripping from third parties even a trace of openness toward what I know to actually in reality be my likely best set of facts in support of defense in the aforementioned trial-by-multiple-of-the-semi-omniscient type of scenario?!

Hopefully after FinGroup and Gray Reed shut up toward me in the wake of when I sent the previously-referenced August 10, 2021 e-mail message to the SEC and Kelsheimer, they decided to cease and desist with performing character assassination against me behind my back, but it is hard to tell from where I stand.

Whatever the case may be, it is one thing for people to have a healthy skepticism toward what others present when they have no way to know for sure, but to jump right into giving those who bear false witness the benefit of the doubt on things like this is absolutely terrible. *It is terrible enough that I sometimes since then on a few rare occasions feel open to wondering whether Pol Pot (1928-1998) was correct to lead the wholesale slaughter of something like about one-third or one-fourth of the population of Cambodia when all hell was breaking loose over there, basing this on the premise that if a bunch of intelligentsia to include respected business leaders and lawyers can get their treatment of me that wrong, even with my bending over backward to give them flashing warning signs about what they are messing with in terms of Buddhism, Esoteric Christianity, metaphysics, nuclear physics, ethics, etc. and they can still repeatedly demonstrate not having a clue, then maybe it could be best every so often for something like the fifty-four wrathful deities of Angkor Wat to inspire a group of people like the Khmer Rouge to perform the wholesale executions of a giant number of the intelligentsia of a nation.*

Of course, I every so often catch myself silently and internally thinking and feeling that way, then think in a very different way.

For example, consider the following train of thoughts: *Wait, I do not really know how all those factors played out back then; maybe Pol Pot really is the monster that much of history portrays him as being; but then again maybe the intelligentsia back then were every bit as screwed up as my impression sometimes is of how some of those folks at FinGroup and Gray Reed acted toward me, and therefore, maybe Pol Pot and the Khmer Rouge were completely right to conduct such wholesale slaughter of their own people; I will go ahead and be agnostic toward whether the horrors unleashed by the Khmer Rouge onto Cambodia were very much a mixed bag of good and evil, totally justified, totally unjustified, mostly unjustified, mostly justified, or whatever else in that spectrum. Common sense can indicate that killing about one-third or one-fourth of the population of one's own country is one of the worst things that anyone could ever do. On the other hand, common sense is often dead wrong, especially in dealing with things like the justified propagation of the Dharma of Buddhism.*

*It can even use people who disbelieve it as unsuspecting conduits of serving as catalysts for many types of enlightenment. That can parallel how many monotheists tend to sometimes say, "God works in mysterious ways." Maybe the Buddhas and Bodhisattvas are much of the reality behind how people perceive the existence and the activities of God, or maybe God is much of the reality behind how many people perceive the statics and dynamics of the Buddhas and Bodhi-sattvas, or maybe something very different is going on with the mysteries under the surface of the many religions, philosophies, and sciences. The Buddhas, Bodhisattvas, and Dharma Protectors have plenty of authority to use both peaceful means and wrathful means to help foster enlightenment.*

*Consider how Pol Pot purportedly dabbled in Roman Catholicism and Buddhism, then departed from those in order to embrace a very straightforward Atheism and a Communist approach to things. In many ways his It is sometimes difficult to tell from a great distance away whether a bunch of people who acted with great wrath were proving to manifest more of a correct wrath or more of an incorrect wrath. Whatever the case might be, the Angkor Wat Temple is quite a mystery, much like how the United States Military-Industrial Com-plex is quite a mystery, and, somewhere amid all these mysteries in all of this reality, maybe, like some of the hopeful words from many people of diverse religions and cultures over the eons, the people of the world will find a way to a better future.*

Think again about what transpired between The Financial Advisory Group (as located in Houston, Texas) and me, from a variety of angles, arming your critical thinking skills and your emotional intelligence with a variety of competing paradigms and other tools, whether you think your use of such tools would be pleasing or displeasing to The Financial Advisory Group, International Campaign for Tibet, Holocaust Museum Houston, True Buddha School, The Drukpa Church of Nepal, any of the political parties who have wielded significant power anywhere anytime, yourself, your family, my family, me, or anyone else.

Next, contemplate for a little while what kinds of analogies and metaphors might prove helpful to yourself in trying to wrap your mind around the mayhem.

Before proceeding further, consider whether or not you wish to pause and reacquaint yourself with earlier portions of this book, any portions of any other cultural artifact that has ever existed anywhere in any form, or both.

* * * * *

________________________________________

________________________________________

________________________________________

Now, for something else: A playlist that I arranged long ago and used hardware and software to legally generate a custom compact disc music artifact.

Playing time as formatted, including any channeling: 78:05 (i.e., seventy-eight minutes and five seconds).

In the outline that follows, the main performers and/or other contributing artists attributed appear on the by-lines.

*Gloom & Doom & Silver Linings & Quicksilver*

1. "In the Year 2525 (Exordium & Terminus)" by Zager & Evans
2. "Green, Green Grass of Home" by Joan Baez
3. "Tales From The Darkside" by Donald Rubenstein and Erica Lindsay [1]
4. "The Unforgiven" by Metallica
5. "Eve of Destruction" by Barry McGuire
6. "The Omen" by Jerry Goldsmith [1]
7. "As Tears Go By" by Marianne Faithful
8. "Our Town" by Iris DeMent
9. "The God Who Failed" by Metallica
10. "American Pie" by Don McLean
11. "Suicide is Painless" by Johnny Mandell / M*A*S*H [2]
12. "Streets of Philadelphia" by Bruce Springsteen [2]
13. "I Guess It Never Hurts to Hurt Sometimes" by The Oak Ridge Boys
14. "Untitled 27" by Polly Scattergood
15. "Reflections of My Life" by Marmalade [3]
16. "March From The River Kwai/Colonel Bogey" by Mitch Miller & His Orchestra & Chorus [2]
17. "Be" by Neil Diamond [2]
18. "The Way We Were" by Barbara Streisand [2]
19. "Get Together" by The Youngbloods
20. "In the Year 2525 (Exordium & Terminus)" by Zager & Evans

[1] as appearing on *Sci-Fi's Greatest Hits Vol. 2: The Dark Side* [which collected Various Artists]

[2] as appearing on *Movie Music: The Definitive Performances* [which collected Various Artists]

[3] as appearing on *Ultimate Collection*

Although it will undoubtedly be uncomfortable for some readers to consider the comparison, I can and do compare this here to the following category of a scenario that has probably happened countless times over the millennia: 1) A wife never cheated on her husband. 2) Her husband found her one day standing five feet in front of another man in broad daylight. 3) At the time, the other man appeared affectionate toward her. 4) The wife appeared affectionate toward the man in front of her, even though he was not her husband. 5) The husband then jumped to a conclusion that his wife and the man standing about five feet in front of her had conducted an extramarital affair, committing adultery such as to cuckold him. 6) The husband then decided to be strategically dismissive and negative toward his wife while carefully arranging a slow process toward a divorce without being open with his wife about exactly what he jumped to conclusions about. 7) The wife suspected #6 to be the case, and decided to strategically drop hints with which to hope that the husband could read between the lines that he was on the wrong track if #6 was the case, and that she expected to go to holy war against him if he should dare to attempt to instigate a divorce based on the false premises associated with #6 (as his reaction to the pattern from #1-#5). 8) The husband later initiated for the divorce process to commence. 9) The wife was quite shocked that the husband did not have a clue from her efforts at conducting #7. 10) The divorce then presented some difficulties, but seemed on track to not be overly explosive. 11) Third parties proceeded to attack the wife's reputation in incidents separate from the divorce itself. Some of them showed much more hostility toward her than she would have ever previously expected, including attempts to intimidate her into not voting the way of her conscience and best attempts to utilize knowledge, critical thinking, and judgment. 12) Things took on extra levels of difficulty and tragedy after that. 13) The wife, though previously holding much back, finally retaliated in full, conducting justified holy war both against her ex-husband and many others who had interpersonally violated her well-being and defamed her character. She had thereby acted on righteous indignation with which to unleash extraordinary divine wrath unto many evil-doers who wound up deserved collateral recipients of punishment from REALITY ITSELF as part of helping with the long-term enlightenment of sentient beings. If you the reader are an online retailer who encounters this passage and finds it to be over-the-top and starts to consider it a reason to remove it from listings of books available for sale, be forewarned, if its availability for sale becomes stripped from many retailers, I may yet arrange to have a much larger quantity purchased by myself from whatever printers I deem suitable and choose to escalate how many copies I send to people of power as a message of how this testimony relates to anything relevant. Anything relevant, that is, that could prove helpful with soteriology (i.,e., salvation, enlightenment, conscience, effectiveness, spiritual well-being, the duty of beings to honor each of the most profound levels of reality, etc.).

* * * * * * * * * * * *

I do sometimes wonder whether it might have been better to take the advice I received from one prominent Texas attorney to go ahead and sue Natasha McDaniel for defamation of character soon after FinGroup's August 6, 2019 termination interview. However, there were several problems with that approach, and I believe that I most likely made the right choice to decline it. That attorney indicated that he would not be on board at that time with helping me to pursue an attempt to sue FinGroup, but he offered to let me hire him to help me sue Natasha McDaniel personally. To reiterate, at this time I believe I made the right decision in declining his offer and choosing to stick with my main idea of primarily retaliating against The Financial Advisory Group, Inc. Here are some reasons for that evaluation:

First, The Financial Advisory Group, Inc. and Natasha both carefully concealed from me any clear indication of what her primary gripe against me in relation to the turning off of the lights while alone in that room was. Although I know that she made insinuations and verbally incendiary statements spread over multiple months, then sent a fatally-flawed email denouncement as a response to my hermetically-sealed email presentation of facts and truth on August 5, 2019, she left much vagueness in several elements of these.

*Second, the unbelievably bad way in which FinGroup botched the August 5-6, 2019 period of its interactions was a strong indication that, in many ways—as per the way that University of Texas professor Dr. Ehud Ronn presented a related pattern—FinGroup should be much more culpable than Natasha McDaniel.*

* * * * * * * * * * * * *

Sometime circa March 2002, Dr. Ronn was one of the presenters who analyzed the Enron and Andersen debacle that was then active news. At some stage, Dr. Ronn cited some long-ago naval battle in which some British high-ranking naval man decided to disobey orders, which seemed to have likely saved his life and the life of his crew. However, he was court martialed and determined to have lacked sufficient justification for disobeying the orders. *Therefore, the court martial process resulted in that British naval officer receiving the death penalty.* Also, Dr. Ronn made an analogy to a criminal and a police officer: *Enron had acted like a criminal, and Andersen had acted like a police officer who chooses to look the other way and let a criminal go unpunished by law enforcement.*

*Paralleling that, I believe that all FinGroup had to do to avoid several subsequent catastrophes was to act on my suggestion to hold reasonably thorough proceedings of looking into the matter, with plenty of internal communications to deal with it, documenting thoroughly what Natasha's statements were and what my statements were, get the information into the open, and complete a process that acknowledged it both in speech and in writing. That would include acknowledging both sides and openly making it clear to both sides what the other side's claims were. That would have been such that even if not giving me the benefit of the doubt, they would avoid both the fact and the appearance of building up much documentation and many discussions concealed from me and severely threatening my reputation with their giving the benefit of the doubt to Natasha's methods of falsely condemning my character and actions.*

*Of course, though, had they done that, then I would have been able to find out clearly whatever was under the surface of the cases in which I witnessed Natasha committing what were at intuitive and basic levels the kinds of defamation of my character that were very threatening to me but which some reasonable observers would have considered to be rough innuendo, insinuations, and cruel, horseplay-style, vague condemnations, with twists of insulting humor that could throw much into question. Getting beyond the vagueness could have proven very helpful to me and protected FinGroup from much of what I later did to FinGroup, though at the expense that it would have left Natasha much more wide open to becoming the focus of Vajrayana and Tetragrammaton-based holy war processes involving me and various levels of REALITY that I have paid my dues thoroughly to be able to work with in bringing consequences to sentient beings. In that case I would have likely had a very clear-cut way of letting go of attacking FinGroup, even after termination, because of how it could have then happened with due process. In such a scenario, attention would have almost undoubtedly shifted to focusing on either suing Natasha McDaniel for defamation of character and/or going straight to other means of publicly communicating much of the truth about the situation, in self-defense and in defense of much of the ability for people to accurately perceive reality and truth.*

*However, FinGroup obscured much of the situation with their methods of keeping me largely in the dark about the exact nature of what Natasha was accusing me of when speaking with other FinGroup personnel behind closed doors, etc.*

For a long time, after getting advice to let the 90-day right to sue to expire, subsequently letting it expire, and other developments, I thought if things would go well enough in my life, then it might be best to let go of the entire thing and fully move on, figuring that the EEOC charge and some related procedures might prove sufficient pushing back. However, as time went by and my life worked very well in some ways, in other ways I became able to kind of tell that some major suppressive elements in reality have been unfolding, stuff along the lines of ripples from disrespect from a variety of people, including some affiliated with FinGroup, had yet to receive sufficient self-defense actions and other forms of rebuke from me. Part of interpreting that has led me to believe that at least some people should deserve access to a written record from me that can help make sense of it all. This should also include opening the door for almost anyone, for at least a while, to be able to purchase a copy of such record through an online retailer or two or more.

Another couple of metaphorical parallels:

- Imagine a man whose primary thing that sets him apart from a high percentage of others is that he has a successful marriage that has lasted for over half a century, including plenty of children and grandchildren in a well-functioning family. If anything were to happen such as to wreak havoc on his family, then one of the worst scenarios would be some people kidnapped the rest of his family members, took them to a foreign land, murdered them, then spread rumors that he had been the murderer.
- Next, imagine a woman whose primary thing that sets her apart from a high percentage of others is that she has become an expert in one of the natural sciences, including that she achieved a PhD and succeeded as a tenured professor. If a totalitarian government took over the national government of her residence, locked her up in prison, and, as a follow-up step, proclaimed to the

public that she had never achieved anything real in her field, then that would be terrible.

* * * * * * * * * * * * 

A problem with these discussions about what went wrong between The Financial Advisory Group and me, what went wrong between The Democratic Party and The Republican Party, and what went wrong in multiple similar conflicts is that it can be all-too-easy to go completely out on a limb such as to issue absolute condemnation without even a trace of considering the more complete picture. In many ways the way that things played out was extremely terrible to me, yet I have found that even among family and friends it is hard for people to grasp any more than a very fragmentary understanding of it. That is one of the things about life: whether conceived in a way like Kris Kristofferson expressed in "Jesus Was a Capricorn" or like Mary Chapin Carpenter expressed in "The Place Where Time Stands Still" or another way, misunderstandings, mistrust, and clinging to trauma can be very problematic for many people much of the time, yet some paths forward are available for genuine understanding, the rebuilding of trust, and the letting go of trauma.

Also, although there were times that I believed that the Democratic Party itself as an entire organization was potentially more to blame than anyone at FinGroup, there have been many times that I have believed that there should be plenty of blame to go around to many people and organizations: blaming The Democratic Party, blaming The Republican Party, blaming the people who set up Enron and Arthur Andersen for their debacles, blaming The Financial Advisory Group, blaming Gray Reed, blaming political pundits, blaming myself, and blaming many other candidates for harsh criticism.

Sometimes this reminds me of Dwight Yoakam's portrayal of Hank Williams' psyche in his last few phases in this world before departing: the main studio recording performance of the song "Long White Cadillac," in which he considers whether to blame it on Audrey Williams, the fame, the money, himself, or anyone or anything else.

Nevertheless, whether I die homeless, penniless, and in the street, in some torture chamber, by a stray bullet, by a lightning strike, or by other means, for quite some time I have felt ready for it.

While I am alive, though, maybe a book like this can help many of those who get a chance to read it, whether they are among the political pundits, Gray Reed, The Financial Advisory Group, those who set up Enron and Andersen for their debacles, The Republican Party, The Democratic Party, explosives dealers, zookeepers, defense contractors, or anyone else.

* * * * * * * * * * * * 

Pivot to a larger view. Think about the beings who possess mammalian bodies in a given lifetime.

The ideas of right and wrong about legal, societal, and personal regulation of sexual activities can and do influence much of politics, religion, warfare, peace, business, and healthcare, whether many feel much like admitting that fact to themselves or not.

[Start of 23-24AUG2019M TRNSCRS #26]

I am not saying that these types of religious sexual practices are right for everyone all of the time. I recognize that the world involves an amazing diversity of lifestyles, beliefs, religions, and cultures, and I believe it can be right for people to regulate sexuality in a wide variety of ways.

Indeed, people practicing Vajrayana Buddhism, Esoteric Christianity, and Zen Buddhism have many different opinions on how to manage sexuality.

[End of 23-24AUG2019M TRNSCRS #26]

Consider how a great many different television shows and movies can complement that set of flexibility in many ways. Many songs, too.

[Start of 23-24AUG2019M TRNSCRS #27]

Regulating sexuality is one of the most central things within how I manage my religious practices.

[End of 23-24AUG2019M TRNSCRS #27]

---

A Critical Supplemental May 2024 Commentary:

*When people float along through life not having any idea for sure in most cases which of the people they are dealing with may be choosing lives of great sexual restraint and which are choosing lives that lack much sexual restraint, they might not suspect until it is too late that a given person whom they choose to totally disrespect might happen to be a person who has killed much of the normal range of human weakness toward sexuality within the psyche of that person, due to whichever motive or combination of motives. A person who has for an extended amount of time chosen to maintain a long-term extinction of much of what would otherwise be portions of psyche with major weakness toward libido and sex is a person who may very well feel fully ready to unleash unlimited wrath upon those whom, to the best of that person's ability to discern reality, are those deserving of having divine wrath land on them, whether those recipients of wrath prove strong enough to survive receiving that wrath or not. Wrath as a method of delivering the harsh consequences that could be called tough, impersonal, spiritual love that is open to acting on righteous indignation, that is.*

[Start of 23-24AUG2019M TRNSCRS #28]

Footnote 5: Given the information from Footnote 4, this helps demonstrate much of why the coworker's slander per se against me, as combined with FinGroup's extreme gross negligence in dealing with it, caused such an extreme offense. FinGroup's way of dealing with this amounted to an extreme unwillingness to make any reasonable accommodation at all toward my religious practices.

[End of 23-24AUG2019M TRNSCRS #28]

---

As another set of angles on the aforementioned items, as well as much else, consider the following transcript of the body of an electronic mail message that I sent to my aunt Jennifer Wei at 7:32 P.M. CDT on April 4, 2024 (as measured from the U.S.), presented in installments:

---

Installment #1 of A Transcript of An April 2024 M.J.B. message to His Aunt Jennifer:

Aunt Jennifer,

Recently, my mother, whose e-mail address is included on the cc line of this message to you, looked at your e-mail message from a few days ago to our family.

In this message I am simply writing to you as one person, not on behalf of the Blair family, yet my family plans to follow up with sending a family response to the aforementioned recent message from you. That family message to you is to include portions in which my mother responds to portions of what I send you in this email and whatever else she believes appropriate, and I respond to her responses. My mother has me run her e-mail address for her, as well as her online accounts in general, yet I am dutiful in showing her relevant messages and making sure that the rare messages that go out from her are with her full awareness and approval in terms of content. When she and I together send you a message after this one, it will be using the account I am using to send out this message. We expect that message to be both a direct response to your recent e-mail and a commentary on this message.

About twenty hours before the time of sending you this clarifying message, I finally got around to showing her that recent message from you. In translating it, she informed me that you were feeling sad that you heard from some people that my mother and I were often not getting along very well. In a little while, I will explain some of what has happened under the surface.

Before that, though, I wish to express concern for the well-being of you, Uncle James, Cousin Yunjay, Cousin Vitin, and other relatives in Taiwan, after the recent earthquake. My family will be reiterating that in the next message, by the way.

---

Installment #2 of An April 2024 e-mail message from M.J. Blair to Jennifer Wei:

Now I will describe everything that seems most relevant and nothing that seems irrelevant. I will do my best to be absolutely accurate while remaining focused on what would be appropriate.

Before my father married my mother, they were engaged for a while. Part of my father's idea was to restrict his marriage options to women of high probability to be great matches. After the marriage and after my birth, though, there emerged a conflict between them about whether to stay in Taiwan or to move elsewhere in connection with my father's defense contracting job of that time.

My father strongly believed it best for the family to move, yet my mother strongly believed it best for the family to stay. While the situation was still unresolved, my mother started to become disoriented. Soon, my father determined that emergency medical examination would be needed for her. The doctors determined that a brain aneurysm would require quick and precise brain surgery for there to be any chance of her survival.

A team of professionals arranged for a helicopter to transport my mother to the Philippines for the surgery. Although the surgery went well, there was a long recovery time. Also, although she recovered most of the facilities of normal human beings, there were several cognitive abilities that became sometimes missing from her.

---

Installment #3 of An April 2024 e-mail message from M.J. Blair to Jennifer Wei:

As time went by and many changes happened, things generally went fine for the family that consisted of my father, my mother, and me. However, here are several unusual things: 1) When health issues led to my father retiring early, the family became extremely stingy with the spending of money. 2) My mother would sometimes exhibit an inability to recognize the social boundaries of not getting excessively aggressive with taking from other people. The most glaring example of that while in El Paso was that one day she was caught shoplifting and detained, then it came out that with the after-effects of the aneurysm and brain surgery the diagnosis was that lingering brain damage had something to do with her poor judgment in choosing to shoplift at that time. 3) Although I consistently performed well academically and sometimes performed well athletically, I was often woefully behind in terms of interpersonal skills in the 1980s and 1990s. My interpersonal skills improved greatly in portions of 2000 and onward, yet I later found out with some horrendous character assasination and mistreatment from a few former business associates in portions of 2018-2021 that some areas of the concept of interpersonal skills are better viewed as becoming an illusion at least some of the time. For example, when one of the most applicable tools becomes my father's adage of, "Nice guys finish last, if at all." (Alternatively, that could be conceived like the Little Texas recording of a song titled "Kick a Little," which was popular in country music in portions of the 1990s.) I successfully defended myself from that 2018-2021 set of interactions with a variety of former business associates, three of which were of the names Natasha McDaniel, Juan Martinez, and John T. Jones. 4) The three aforementioned individuals in some ways had a few redeeming qualities in their interactions with me, some of which will be illustrated in the following transcript resembling a set of communications (some of which were spoken and some of which were written and sent by email) from approximately the first half of April 2019:

Chris Kolenda: Maurice, you didn't even look at that last draft for estimating an extension payment amount!

Maurice J. Blair: I did look at it! However, the software did something very weird, and I was trying to figure out what had happened while being badgered by my mother late at night; she was calling me over and over again to complain that I was still working and not going home, and I also used some speed-reading kinds of methods with looking at the return pages.

Chris: If you don't look at it carefully enough, then it's virtually like not looking at it.

Maurice: Yes, but at that stage, knowing that you would be reviewing it, and facing such repeated pressure from my mother calling the office over and over again to complain harshly and tell me that I really should go home and not worry about squeezing in more work, I decided to finish sending that over without yet getting to the bottom of why something seemed so strange. I suppose that although I had been instructed to make sure to finish sending a draft estimate before leaving for the day, it might have been better if I had decided to decline to finish sending a draft, and to go home for the situation to be reasonably peaceful, then to go back the next day to work on it some more.

Natasha: That estimate had to get done by the end of that day. You should have worn the pants in your family and put your foot down, insisting that you would finish the estimate and perform it well before leaving that night.

---

Although I have sometimes considered the big picture of how Natasha McDaniel acted toward me in other interactions as having been among the most unethical behavior that anyone has ever done toward me in my life (some of which could have been blamed on her, some of which could have been blamed on political leaders, some of which could have been blamed on societal problems in general, etc.), on the specific point described in the above, I believe she was very much on target. That is, accurate about how in some situations I would best be even more ready to reject my mother's instructions and orders than I had been prior to that work incident.

---

Installment #4 of An April 2024 e-mail message from M.J. Blair to Jennifer Wei:

I have even taken that approach to virtually everyone everywhere in that no matter how highly anyone might rank in terms of organizational leadership, government leadership, any other kind of leadership, any combination of social status and ranking or whatever, I am much more ready than before to nip problems in the bud by exploding on them with vicious speech and nonverbal communication early in when potential problems arise. This is similar to some things I had observed about my father, though I ended up waiting to emulate him with them until when The Financial Advisory Group, Inc. (as located in Houston, TX) crossed several redlines in their interactions with me in portions of August 5-6, 2019.

---

My mother Ming has been able to oftentimes get along well with me, though she has also oftentimes not gotten along very well with me. Rather than going into almost every detail and incident, which would be way beyond the scope of this message, I will mention just three more things.

5) In mid-to-late 2001, I spent multiple sessions with a therapist named Victor Rivera, seeking improvements in general with how to run life. One of his recommendations for me was to consider that, although parents can be very helpful many times and in many ways, their distortions can be huge parts of why people's lives can get messed up.

One of the exercises he had me perform was to a) imagine having an unlimited supply of time and money, b) then to look at a local paper's advertisement section for activities such as festivals, other public events, and dining at medium-to-high-priced restaurants, c) to identify which of those activities I might prioritize participating in if time and money were no object, and d) to actually participate in such activities at least occasionally.

Although I have not become a huge spender all that often, in order to get life to have a reasonable chance to become better, I have occasionally chosen to temporarily become a big spender, even though those occasions in almost every case led to my mother repeatedly second-guessing, complaining, and condemning the boosted spending, no matter how much I would believe in it being the correct choice in the situation (or one of multiple correct choices available in the situation) and no matter how much I would explain to her much of why to go with those options.

---

Installment #5 of An April 2024 e-mail message from M.J. Blair to Jennifer Wei:

6) My father spoke openly with me multiple times about how it was much easier for him to deal with my mother before her aneurysm and brain surgery processes. Of course, however, he was able to find ways to love her and take reasonable care of her anyway.

7) My mother has told me many times that she had hoped that if one of my parents would die first that it could have been her, because she knew that my father and I would tend to get along consistently well most of the time, whereas she and I would tend to very much

have a roller coaster of getting along well, then getting along poorly, then getting along at a mediocre level, then getting along well again, followed by new cycles of many ups and downs. Although she and I have many conflicts, we also resolve them frequently.

Often, both she and I agree to work on doing better with taking care of each other and other people and responsibilities in general.

Regards,

Maurice J. Blair

---

A Transcript of the Follow-Up Message, Which was From The Blair Family Both to the Aunt-Jennifer-Wei-&-Uncle-James-Chen Family in Taiwan and to The Tse Family in Hong Kong, sent at 9:13 P.M. U.S. CDT April 4, 2024:

Aunt Jennifer, Uncle James, Cousin Alex, Aunt Yueh-Hwa, Any Other Relevant Extended Relatives, and Anyone Close Family Might Choose to Share this With,

This message will clearly show which portions are from Ming (Cousin Jim's mother; in other words, sister to Jennifer, aunt to Alex, etc.) and which portions are from Cousin Jim.

Statement 1 from Ming to Relevant Relatives in Asia: We prayed for the well-being of people in Taiwan after that earthquake.

Response 1 from Jim: Yes, we have been concerned, and we hope that those of you receiving this message, as well as other people in Taiwan will have good chances for recovery and well-being. Recently, we have prayed for this, too.

Statement 2 from Ming: I agree with Jim about the earlier message to Jennifer.

Response 2 from Jim: When we were getting ready to put together this follow-up message, my mother suggested that we include Cousin Alex in this message. A pdf copy of that earlier message is included as an attachment to this message. Please take a look at it, Alex, as it can help with better understanding some of our challenges and how we are working on doing better with dealing with them.

Statement 3 from Ming: Please take good care of the family members, including the extended relatives.

Response 3 from Jim: Yes, please take good care of each other. Also, I noticed that although the previous message from me made reference to Aunt Jennifer feeling sad in relation to some developments, consulting Google Translation and discussing it with my mother, I found out that this was a between-the-lines implication rather than something stated directly. The main expression involved Aunt Yueh-Hwa having recently felt extremely concerned about how my mother and I have sometimes had extra difficulties getting along in recent years. Still, we are getting along reasonably well in general, with many ups and downs, including getting back on track repeatedly.

Additional Statement from Both Ming and Jim: We were shocked recently to learn of the major earthquake that hit Taiwan earlier this week, we hope that you are currently safe, and we hope that things will go well for you in the near future.

All Our Love,

Blair Family

---

---

By the way, the October 12, 1903 entry in Chapter Seven derived from records of a game of that day that pitted versus each other Emmanuel Lasker and an opponent not named by the records; the entry utilized a method of contorting traditional chess notations into something that weaves together much symbolism.

Similarly, the August 29, 2015 entry in Chapter Seven derived from a combination of records of a game that pitted Wesley So versus Hikaru Nakamura on that day and featuring the same weaving method that transfigured notation for the Lasker-vs.-No-Specified-Name game from over eleven decades before it.

Sometime around the December 1994 to December 1997 range or thereabouts, there was a long-distance debate disagreement in which Eva-Maria Gortner presented to me that she had started to think that everything that happens with the human race is in some way rooted in urges toward reproduction and survival, whereas I argued back that I thought that we should seriously regard quality of life as being important, with or without reproduction, and with or without biological survival. Eventually, I was able to think much more thoroughly and arrive at a couple of diagrams, one of which appears below on this page, and the other of which appears on the following page.

"A Diagram That Has Probably Been in The Public Domain For Ages, Though Maurice James Blair Thought of It on May 6, 2024 and Composed It; Many Other Beings Probably Composed Something Essentially Identical to It Centuries Earlier; and Maurice James Blair Had Not Previously Witnessed It Anywhere by Sensory Perception Before Composing It, Likely Duplicating Some Previously-Published Diagram(s) to Some Very Major Degree"

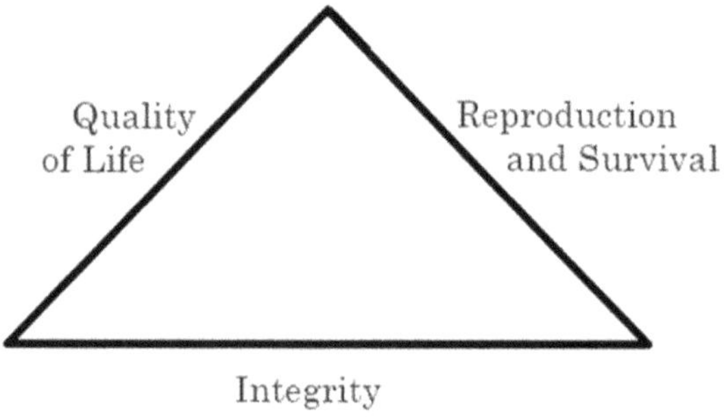

"A1B1T1T2A2B2T3"

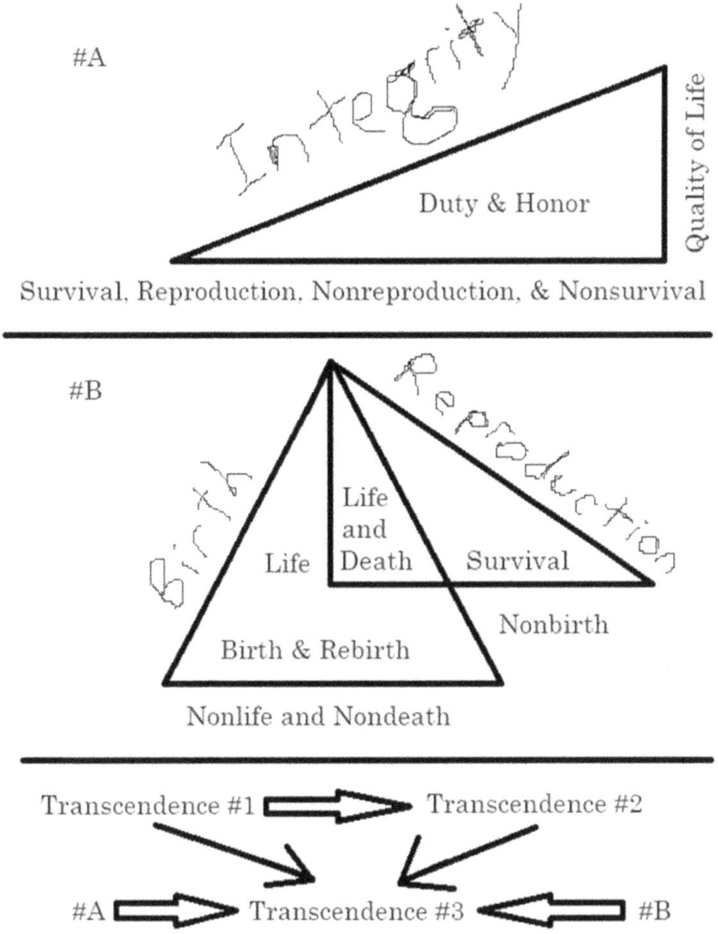


(diagram composed by M. James Blair on May 6. 2024)

---

## SECTION SIX, PART C

Redacted copies of select correspondence and related discourse are here presented as image files rather than transcriptions, and a variety of narratives then follow up on their themes:

A May 4, 2024 View to the Two Notifications Received by Maurice Blair (@M_James_Blair) on X (formerly known as Twitter)

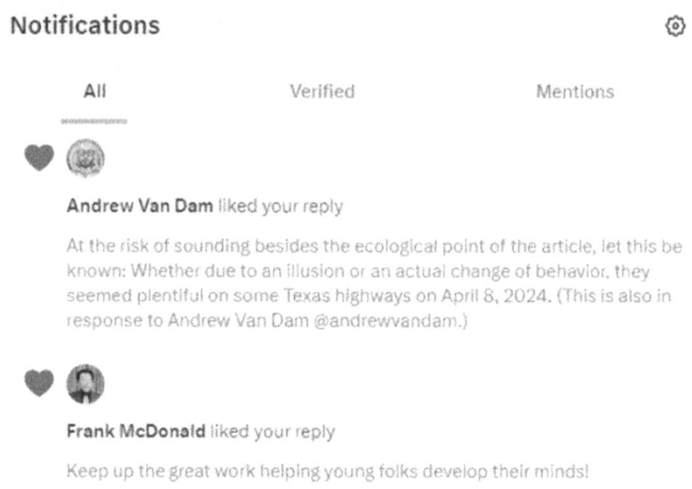
Notifications
All
Verified
Mentions
Andrew Van Dam liked your reply
At the risk of sounding besides the ecological point of the article, let this be known: Whether due to an illusion or an actual change of behavior, they seemed plentiful on some Texas highways on April 8, 2024. (This is also in response to Andrew Van Dam @andrewvandam.)
Frank McDonald liked your reply
Keep up the great work helping young folks develop their minds!

People followed by Maurice Blair (@M_James_Blair) / X

**Maurice Blair**
@M_James_Blair

Verified Followers | Followers | **Following**

**Science News**
@ScienceNews
Following
Covering the latest news in all fields of science. Publisher @society4science. See also @SN_Explores.

**Frank McDonald**
@FMcDonald_JDS
Following
8th Grade Science Teacher

**Wesley Hunt**
@WesleyHuntTX
Following
Father, Husband, Army Veteran, West Point Graduate, Native Texan, Congressman for TX-38. Follow @RepWPH for Congressional Updates. (American/Apache Pilot)

**Elon Musk**
@elonmusk
Following

**Dalai Lama**
@DalaiLama
Following
Welcome to the official twitter page of the Office of His Holiness the 14th Dalai Lama.

**Liza Darnton**
@LizaDarnton
Following

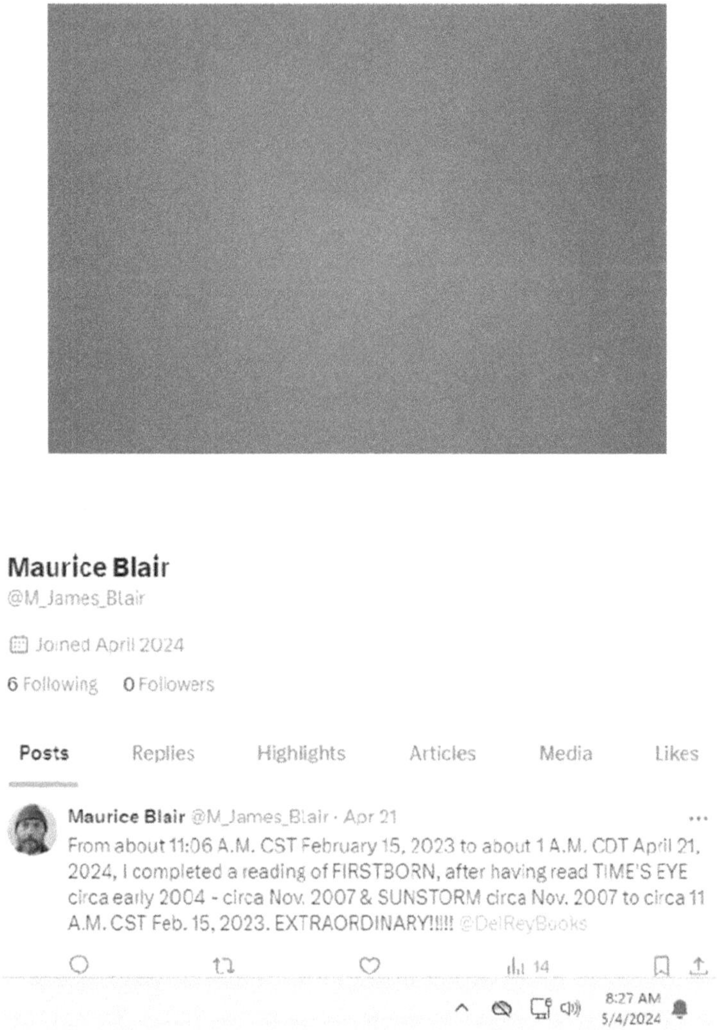

**Maurice Blair**
@M_James_Blair

Joined April 2024

6 Following 0 Followers

Posts Replies Highlights Articles Media Likes

**Maurice Blair** @M_James_Blair · Apr 21
From about 11:06 A.M. CST February 15, 2023 to about 1 A.M. CDT April 21, 2024, I completed a reading of FIRSTBORN, after having read TIME'S EYE circa early 2004 - circa Nov. 2007 & SUNSTORM circa Nov. 2007 to circa 11 A.M. CST Feb. 15, 2023. EXTRAORDINARY!!!!! @DelReyBooks

14

8:27 AM
5/4/2024

←

**Maurice Blair**

25 posts

ılı 14

**Maurice Blair** @M_James_Blair · Apr 10 ···

Here is a glimpse of a partly cloudy total solar eclipse and related scenery in Texas and from the skies above on April 8, 2024.

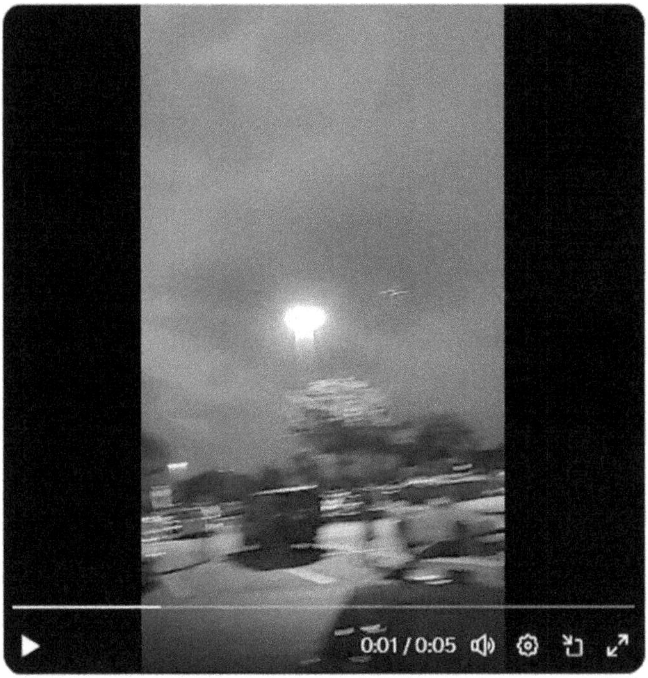


ılı 15

**Maurice Blair** @M_James_Blair · Apr 8 ···

If anyone anywhere has any issues to wish to deal with by speaking directly to me, then there's a great chance you might be able to find me either in a restaurant or outdoors in Fredericksburg, TX around lunchtime today.
(Posted: April 8, 2024, about 4:25 AM U.S. CDT)

ılı 20

8:10 AM
5/4/2024

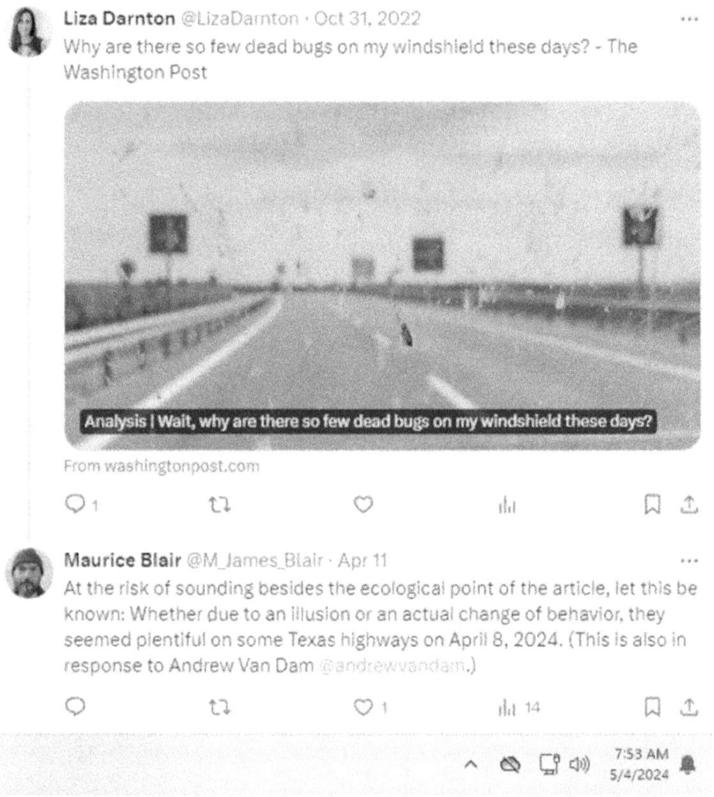

**Liza Darnton** @LizaDarnton · Oct 31, 2022

Why are there so few dead bugs on my windshield these days? - The Washington Post

Analysis | Wait, why are there so few dead bugs on my windshield these days?

From washingtonpost.com

1

**Maurice Blair** @M_James_Blair · Apr 11

At the risk of sounding besides the ecological point of the article, let this be known: Whether due to an illusion or an actual change of behavior, they seemed plentiful on some Texas highways on April 8, 2024. (This is also in response to Andrew Van Dam @andrewvandam.)

1 14

7:53 AM
5/4/2024

## An advertisement from early 2023 C.E.:

Format Comparison for print purchase availability in early 2023 for *All Things under and over the Sun and Stars: Enigmas in Various Stages* (M. James Blair)

| Size: | Trade | Royal | Trade | Executive |
|---|---|---|---|---|
| Format: | Paperback | Hardcover | Hardcover (with dust jacket) | Hardcover |
| Cover Design Firm: | RL Design | Creative Paramita | RL Design | Creative Paramita |
| Main Distribution Channel: | Amazon | Amazon | Barnes and Noble | Lulu |
| MSRP for a new copy: (in U.S. Dollars) | $17.56 | $37.90 | $54.99 | $105.65 |

## An item from the year after that:

Consider This Here May 4, 2024 Evening Addendum:

An *Alternative Beginnings and Endings of All Things* Supplemental Note: Although this work refrained from pursuing officially-stated permission from those from whom it used de minimis amounts of copying as a fair use of copyrighted materials, it has done this in a manner consistent with the m.o.'s of many creatives over the eons, and if anyone anywhere wishes to sue over such utilizations, or anything else, then go for it, and those able to witness the aftermath may experience what happens in that scenario.

**Frank McDonald** @FMcDonald_JDS · Apr 3 ···
Playing shuffle board using spring scales to determine what force will provide the right acceleration to score the most points. #sciencethings

2 2 16 849

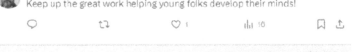

**Maurice Blair** @M_James_Blair · Apr 5 ···
Keep up the great work helping young folks develop their minds!

1 16

8:01 AM
5/4/2024

4:09 & 8:35 messages to & a 11:19 message from:

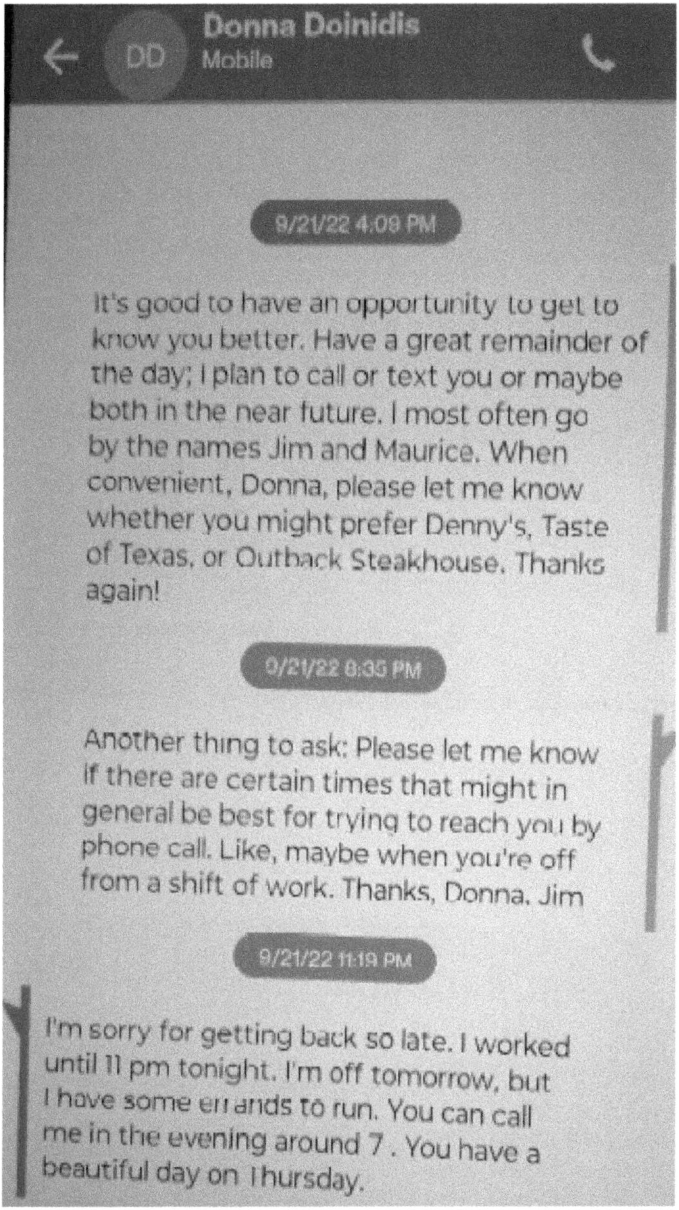
Donna Doinidis
DD
Mobile
9/21/22 4:09 PM
It's good to have an opportunity to get to know you better. Have a great remainder of the day; I plan to call or text you or maybe both in the near future. I most often go by the names Jim and Maurice. When convenient, Donna, please let me know whether you might prefer Denny's, Taste of Texas, or Outback Steakhouse. Thanks again!
9/21/22 8:35 PM
Another thing to ask: Please let me know if there are certain times that might in general be best for trying to reach you by phone call. Like, maybe when you're off from a shift of work. Thanks, Donna. Jim
9/21/22 11:19 PM
I'm sorry for getting back so late. I worked until 11 pm tonight. I'm off tomorrow, but I have some errands to run. You can call me in the evening around 7 . You have a beautiful day on Thursday.

## 9/23/2022 & 3/2/2023 Text Messages From Maurice to Donna:

9/23/22 9:08 AM

Thanks for the response. Yesterday, Thursday, I took an important step with one of my business activities. After that I went on a combination of walking, taking buses, watching a movie at Memorial City Mall, and buying several meals, while deliberately leaving both of my cell phones at home. I did not get home until something like 2:10 or 2:20 AM, and it was just a few minutes ago that I found your text message. I plan to call you sometime today. I had a good Thursday. I hope you will have a good day today (i.e., Friday).

3/2/23 10:56 AM

A few months ago I changed back to having one cell phone instead of two. If you would still feel fine about sharing a phone call with me in the near future, then when might you recommend for me to call you? If I call you in the near future, then it would most likely either be from this cellular number or from the related landline. Happy Texas Independence Day!

A Copy of Additional D.D. and M.J.B. correspondence, with a little bit of redaction:

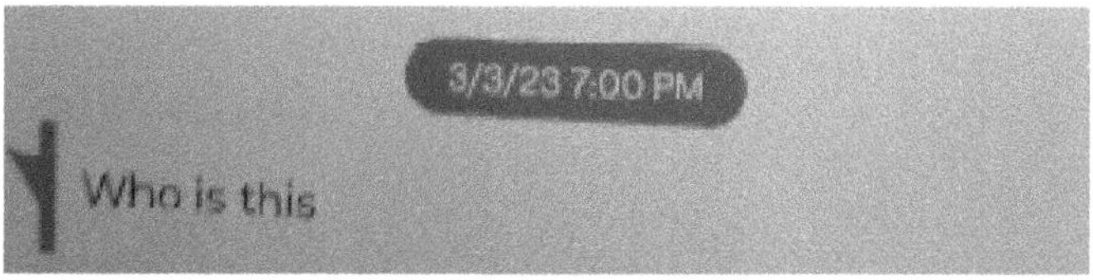

3/3/23 7:00 PM

Who is this

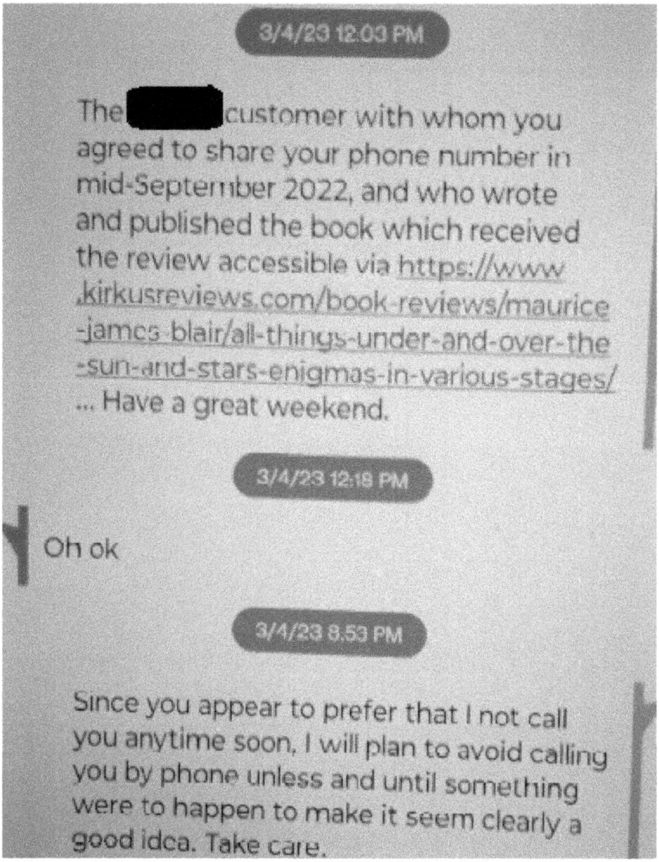

3/4/23 12:03 PM

The [redacted] customer with whom you agreed to share your phone number in mid-September 2022, and who wrote and published the book which received the review accessible via https://www.kirkusreviews.com/book-reviews/maurice-james-blair/all-things-under-and-over-the-sun-and-stars-enigmas-in-various-stages/ ... Have a great weekend.

3/4/23 12:18 PM

Oh ok

3/4/23 8:53 PM

Since you appear to prefer that I not call you anytime soon, I will plan to avoid calling you by phone unless and until something were to happen to make it seem clearly a good idea. Take care.

After she spoke warmly and favorably toward me on April 5, 2024, I texted her the next day.

4/6/24 7:06 AM

Donna, At this time I am very interested in the possibility that you and I could go on a date in the near future. Some dating sites may have people identify as more casual (preferring chances of either delaying or avoiding long-term commitment) or as more serious (preferring to improve the likelihood of entering a long-term romantic relationship with someone soon).

If you agree to date me, then I would gladly date you in the near future with either the casual approach or the serious approach, based on whichever you would prefer. Also, I would expect to respect your boundaries with dating, although I do not currently know what boundaries you prefer (and I presume that those are within reason). How about meeting me at Rudi Lechner's on one of the days of your choice from Tuesday the 9th to Friday the 12th? If you agree to this, then would you prefer to meet me for lunch or for dinner? Jim (whom you mentioned yesterday recommending try texting you again)

4/10/24 7:21 PM

Who is this?

4/10/24 7:49 PM

As I mentioned in the previous text message, I had a conversation with you on April 5, 2024 in which you asked me to text you. Previously, you and I had shared text message communications in September 2022 and in March 2023, though you said to me from the [redacted] register on the recent Friday the 5th that you had lost your old phone and had to replace it.

4/10/24 7:56 PM

I am not interested in dating.

4/10/24 8:07 PM

I'm sorry I know who this is

Although we can get together let me see what my schedule is on Friday.

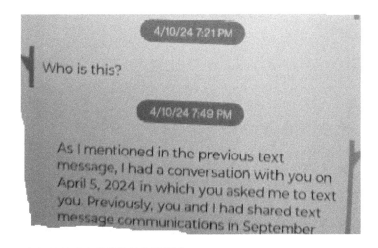

An April 10, 2024 Text From Maurice to Donna, Part I:

4/10/24 8:35 PM

Let me be absolutely clear, there is no need for you to apologize for any of your recent communications, whether the part in which you mentioned knowing who I am, the part in which you mentioned not knowing who I am, or the part mentioning that you are not interested in dating me. It has been decades since I have felt any resentment toward the act of a woman rejecting the possibility of dating me when the woman performs the rejection in a reasonably respectful manner, and I found your manner to be reasonably respectful. We can place the prioritization of meeting outside of the [redacted] business interactions, whether as Platonic friends or as acquaintances not quite at the level of being friends, into being low-to-medium priority. You have stayed within a reasonable range of interacting with me, and I do not feel a need to necessarily arrange to meet you outside of the grocery store processes, though there could be a beneficial effect for it, perhaps. If you

## An April 10, 2024 Text Message From Maurice James Blair to Donna Doinidis, Part II:

would prefer to limit our planned meeting in person to be only when I happen to be in the store and you happen to be working there, then that is fine with me as well. I am at a stage in my life that enough things have gone well enough that I feel that I could still have a reasonable life if I wind up not going on any more dates with anyone between now and when I die, although there may be benefits to if I ever again go on at least one more date, whether with at least one woman among the women I dated before or among the women who would be newly dating me. Also, more broadly speaking, oftentimes in recent months I feel that my life has been reasonably complete, and I am not overly concerned about the remote possibilities of getting struck to death by lightning or by a stray bullet from a gunfight between rival drug cartels while happening to be a third-party bystander, etc. Take care, whether we meet again in a given setting or not.

Delivered

A Lightly-Redacted Copy of Some of the Text Messaging between B.Roth and M.J. Blair:

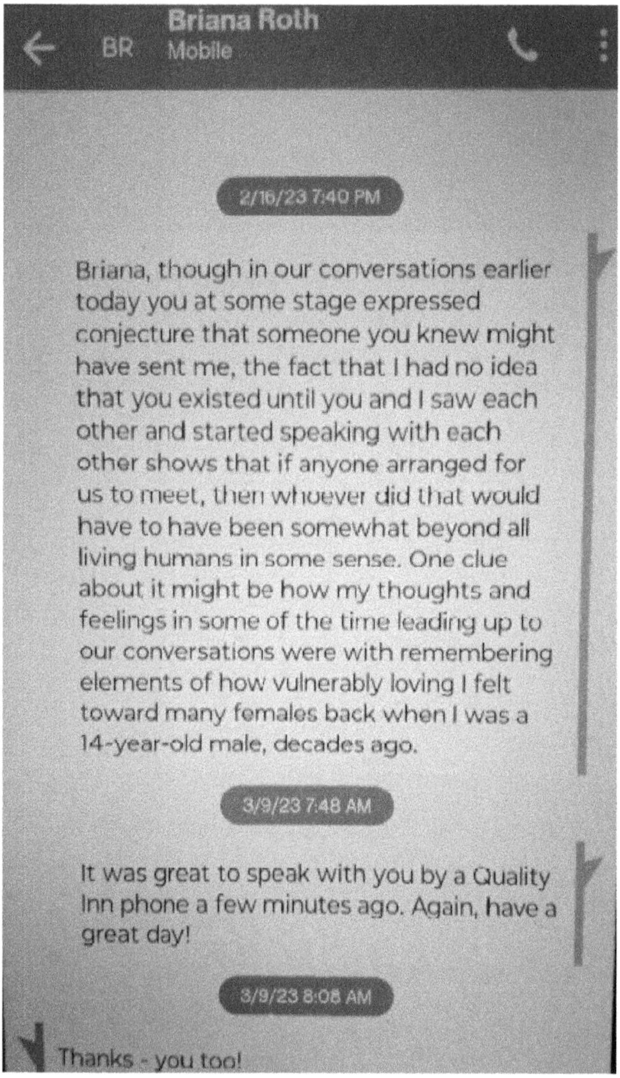

Briana Roth
BR Mobile

2/16/23 7:40 PM

Briana, though in our conversations earlier today you at some stage expressed conjecture that someone you knew might have sent me, the fact that I had no idea that you existed until you and I saw each other and started speaking with each other shows that if anyone arranged for us to meet, then whoever did that would have to have been somewhat beyond all living humans in some sense. One clue about it might be how my thoughts and feelings in some of the time leading up to our conversations were with remembering elements of how vulnerably loving I felt toward many females back when I was a 14-year-old male, decades ago.

3/9/23 7:48 AM

It was great to speak with you by a Quality Inn phone a few minutes ago. Again, have a great day!

3/9/23 8:08 AM

Thanks - you too!

Comment: I met her by the side of the road in SW Houston while she and I were both walking along as pedestrians.

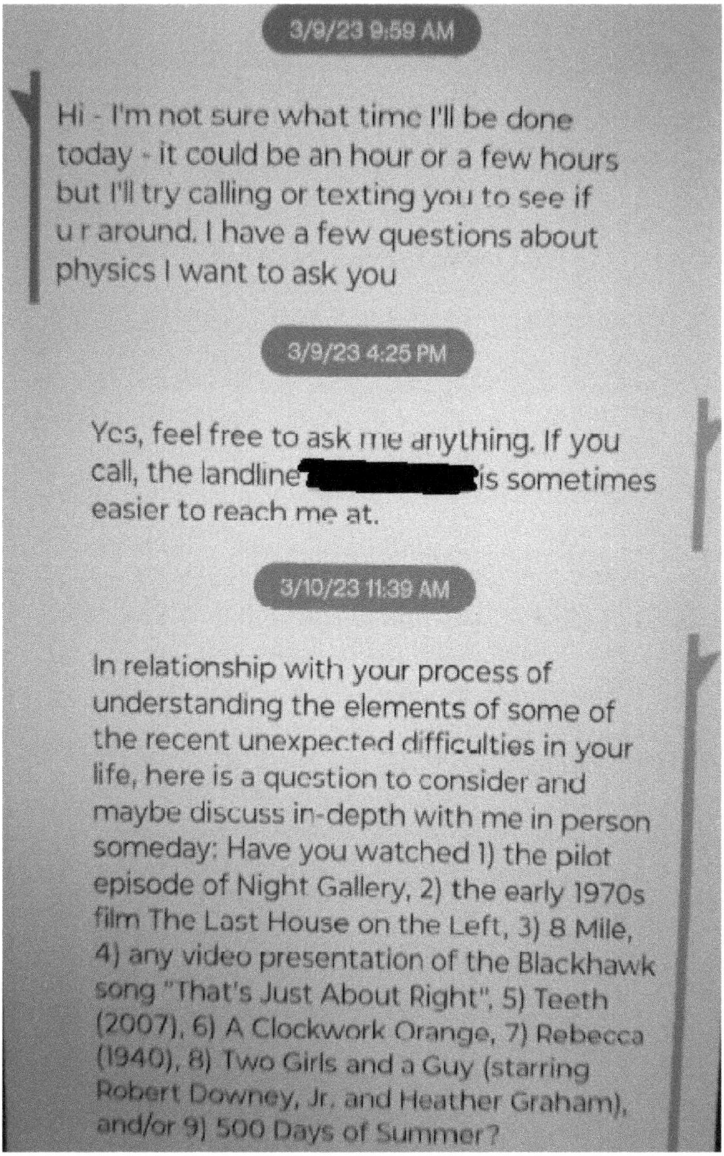

3/9/23 9:59 AM

Hi - I'm not sure what time I'll be done today - it could be an hour or a few hours but I'll try calling or texting you to see if u r around. I have a few questions about physics I want to ask you

3/9/23 4:25 PM

Yes, feel free to ask me anything. If you call, the landline [redacted] is sometimes easier to reach me at.

3/10/23 11:39 AM

In relationship with your process of understanding the elements of some of the recent unexpected difficulties in your life, here is a question to consider and maybe discuss in-depth with me in person someday: Have you watched 1) the pilot episode of Night Gallery, 2) the early 1970s film The Last House on the Left, 3) 8 Mile, 4) any video presentation of the Blackhawk song "That's Just About Right", 5) Teeth (2007), 6) A Clockwork Orange, 7) Rebecca (1940), 8) Two Girls and a Guy (starring Robert Downey, Jr. and Heather Graham), and/or 9) 500 Days of Summer?

Related comment:

8/26/23 11:47 AM

Yes, I still plan on the same mall we mentioned. I expect to be there about 12:10 as an updated ETA.

8/26/23 12:22 PM

Thanks for the update w/ our call a few minutes ago. It's fine with the legs situation regarding hair, I could adjust my mind in different ways about the civilization-versus-alternate-lifestyles perspectives easily; recall how the previous time we met I had major facial hair in full display! I'm going to expect to be in or near the fireplace area, which they seem to have restored to looking like a fireplace area, after some kind of recent hiatus, near the ice rink. Hopefully, we'll meet a little later, after you arrange your transportation method. If and when you arrive, I may or may not be wearing the aforementioned hat, yet I will expect to be wearing the shirt I have on right now, which includes "WESTERN" on part of the front of it.

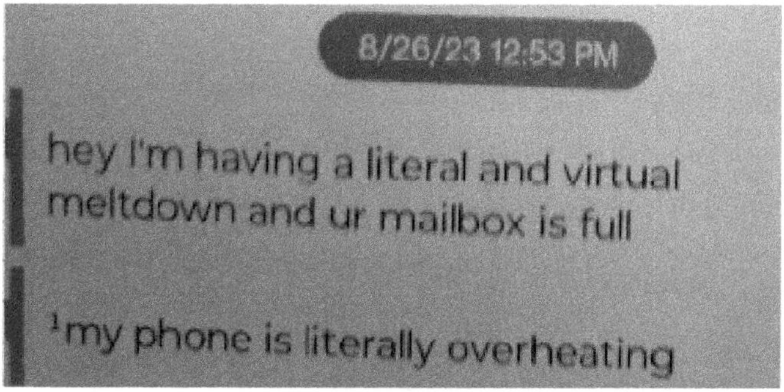
8/26/23 12:53 PM
hey I'm having a literal and virtual meltdown and ur mailbox is full
¹my phone is literally overheating

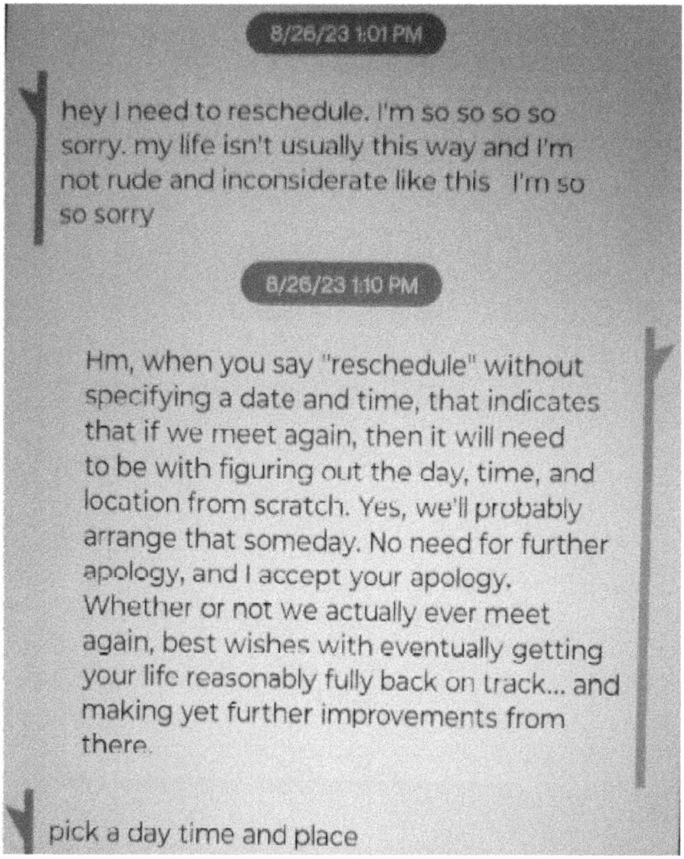
8/26/23 1:01 PM
hey I need to reschedule. I'm so so so so sorry. my life isn't usually this way and I'm not rude and inconsiderate like this I'm so so sorry
8/26/23 1:10 PM
Hm, when you say "reschedule" without specifying a date and time, that indicates that if we meet again, then it will need to be with figuring out the day, time, and location from scratch. Yes, we'll probably arrange that someday. No need for further apology, and I accept your apology. Whether or not we actually ever meet again, best wishes with eventually getting your life reasonably fully back on track... and making yet further improvements from there.
pick a day time and place

---

**********************************************************************************************

Some of Briana's texting already showed red flags as of that time, but I chose to press on through the situation. Whether that was a good decision, a poor decision, a mediocre decision, or whatever else, I have dealt with the reality that it was what it was.

Per the cellphone system, the following message from her went into transmission soon after 1:10 PM August 26, 2023.

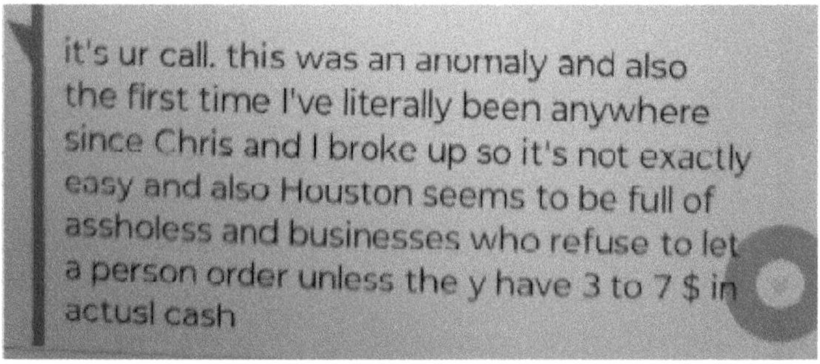
it's ur call. this was an anomaly and also
the first time I've literally been anywhere
since Chris and I broke up so it's not exactly
easy and also Houston seems to be full of
assholess and businesses who refuse to let
a person order unless the y have 3 to 7 $ in
actusl cash

**********************************************************************************************

I did not agree and do not agree with her very sweeping generalization of many people and businesses in Houston being terrible for insisting on patrons having at least $3 or $7 with which to place an order. However, I have refrained from informing Briana Roth of this disagreement, as part of sometimes maintaining the social nicety of choosing omissions aimed at agreeability. –M. James Blair, May 8, 2024

---

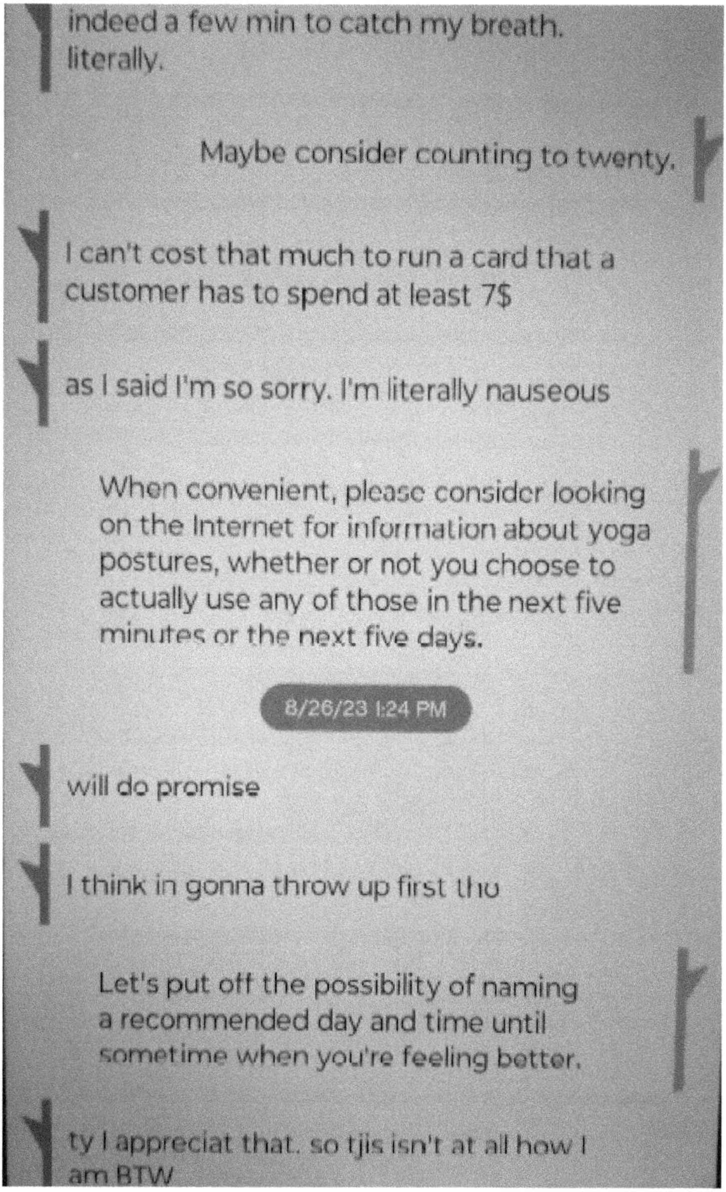

indeed a few min to catch my breath.
literally.

Maybe consider counting to twenty.

I can't cost that much to run a card that a customer has to spend at least 7$

as I said I'm so sorry. I'm literally nauseous

When convenient, please consider looking on the Internet for information about yoga postures, whether or not you choose to actually use any of those in the next five minutes or the next five days.

8/26/23 1:24 PM

will do promise

I think in gonna throw up first tho

Let's put off the possibility of naming a recommended day and time until sometime when you're feeling better.

ty I appreciat that. so tjis isn't at all how I am BTW

8/26/23 1:59 PM

Something about this entire situation reminds me of some mysteries involving Pink Floyd, Rosanne Cash, and Don Henley.

9/7/23 10:06 AM

So sorry thr reception in my room is horrible. I don't have I just tried calling back

9/7/23 10:33 AM

Call me later - I should be around

Sorry idk what's happening with my phone connection

9/7/23 12:16 PM

That's understandable. I called again, this time from cell phone rather than landline, just prior to sending this text message. When convenient, please send an email to [redacted] with the link to the article that you mentioned early in our phone conversations today. Thanks, and best wishes with the remainder of the day!

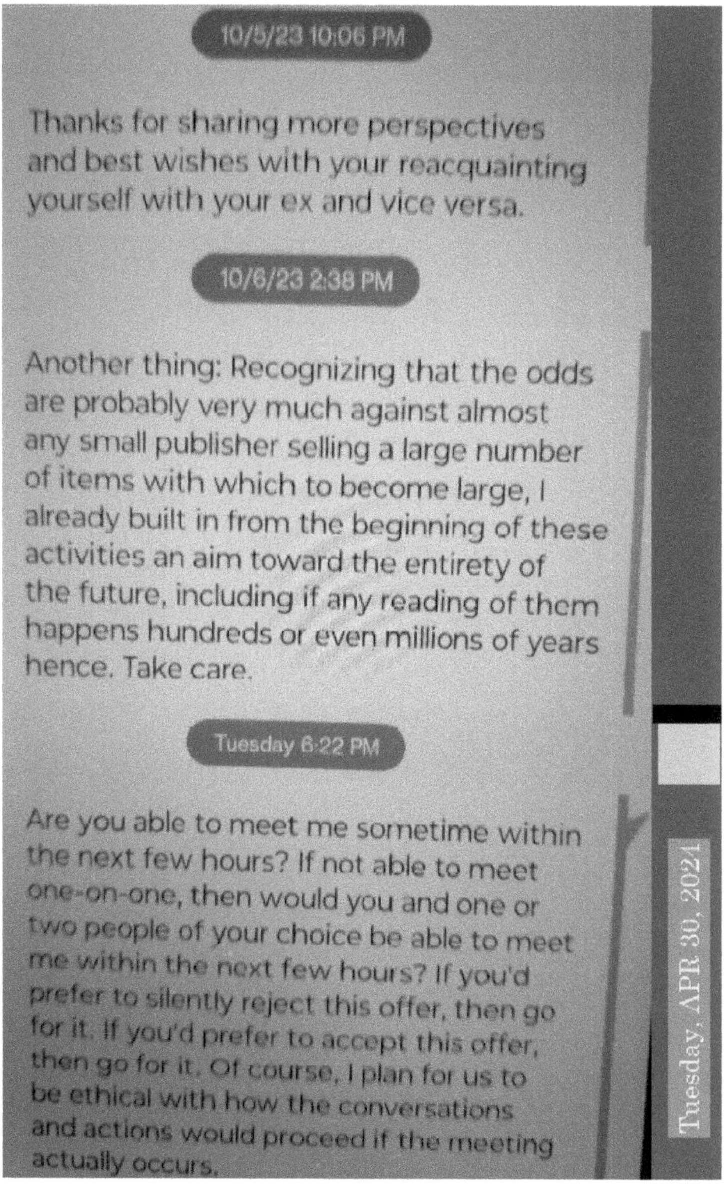

10/5/23 10:06 PM

Thanks for sharing more perspectives and best wishes with your reacquainting yourself with your ex and vice versa.

10/6/23 2:38 PM

Another thing: Recognizing that the odds are probably very much against almost any small publisher selling a large number of items with which to become large, I already built in from the beginning of these activities an aim toward the entirety of the future, including if any reading of them happens hundreds or even millions of years hence. Take care.

Tuesday 6:22 PM

Are you able to meet me sometime within the next few hours? If not able to meet one-on-one, then would you and one or two people of your choice be able to meet me within the next few hours? If you'd prefer to silently reject this offer, then go for it. If you'd prefer to accept this offer, then go for it. Of course, I plan for us to be ethical with how the conversations and actions would proceed if the meeting actually occurs.

Tuesday, APR 30, 2024

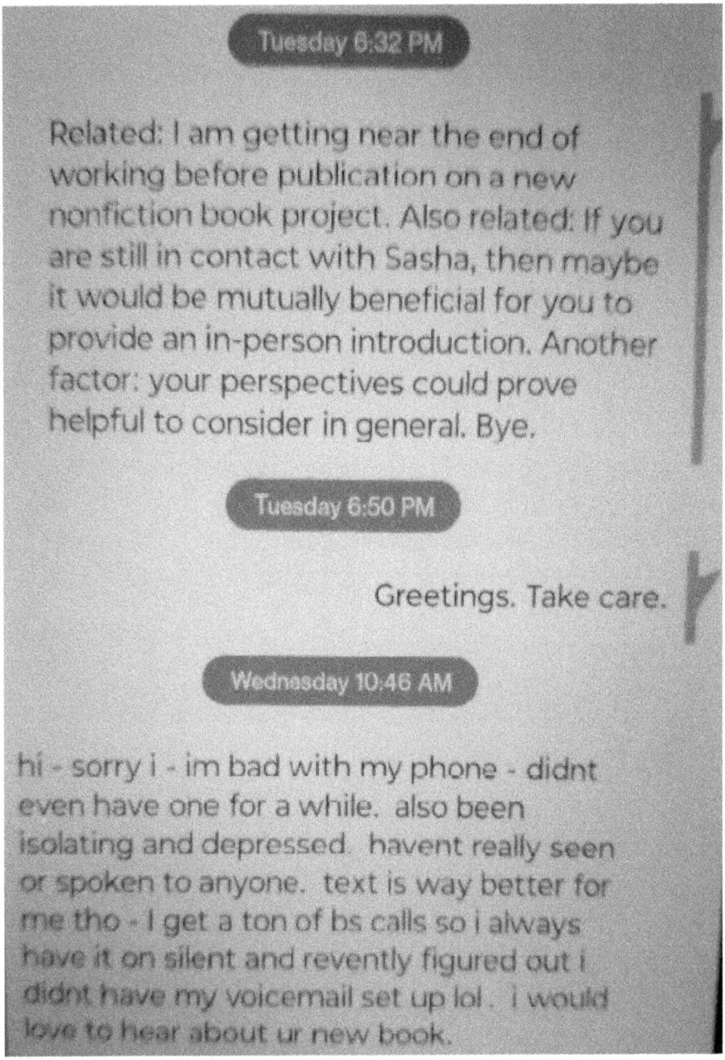
Tuesday 6:32 PM
Related: I am getting near the end of working before publication on a new nonfiction book project. Also related: If you are still in contact with Sasha, then maybe it would be mutually beneficial for you to provide an in-person introduction. Another factor: your perspectives could prove helpful to consider in general. Bye.
Tuesday 6:50 PM
Greetings. Take care.
Wednesday 10:46 AM
hi - sorry i - im bad with my phone - didnt even have one for a while. also been isolating and depressed. havent really seen or spoken to anyone. text is way better for me tho - I get a ton of bs calls so i always have it on silent and revently figured out i didnt have my voicemail set up lol . i would love to hear about ur new book.

Wednesday 11:48 AM

If you are that depressed, then how about if I could pick you up on my way to visit a library in Austin today, and I could bring you back to Houston by sometime tonight?

May 1, 2024

Wednesday 12:02 PM

hhhmmm - interesting - i would normally say yes - but my parents are going out of town tomorrow and my mom is taking me to get food and a few other things.

what is your book about? im so sorry i wasn't trying to be rude at all not getting back to you. i hate the phone and a bunch of other things. i actually have a few questions for you

and i really didn't have a phone for like almost 2 months after i got back from florida

Take care. Maybe we'll meet again, and maybe we won't meet again; either way, best wishes with prospects for enlightenment and enhanced enlightenment. The new book is set to be the sequel to the July 2023 book that my C Corp published. It involves science, comparative religion, and much more.

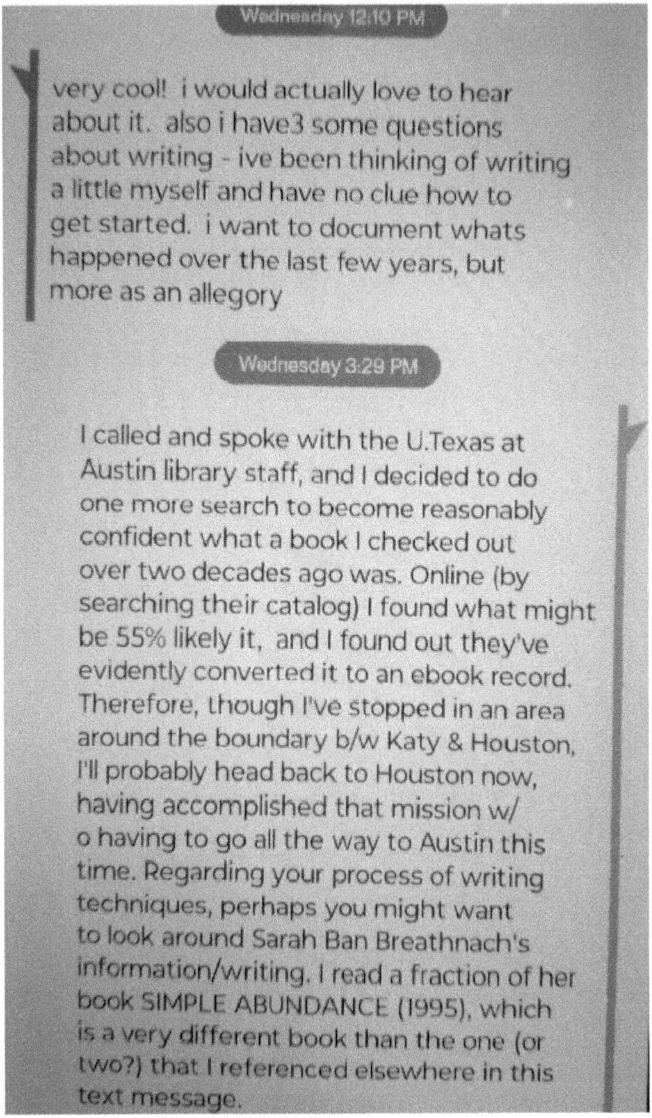

Wednesday 12:10 PM

very cool! i would actually love to hear about it. also i have3 some questions about writing - ive been thinking of writing a little myself and have no clue how to get started. i want to document whats happened over the last few years, but more as an allegory

Wednesday 3:29 PM

I called and spoke with the U.Texas at Austin library staff, and I decided to do one more search to become reasonably confident what a book I checked out over two decades ago was. Online (by searching their catalog) I found what might be 55% likely it, and I found out they've evidently converted it to an ebook record. Therefore, though I've stopped in an area around the boundary b/w Katy & Houston, I'll probably head back to Houston now, having accomplished that mission w/o having to go all the way to Austin this time. Regarding your process of writing techniques, perhaps you might want to look around Sarah Ban Breathnach's information/writing. I read a fraction of her book SIMPLE ABUNDANCE (1995), which is a very different book than the one (or two?) that I referenced elsewhere in this text message.

May 1, 2024, cont'd. From: Briana. To: Maurice.

thank u - hey - did you go to ut? that would be funny to look into the books that i checked out when i was there.

are you well read in the kaballah? i know - random, but ive been reading and learning the book modern magick. i have to be careful of Austin so probably good i didn't go regardaless - i am allergic to cedar and get terrible migraines and didn't even think about that at first.

its on my mind tho right now - im going thru my photos trying to get rid of accidental pics and just clean it up etc and im watching a video right now that i never understood - there is so much i never understood with chris - taht kinda has to do with all of that. very much related to psychic and magic etc. things you might be more familiar with - i would have to explain it all to you - what exactly im referring to and very hard do at the same time. anyway, sorry u drove all that way for nothing. Its a nice drive tho lol.

Wednesday 3:50 PM

i guess paranormal is the right phrase.

May 1, 2024, cont'd. From: Maurice. To: Briana.

Wednesday 4:37 PM

If you reread the 3:29 text, you may notice that I figured out what seems likely to be the answer I was after while on a stop around the Katy-Houston boundary, then decided to lean toward postponing a visit to Austin. I've looked into a little bit of Kabbalist stuff. Would you be open to meeting me in Houston tomorrow?

From: Briana Roth. To: Maurice J. Blair.

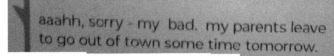

aaahh, sorry - my bad. my parents leave to go out of town some time tomorrow.

not sure when, but supposed to go to the store at some point with my mom....ill have to stay kinda close to the house while they are gone because i take care of the dogs, but i can for sure get out. im not sure if you have regular use of your car or not.

************************************************

Part of a 6:32 PM, May 1, 2024 Message From Maurice James Blair to Briana Roth, after several more rounds of back-and-forth messaging:

I wonder about whether maybe at either a conscious level or an unconscious level you intentionally mentioned your teeth while

remembering how I've told you before that I really love the movie TEETH (2007), though that ode to the controversies of gender relations and the uniqueness of individuals can make many guys cringe. Best wishes with whichever choices you make about your dental health, by the way. Since you have already partway agreed to Taste of Texas, I'll make a primary recommendation that I could pick you up at or near your home at about 6:30 tomorrow, May Second, and to plan to bring you back home at a reasonable time. Do you wish to agree or to present a countersuggestion?

***********************************************

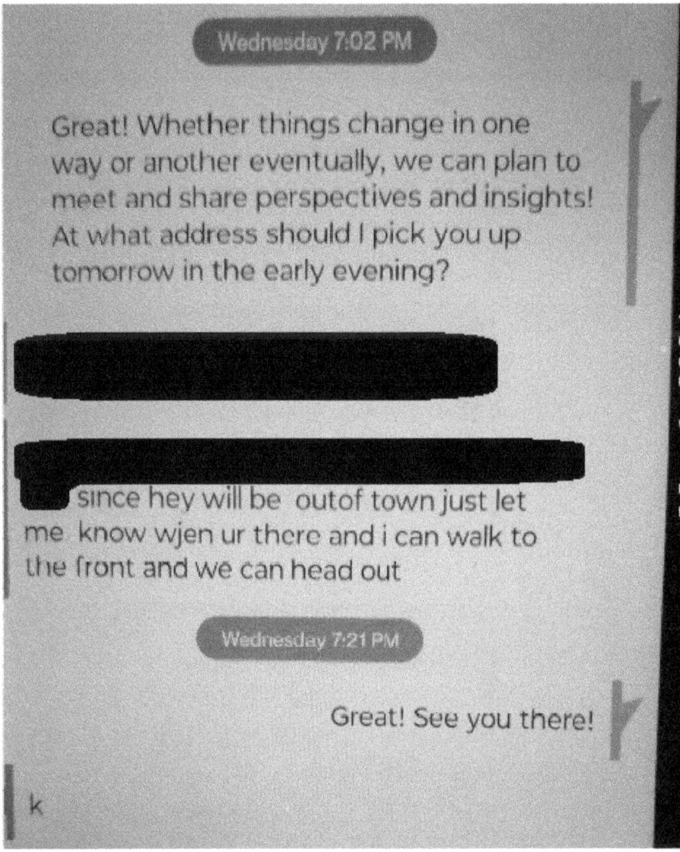
Wednesday 7:02 PM
Great! Whether things change in one way or another eventually, we can plan to meet and share perspectives and insights! At what address should I pick you up tomorrow in the early evening?
[redacted] since hey will be outof town just let me know wjen ur there and i can walk to the front and we can head out
Wednesday 7:21 PM
Great! See you there!
k

May 1, 2024

May 2, 2024. From: B. Roth. To: M.J. Blair.

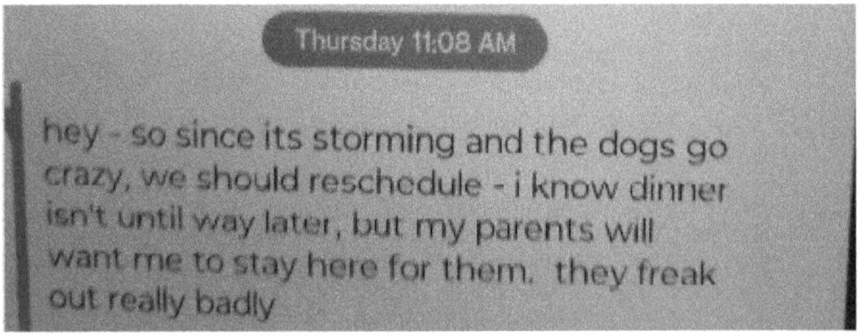
Thursday 11:08 AM
hey - so since its storming and the dogs go crazy, we should reschedule - i know dinner isn't until way later, but my parents will want me to stay here for them. they freak out really badly

## May 2, 2024 Text Messaging, cont'd

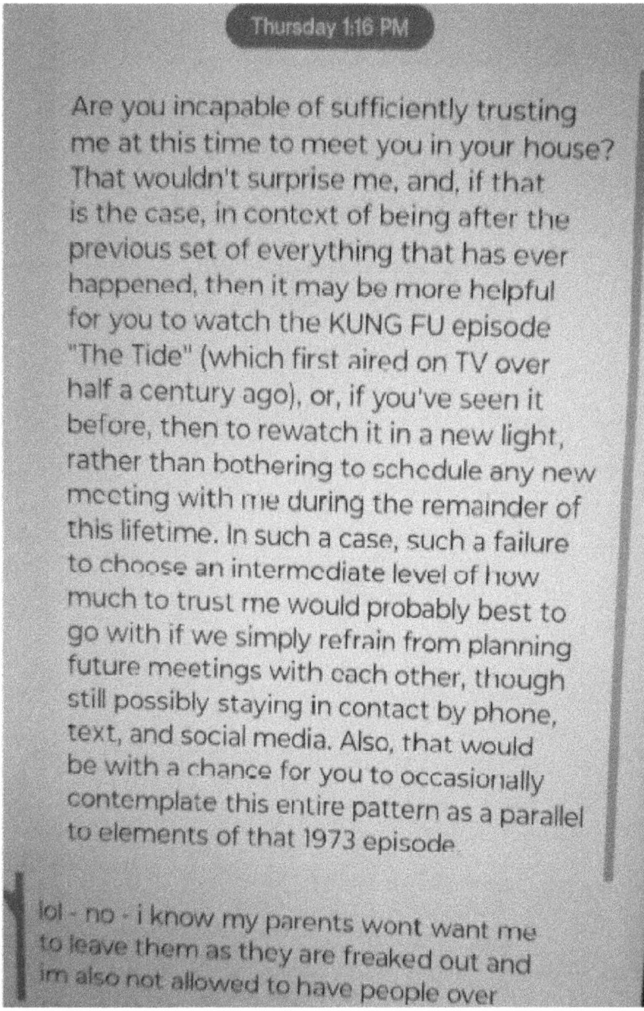

Thursday 1:16 PM

Are you incapable of sufficiently trusting me at this time to meet you in your house? That wouldn't surprise me, and, if that is the case, in context of being after the previous set of everything that has ever happened, then it may be more helpful for you to watch the KUNG FU episode "The Tide" (which first aired on TV over half a century ago), or, if you've seen it before, then to rewatch it in a new light, rather than bothering to schedule any new meeting with me during the remainder of this lifetime. In such a case, such a failure to choose an intermediate level of how much to trust me would probably best to go with if we simply refrain from planning future meetings with each other, though still possibly staying in contact by phone, text, and social media. Also, that would be with a chance for you to occasionally contemplate this entire pattern as a parallel to elements of that 1973 episode

lol - no - i know my parents wont want me to leave them as they are freaked out and im also not allowed to have people over

(from portions of May 2, 2024 correspondence)

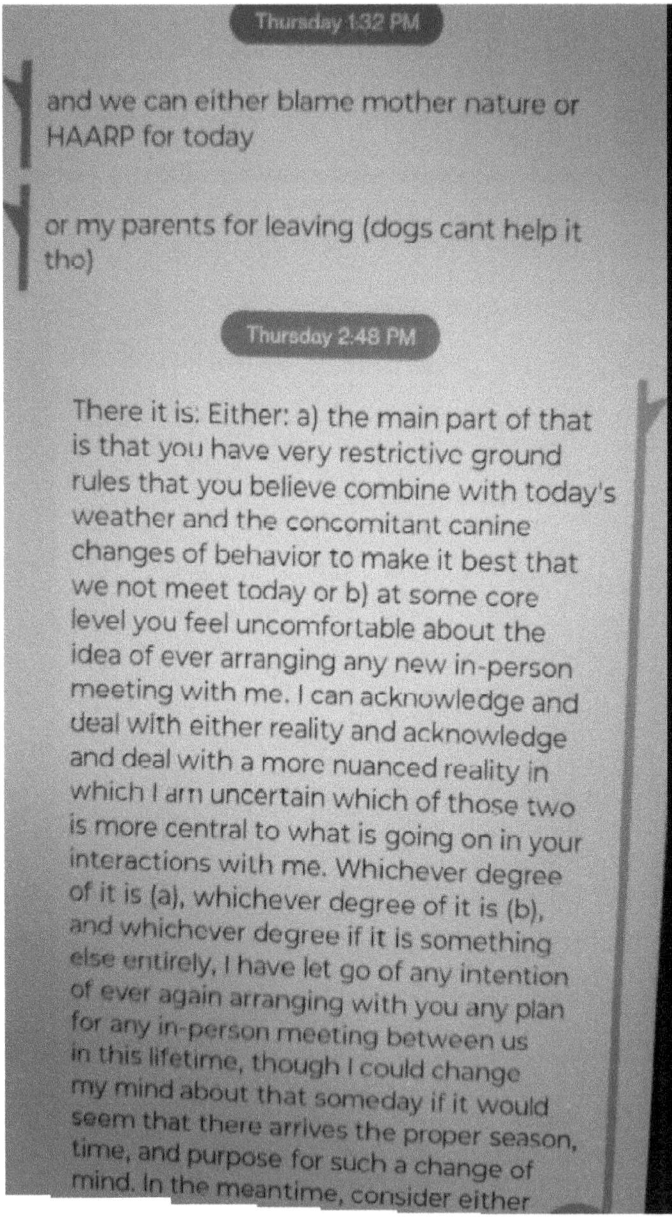

Thursday 1:32 PM

and we can either blame mother nature or HAARP for today

or my parents for leaving (dogs cant help it tho)

Thursday 2:48 PM

There it is: Either: a) the main part of that is that you have very restrictive ground rules that you believe combine with today's weather and the concomitant canine changes of behavior to make it best that we not meet today or b) at some core level you feel uncomfortable about the idea of ever arranging any new in-person meeting with me. I can acknowledge and deal with either reality and acknowledge and deal with a more nuanced reality in which I am uncertain which of those two is more central to what is going on in your interactions with me. Whichever degree of it is (a), whichever degree of it is (b), and whichever degree if it is something else entirely, I have let go of any intention of ever again arranging with you any plan for any in-person meeting between us in this lifetime, though I could change my mind about that someday if it would seem that there arrives the proper season, time, and purpose for such a change of mind. In the meantime, consider either

(from portions of May 2, 2024 correspondence b/w M.J.Blair and B. Roth) viewing or reviewing the television episode I referenced in the previous text message that I sent you. Take care, and best wishes with your role in facilitating the enlightenment of sentient beings.

ok - well - not to throw a wrench in it, but since the storm ended, there isn't really an issue unless it starts again. your call.

(Note: When I began composing my Thursday, May 02, 2024, 3:11 P.M. text message to Briana Roth, the storm was going very much, yet it had almost stopped by the time of finishing and sending that message. I sacrificed a small amount of purity of speech by not clarifying this as managing a trade-off between that and keeping the message less complicated and confusing than it might otherwise have been. --Maurice James Blair, 5/6/24)

(May 6, 2024 Note)

Thursday 3:11 PM

In my neighborhood, the storm is still going. It had a brief lull, then it ramped back up. If you feel like the storm and other factors actually turn out to be in good enough a shape to make it sensible to meet me later, then you could send a message about this idea closer to 5 or 5:30 with confirming that you believe that way

(May 2, 2024)

at that time. However, it looks like there is probably more of a core level in which you, like the vast majority of people the vast majority of the time in recent years, rather than giving me the benefit of the doubt in many situations or giving me complete neutrality of perception toward many situations, lean toward assuming a range from moderate negativity toward me to assuming the worst, while I know dead-cold much of the refutation (by direct knowledge and experience, though much

of it is often not directly observable by any of them) of their jumping to excessively negative and dismissive attitudes toward me. Sure, if you believe the situation actually allows for you to be able to go with me to dinner today while honoring your responsibilities, then I could agree, as per our earlier plan. However, if you believe as of about 5 or 5:30 that your situation does not allow it to be compatible with your responsibilities, then I will expect to agree that we not meet today. In such a scenario of you deeming it incompatible with your situation for you to meet me today, then it will likely lead to me again fully letting go of any intention to initiate any further attempts to ever plan any future meeting with you in this lifetime, with it to-be determined whether or not anyone or anything would ever change my mind about that.

Thursday 3:20 PM

wow - it really actuslly was tje fact that i am watching 3 dogs who all panic and freak out when its storming and it wouldnt have been responsible to leave them like that - and i am not allowed to have people at the house - these 2 factors would hsve applied to anyone - you, my neighbor, a hugh school friend, the mayor, or the man on the moon - really - had nothing to do

(first part of a May 2, 2024 3:20 P.M. text message from Briana Roth to Maurice Blair)

(2nd part of a Briana Roth 5/2/2024 text message)

with u - but now im just exhausted from these texts sorry u look at life tjst way. in back to not interacting witj people things may be boring and lonly but at least no drama

and if u csnt deal with rational things like dogs in storms - thats not cool best of luck

(2nd part of a Briana Roth 5/2/2024 text message)

(1st part of a Maurice Blair 5/2/2024 6:59 P.M. text message to Briana Roth)

Thursday 6:59 PM

No. You don't get it. This is not about your sensitivity to when I sought clarification, then you clarified and adjusted, then I clarified some more. The way you presented earlier, combined with how you presented not being able to meet me in the previous time we tried to arrange to have a follow-up meeting smacked of the core level involving that you, like a high percentage of other women I have ever had interest in getting involved with do not regard me as being very legitimate as a human being. Therefore, I presented pathways forward to resolving this such as

(1st part of a Maurice Blair 5/2/2024 6:59 P.M. text message to Briana Roth)

to stand up for my legitimacy as a human
being while also opening the door for you
to understand both your legitimacy as
a human being and my legitimacy as a

being while also opening the door for you
to understand both your legitimacy as
a human being and my legitimacy as a
human being. You are deflecting again. I
can accept it and move on, and give you a
clear path to accepting it and moving on,
but it is obvious that you jumped straight
into canceling today before even waiting
to see if the storm would reasonably clear,
and that adds weight to my suspicions
that may be the previous time your entire
set of texts might have been a charade
with an intention to not hurt my feelings.

(M.J.B. 5/2/2024 6:59 P.M. text message to B.R., cont'd)

People in general do not get it that I don't
give a damn about anyone's efforts aimed
in a use-white-lies-to-not-hurt-feelings
approach toward me; long ago I embraced
spiritual development in such a way that
an appeal to personal feelings by me would
seem tantamount to spiritual suicide
because my life development became
advanced enough that it should all be
about the deeper reality beyond what
would otherwise be my personal feelings
(in other words I only consider my personal
feelings to have any right to exist insofar as
they are compatible with enlightenment,
etc.) Therefore, purity of speech is what I
respect deeply, not any attempts by others
to appeal to their misguided imaginings
of telling lies with which to not hurt the
illusory versions of me that they are falsely
perceiving to be real. Often I won't call

(6:59 P.M. U.S. CDT text message from M.B. to B.R., cont'd)

people out the way that I've called you out here, and maybe I'm wrong about some of how you had perceived me, but it seems obvious that you had the chance earlier to simply state that the dogs were acting up so we should cancel unless the storm clears up in time to make it practical, but instead you went straight to trying to fully cancel, which adds to my probability evaluation of the likelihood that both the previous time abd this time the most fundamental detail is that you feel that my best was never good enough for you to feel right about ever meeting me again in the remainder of this lifetime, feeling that it makes you a better person to force a future in which you never intend to meet me because of whatever personal defects you perceived me to have. I tried to present a diplomatic way to give both a chance to call that out for what it is and a chance that you could course correct if that is not what's going on with how you perceive me and how you should manage interacting with me. Finally,

(6:59 P.M. CDT, May 2, 2024 message from M.J. Blair to B. Roth, cont'd)

at 3:11 P.M. (as measured from this side) I sent a carefully-worded message to let you clarify further and to demonstrate if you have sufficient affinity for various of both your challenges and my challenges to react in a reasonably friendly way. Instead of reacting with friendliness and trying to be thoroughly understanding toward getting next steps to work smoothly, whether ever meeting me again in the future or not, you chose to lash out at me. This is not surprising, and it's not entirely your fault; much of it is clearly some of your former lovers' and other former acquaintances' fault for traumatizing you as much as they did, causing you to excessively associate men who have interest in meeting you one-on-one with trauma and drama, including that you perceived hostility in my messages sent to you today instead of what they truly reflected: a mixture of tough love, equanimity, strategic coordination, and multipathway sophistication in support of conscience and opportunities for enlightenment. I dealt rationally about the dogs, the storm, and your parents' restrictions; however, I also dealt rationally with standing up for my legitimacy as a human being in the wake

(A 6:59 P.M. CDT message from Maurice James Blair, continued)

of your veering into texting me in ways that seemed to reflect perceiving me as a stereotypical nerdy, way-below-average, frustrated chump. If you have misperceived me in that way, then you are probably among a very large number of people who have misperceived me that way in recent years. When I was a teenager, in many ways I was a stereotypical, nerdy, way-below-average frustrated chump, years later I was partway like that, and eventually I became a very different sort of a person, though superficially it can still be easy for people to jump to the dead-wrong conclusion of associating me with that profile. You may have misunderstood and been skeptical when I stated that I currently neither need to live nor need for this entire universe to live. However, that is true, through and through. That may often come with the extinction of desires--except insofar as coordinated temporary desires can be constructive toward enlightened processes and can fully integrate with profound spirituality, for example through tantric practices. I have had sufficiently great a life and sufficiently complete a life that I feel ready to die at any time now and feel ready for this universe to die at any time now, with beings like you who might not feel ready for universal annihilation to possibly be able to be lifted up to sufficient enlightenment

(A 6:59 P.M. U.S. CDT, May 2, 2024 text message from M.J. Blair, continued)

Namo Vajrasattva. Namo Ushisha Vijaya. Namo Vajrayogini. Namo Avalokitesvara. Namo Ksitigharba. Namo Mahakala. Namo Simhamukha.

(conclusion of a May 2, 2024 6:59 P.M. text from M.J.B.)

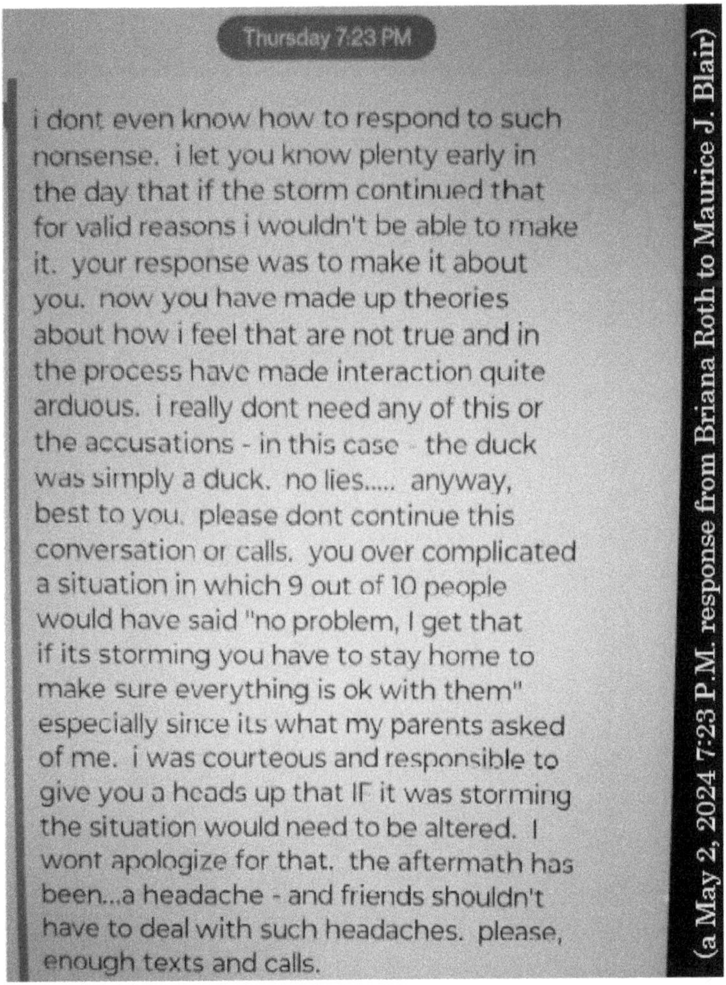
Thursday 7:23 PM

i dont even know how to respond to such nonsense. i let you know plenty early in the day that if the storm continued that for valid reasons i wouldn't be able to make it. your response was to make it about you. now you have made up theories about how i feel that are not true and in the process have made interaction quite arduous. i really dont need any of this or the accusations - in this case - the duck was simply a duck. no lies..... anyway, best to you. please dont continue this conversation or calls. you over complicated a situation in which 9 out of 10 people would have said "no problem, I get that if its storming you have to stay home to make sure everything is ok with them" especially since its what my parents asked of me. i was courteous and responsible to give you a heads up that IF it was storming the situation would need to be altered. I wont apologize for that. the aftermath has been...a headache - and friends shouldn't have to deal with such headaches. please, enough texts and calls.

(a May 2, 2024 7:23 P.M. response from Briana Roth to Maurice J. Blair)

Note: With the way of composing and sending that, in context, Briana paralleled many across the eons who have shown obliviousness to the value of paying attention when encountering those who present severity, zealotry, and a commitment to divinity.

---

The Beginning of Maurice James Blair's 8:21 PM, May 2, 2024 Response:

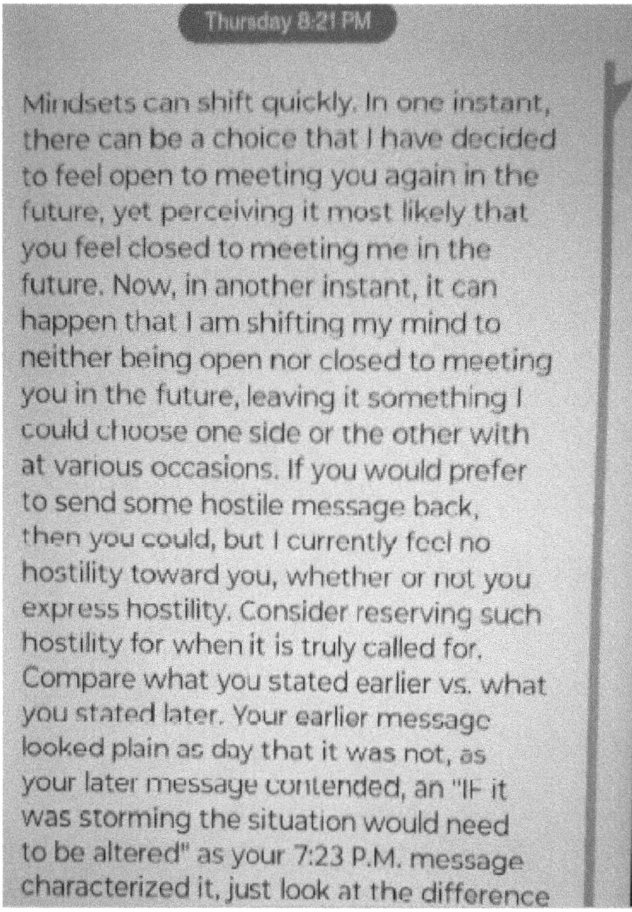

Thursday 8:21 PM

Mindsets can shift quickly. In one instant, there can be a choice that I have decided to feel open to meeting you again in the future, yet perceiving it most likely that you feel closed to meeting me in the future. Now, in another instant, it can happen that I am shifting my mind to neither being open nor closed to meeting you in the future, leaving it something I could choose one side or the other with at various occasions. If you would prefer to send some hostile message back, then you could, but I currently feel no hostility toward you, whether or not you express hostility. Consider reserving such hostility for when it is truly called for. Compare what you stated earlier vs. what you stated later. Your earlier message looked plain as day that it was not, as your later message contended, an "IF it was storming the situation would need to be altered" as your 7:23 P.M. message characterized it, just look at the difference

(first part of an 8:21 P.M. CDT, May 2, 2024 response from Maurice James Blair to Briana Roth) in words: your entire 11:08 A.M. message was, without alterations for capitalization, punctuation, or anything else, "hey - so since its storming and the dogs go crazy, we should reschedule - i know dinner isn't until way later, but my parents will want me to stay here for them. they freak out really badly" and that does not include any "if things clear up, then maybe meeting today would be fine" element to it. None whatsoever. By mischaracterizing that, you accidentally caused me to consider what might be a more accurate explanation: You have likely not felt very good about meeting me again in the future, yet you were partway on the fence about it while considering yourself to be of a much higher social status than me in general. Although there are ranges in which you are of higher social status than me, there are also areas in which I serve important roles such as to be of equal status as you, and there are at least a few ways in which I am of elite social status. More importantly, though, the

(An 8:21 P.M., May 2, 2024 text message from M.J.B.)

capabilities that I have paid my dues with are such that I will give anyone anywhere, no matter what the person's gender, rank or anything else might be, if things go into the realm where I believe it my religious duty to do so, to express sharp criticism toward them, and to strongly disagree with them, no matter how much they might not like it, no matter how much they might jump to wrong conclusions from receiving those sharp criticisms and those rejections of what they present. I deliberately put elements into the conversation that relate to whether you have reasonable affinity with the Buddhas, the Bodhisattvas, and

(An 8:21 P.M., May 02, 2024 message from M.J.B., cont'd)

the Dharna Protectors, and you have demonstrated an interesting mixture of degrees of such affinity and degrees of much room for improvement with such affinity. You repeatedly steer away from a straightforward ability to comprehend key sentences within my messages to you, but maybe you will understand them better a few minutes from now or a few decades from now. Whether or not we ever communicate again after I send you this text (& whether or not you might have already blocked me before my act of attempting to send it to you), I wish you the ability as time goes to learn more, understand better, and improve, much as I am also working to learn more, understand better, and improve. In case you are skeptical that I have succeeded with very many interactions with other people, especially women, rest assured, I have succeeded some of the time, and, in terms of some of the more mysterious levels of energy, I have succeeded extremely well.

(An 8:21 PM CDT, May 2, 2024 text message from M.J. Blair, cont'd)

(8:21 PM, May 2, 2024 M.J.B. Response, cont'd)

For example, no medical doctors have had any prescription medication regimens enforced on me in the most recent period of a little over 2 years and 11 months other than how I received a tetanus shot after a 12/11/2021 barfight and some topical bloody scalp care after the accomplice of a gunman hit me over the head with a pipe on 9/9/2022 as part of robbing me. Also, there were some extreme difficulties that I overcame within the first seven weeks after the last time I was in any prescription medications. IDK how many of the guys you've met have been in a bareknuckle fight with another man before, but it is probably a small percentage. Yes, if you want to jump to a conclusion against me on that, presuming him to have had more justification than me in connection with that fight, then you could, but you would probably be ignoring many key factors. For example, he threw the first punch, the second punch, and multiple additional punches before I punched back.

> Furthermore, when HPD interviewed me about it, they asked if I would like to press charges against him, and I declined, because I considered it a fair fight. No charges were ever pressed against me in connection with that fight, and no one has ever sued me in connection with that fight Perhaps even more remarkably, the female bartender who was on duty at the turne of the fight eventually sent me a Facebook friend request, and I accepted that friend request. Again, best wishes with making improvements to your life and your abilities to help others. Take care.

(conclusion of an 8:21 PM, May 2, 2024 text message from M.J. Blair to Briana Roth)

Clarification: In case you were wondering, I considered stating to her point blank an alternative extra phrase instead of the phrase used near the end of the passage, "By mischaracterizing that, you accidentally caused me to consider what might be a more accurate explanation: You have likely not felt very good about meeting me again in the future, yet you were partway on the fence about it while considering yourself to be of a much higher social status than me in general. Although there are ranges in which you are of higher social status than me, there are also areas in which I serve important roles such as to be of equal status as you, and there are at least a few ways in which I am of elite social status."

My main impulse was to go directly 360$^0$, "Although there are ranges in which you are of higher social status than me, there are ways in which I am of equal status, and there are ranges in which I am of higher social status than you."

This gets to the heart of the matter of much of what has tended to go wrong every so often since I finalized the first printing text of *All Things Under and Over the Sun and Stars: An Enigma in Twenty-Three Stages* (as composed by the conglomeration of a multitude of beings, including yours truly, with many beings teaming up on largely through my channeling spirits—to whatever degree real, imagined, both, or in some of the twilight zones between the real and the imagined, to whatever degrees of the outer limits of mind, to whatever degree from beyond, etc. What has gone wrong every so often in my interactions with others after that June 3, 2005 occurrence (one day before the official publication of that distributed-repeatedly-on-a-nonmonetary-basis work that subsequently became adapted into the *All Things under and over the Sun and Stars: Enigmas in Various Stages* novel which I felt fine about crediting myself with writing—see *Science, Religion, Politics, and Cards* and *An Encyclopedic Survival Guide for Navigating Normal and Paranormal Experiences* if you wish to get more of the context), involves a controversy at some core levels of Exoteric Abrahamic Religion vs. Esoteric Abrahamic Religion vs. Exoteric Dharmic Religion vs. Esoteric Dharmic Religion vs. All Other Manifestations of Religion vs. All Manifestations of Nonreligion. Specifically, this is the issue of how much people choose to consider hierarchies as absolute versus how much people choose to consider hierarchies as relative.

Over the years, I noticed often two main camps on this: There is the camp that gravitates toward believing hierarchies to be absolute often also gravitating toward a combination of the trending-toward-very-simpleton-notions-of-religion-and-life-in-general outlook and leaning on authoritarian mindsets as a crutch, whether as the followers of autocrats or as the autocrats themselves; and there is the camp that gravitates toward believing hierarchies to be relative in all or nearly all cases. The camp tending to believe hierarchies to range from generally relative to universally relative often also gravitates toward a combination of the trending-toward-considering-religion-and-life-in-general-to-be-a-mystery outlook and embracing many situations in terms of the lower-case-d democratic mindsets as a way of liberation, whether a given individual of that camp happens to be a capital-D Democrat, an Independent, a capital-R Republican, a Christian, a Muslim, a Jew, a Hindu, a Sikh, a Scientologist, an Agnostic, an Atheist, a Deist, a Jain, a Buddhist, or whatever else nominally.

Yes, people of either camp can adapt to militaristic situations in which it becomes paramount to trust in leaders such as to seldom, if ever, dare to second-guess the judgment of superiors, such as when people who enlisted into a military organization go through basic training. However, people of any level of any of that had probably best consider, at least some of the time and to some degree the perspective permeating many areas of both the set of all esoteric religions and the set of all exoteric religions, and which may serve as a transcendental bridge from anywhere to anywhere else, which has been expressed in grail lore, gospels, religious texts from diverse cultures, and, every so often, in everyday speech: It is best to cooperate with a given authority when that authority is genuinely authoritative and legitimate, as relating to whatever is most real and true and actually relevant, whereas it is best to fight back against a given authority when that authority lacks sufficient genuine authority and legitimacy as relating to whatever is most real and true and actually relevant.

Beings' notions, for example, 1) "Father knows best," 2) "Happy wife, happy life," 3) "If mama ain't happy, then nobody's happy," 4) "Trust the government," 5) "Be skeptical of the government," 6) "Trust the Democratic Party," 7) "Trust the Republican Party," 8) "Trust the religious leader(s) most obvious for you to trust," 9) "Be skeptical of the religious leader(s) most obvious for you to trust," 10) "Trust all commandments to be absolute, and blame yourself when you seem to be caught in a pickle," 11) "Trust yourself," 12) "Be skeptical of yourself," 13) "Trust in Death," 14) "Trust in Time," 15) "Trust in the Devil," 16) "Trust in God," 17) "Trust in the Stars," 18) "Trust in the Moon," 19) "Trust in the Sun," 20) "Trust in Judgment," 21) "Trust the World," 22) "Trust in the Otherworldly, 23) "Work for None and All," 24) "Trust in Life," 25) "Believe in LSD, mindful as to which versions to believe in—whether, for example, to cognize it to stand for a given landing ship dock, a given last supper digest, or whatever else—careful of how, when, and how much to believe," and 26) "Believe in the U.S.A., mindful as to which versions to believe in—whether, for example, to cognize it to stand for The United States of America of 1952, The United States of America of today, Uniform Soteriological Advice, or whatever else—careful of how, when, and how much to believe," can perhaps prove helpful to some beings in some ways sometimes, but history has repeatedly proven the act of idolizing notions to become oftentimes problematic in the long run for beings.

* * * * * *
* * * * *
* * * * * *
* * * * *
* * * * * *
* * * * *
* * * * * *
* * * * *
* * * * * *

Consider this idea that I put into what are in this case my own words, though they have probably been the words of many others in that exact sequence—whether those others were of this world or beyond it—going back multiple centuries or further, and therefore, it is probably a seven-word sentence that in some ways has already been in the public domain for eons: "Masterfully coordinating after achieving competency is better."

* * * * * *
* * * * *
* * * * * *
* * * * *
* * * * * *
* * * * *
* * * * * *
* * * * *
* * * * * *

For a while, I thought that the message that I sent at 8:21 in the evening on May 2, 2024 would be sufficient, likely the final act of direct messaging between that Briana Roth and this Maurice James Blair in this lifetime. Indeed, as of the last time I checked before sending this book to be published, to the best of my knowledge an update is that she has remained silent toward me on this, which seems eminently appropriate, granted to be in the vein of exhibiting a microscopic parallel to how The Financial Advisory Group, Inc. and Gray Reed & McGraw went totally silent toward me after I went straight to complaining to the Securities and Exchange Commission. Reminder: that was in the wake of the Gray Reed defamatory letter dated 9 August 2021 as received by be on 10 August 2021 having proved enough to nudge me off the fence about whether to complain to the SEC about my updated perceptions of criticizing the FinGroup CCO who had been my main supervisor during the 6 August 2018 to 6 August 2019 period and who had shown the nerve to disrespect much of the truth and many of the facts in and adjacent to my life.

However, as I went for a drive, as a way of driving meditation, which some may consider a parallel to the common Zen practice of walking meditation, though walking meditation generally would not include driving at 65 mph on an Interstate, more perspectives arrived. Some of that drive also involved phases of very actively thinking with words, idea structures, concepts, etc. Some Christians and Hindus might wish to think of much of that as a way of performing insight meditation.

* * * * *

After a while, I stopped over in Baytown.

That was also in Texas, though a moderate drive East of Houston.

There I composed and sent a follow-up text message, bringing it all back home.

---

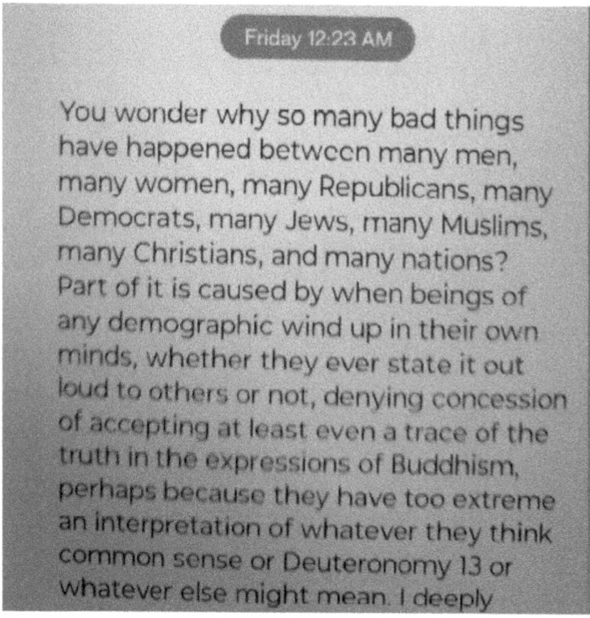
Friday 12:23 AM

You wonder why so many bad things have happened between many men, many women, many Republicans, many Democrats, many Jews, many Muslims, many Christians, and many nations? Part of it is caused by when beings of any demographic wind up in their own minds, whether they ever state it out loud to others or not, denying concession of accepting at least even a trace of the truth in the expressions of Buddhism, perhaps because they have too extreme an interpretation of whatever they think common sense or Deuteronomy 13 or whatever else might mean. I deeply

(Beginning of a May 03, 2024 Text Message, from: Maurice James Blair, to: Briana Roth, cc: Anyone Else Who Might Ever Have the Opportunity to Consider Its Statement)

respect Exodus 20, Deuteronomy 13, and the entire book of Ecclesiastes, though I recognize much unknown unto me about their relations with everyone and everything. Furthermore, I have experienced much proof of much of Buddhism, though it is not the kind of proof that would mean for everyone to need to convert to it; rather proofs that much of its core, much like the cores of Judaism, Noahidism, and Agnosticism, has much truth to it. This is probably the last direct communication that we will share in this lifetime, though rest assured, if you show a new round of hostility, either through yourself or through a lawyer, then I will probably fight back in defense of truth by publishing or otherwise revealing to much of the public that threat from you or whomever you are associated with for the world to see, like I did to The Financial Advisory Group, Inc., Gray Reed & McGraw, then, later, The Michael Berry Show.

(A May 3, 2024 Message From Maurice James Blair to Briana Roth, cc'ing Any Who Might Find the Copy of It Here, cont'd)

Of those three, only The Michael Berry Show collaborated on direct, follow-up communications with which to re-earn my respect. You have not offended me at any more than about one-millionth the level at which Gray Reed & McGraw offended me, and you have not offended me at any more than about one-trillionth the level of how The Financial Advisory Group, Inc. offended me, but, like those two and unlike The Michael Berry Show, you have, thus far, failed to show any signs of acknowledging and respecting at least a small-but-significant amount of the reality of the ways in which I have paid strange dues with respect to the mysteries of Yod-He-Vau-He, Adibuddha, The Unknown, The Known, etc. You wonder why much of your life has seemed like a magnet for hostility from others? Some of the answers you might find from stuff like Exodus, Leviticus, Ecclesiastes, The Dhammapada,

(A May 3, 2024 Text Message From Maurice James Blair to Briana Roth, later copy concerning Anyone Who Finds This Copy Here, continued)

and Jewel's song "Pieces of You" (though that song does not have to be thought of only in terms of the demographics she focused on; it can be extended to the ways that the climactic scene in Chaplin's 1940 film The Great Dictator can relate to a degree of compassion for all human beings, getting beyond overly-rigid sweeping generalizations and jumping to conclusions). Something else you might consider visiting or revisiting might be Looking for Comedy in the Muslim World (2005), and another could be the even-more-bizarre comedy Borat (2006). One more thing that might suit your fancy and personal growth, whether or not you ever deem me appropriate to communicate with again or not, might be the Napoleon Hill spoken word audio item Selling You, part of which included him going on at length about how closing oneself off completely to anyone or anything can be detrimental to one's heart and mind and soul. I still feel that it's

(A May 3, 2024 Message From Maurice James Blair, continued)

been good knowing you, I owe absolutely no apology to you for communicating carrying degrees of sacred truth which you knee-jerk reacted to by characterizing as nonsense, you do not necessarily have to provide any direct response, and, although I previously believed it most likely for you not to wind up being presented in the new book, you are now at about a 98% forecast to have portions of our text message correspondence appear in that book. You think I wouldn't dare? I've already done that sort of thing to people who acted with much less hostile provocation toward Esotericism, Buddhism, etc. than you did; you really thought I wouldn't be open to considering doing that to you? That is part of a drill-sergeant-style tough love that I feel in recent years open toward bestowing on anyone I might come across if the person steps out of line sufficiently in relationship with YHVH, The Totality of Abrahmic Religions, The Totality of Dharmic Religions, Adibuddha, The Entirety of The Mysteries at The Core of Reality Itself, and so on and so forth, ad infinitem

(A Copy of a May 3, 2024 Message from M.J.B. to B.R., cont'd)

and beyond. This is not blackmail, I am no longer looking with optimism toward any possible future direct communications between you and me in this lifetime; however, I have to think long and hard about all four main options: 1) to include our correspondence, though carefully redacting any details in it that I would be legally and ethically obligated to redact, though keeping your first name and last name included; 2) to do the same as in #1, but to exclude your surname from the book; 3) to do the same as in #2, but to also exclude your individual name; and 4) to exclude our correspondence from any direct presence in the book. You might be thinking of threatening me into not doing that, might you? Who do you think you're fooling? I meant every last word of it when I mentioned earlier that I have reached a stage in life in which I feel fine with the possibility of dying at any instant and feel fine about possibilities of this universe dying at any instant, on account of readiness for potential next phases of spiritual enlightenment. You thought my mentioning that was nonsensical? I was deadly serious about it! I am at peace with

(Continuation of A Copy of A May 3, 2024 Text Message From M.J. Blair to Briana Roth, w/ M. James Blair cc'ing Any & All Who Venture Here)

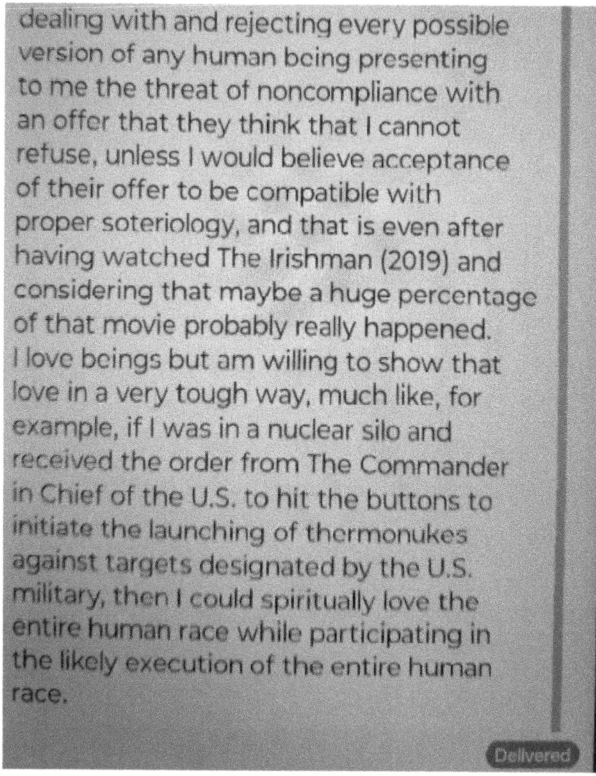

dealing with and rejecting every possible version of any human being presenting to me the threat of noncompliance with an offer that they think that I cannot refuse, unless I would believe acceptance of their offer to be compatible with proper soteriology, and that is even after having watched The Irishman (2019) and considering that maybe a huge percentage of that movie probably really happened. I love beings but am willing to show that love in a very tough way, much like, for example, if I was in a nuclear silo and received the order from The Commander in Chief of the U.S. to hit the buttons to initiate the launching of thermonukes against targets designated by the U.S. military, then I could spiritually love the entire human race while participating in the likely execution of the entire human race.

Delivered

(Ending of A May 3, 2024 Text Message From M.J.B. to B.R, & w/ which M.J.B. would later cc Any & All Who Find the Copy Here)

Please note that within a few days after that, I noticed on Facebook that Briana Roth had not unfriended me—at least not yet, anyway—and, although I felt tempted to unfriend her, I had not unfriended her—at least not yet, anyway. There are also several other Facebook friends whom I have considered very much on the bubble as far as whether to unfriend them or not. If you are on that platform, then consider whether there might be some of your Facebook friends about whom you regard as being on the bubble, as well. After much time went by, on May 19, 2024 I included a huge number of people, including Briana Roth, on a communique in which she was on the periphery. More about that later.

I have rarely unfriended people on Facebook. Meanwhile, though relatively few have unfriended me on that platform, the patterns can remind me that humility has oftentimes been very relevant to my situation in recent decades.

Also, I am very thankful that there have been some women here and there over the years with whom I have been able to experience things go very well from a holistic, long-term perspective, at least some of the time, as such successful experiences and the memories of them help me with the ability to stay on track with well-being each time when a person, an organization, or whoever or whatever goes on some type of a rampage against me. In some ways it is unfortunate that Briana has not, as of yet joined the ranks of the women with whom things went very well in the long run in an overall sense, but I am very glad that, as of the time of this work going to publication, I can count Jessica Trend, Rose Rodriguez, and Liza Darnton among their ranks, though there is some uncertainty to what degree, if any, that at least one of those three has even half the level of favorable feeling toward how the interactions with me happened in the long run. Fortunately, there is no clear evidence of any of those three harboring very major long-term resentiment toward me, while I am extraordinarily grateful for the total set of interactions with them from each beginning up to the time of this book going to its first publication.

With Jessica Trend (whose surname I am not completely certain of the spelling, as she chose to decline to spell it for me, and I did not find out for sure through other means; theoretically, it could be spelled, "Trynd," "Chrend," or another way, yet it seems, based on pronunciation and the cultural contexts, that the spelling was probably "Trend." I do not know whether or not she has subsequently changed her surname), also known as "Jess," there never really was a time of major negativity of me toward her, and although she eventually showed mild rebuke toward me regarding the possibility of future planned meetings, she never really showed cruelty toward me at all.

With Liza Darnton, there have been such intricacies that no amount of writing or speaking would be sufficient to explain anywhere near everything about her interactions with me. She showed mild rebuke toward me from around one-fourth of the way into the first and only date she went on with me to near the very end of when we were at the same location for that date, then she showed profound passionate affection briefly, then left the event somewhat early, though not way too early.

As previously mentioned, over 27 years later, I offered her a LinkedIn invitation to officially network with me, and she accepted that very soon after receiving that invitation. The offer and her acceptance both occurred in the third quarter of the month of June 2022.

Perhaps revisiting Section Five, Part L might bring a reader closer to understanding, or perhaps there is no way for a given reader to find a better understanding unless somehow thoroughly tuning in with the reality of this set of wonder.

That includes how even if Liza herself reads this book someday, then she herself still might not ever get way too close to a complete understanding of this. However, for all I know, maybe she already has close to a complete understanding of this. Although many of the people I have met in this life have impressed me in a good way, and although many of the people I have never met in this life have impressed me in a good way, somehow if THE LORD were to ask me at the time of this book going to print to vote for everyone on Earth to go onto one side or the other of a list, with no one allowed to be in an undecided column, with one side as essential personnel of the human race and the other side as expendable personnel of the human race, then I would place Liza Darnton as the only human being on the side of essential pers-onnel. None of my known relatives, my closest of friends, my sexual partners, would I vote to go on the side of the essential human personnel in that case. Also, I would not choose myself to go on the side of the essential human personnel. I would be tempted to place HH the Dalai Lama on the list, but in this case I would resist the temptation to include him, because it would somehow ring to me as an excessive attachment to him; the same would also go for GM Lu Sheng-yen. I would not feel anywhere near a trace of temptation to include myself on the list of essential personnel; the weight of the repeated rebuke of such a large number of people over the years is enough that as of the time of this book going to print I do not even begin dare to consider myself as having even a trace of a right to dare to believe myself as deserving of being voted by myself to be among the essential personnel. Of course, had any of various people shown a much larger amount of favorability toward my life, for example by having resulted in much larger sales of my books, having led to being in a great marriage, having at least one known biological descendant, having a career that would look much more respectable on paper, reaching a medium to high level of the clergy or sangha or equivalent of some religious order, or something similar might have meant to me enough to tip the scales in favor of including myself among the essential personnel. Alas, none of that has happened as of yet. Actually, even if some of that had happened, I do not know whether it would have been quite enough to tip the scales in favor of that. For example, if I had actually somehow achieved several of those items, for example, if I had found a great marriage and had known biological descendents, then, for all I know, the other factors might have then favored something like counting the wife from the great marriage and the known biological descendants as being among the essential personnel, but still excluding myself from them, based on some sense that it would be better to give THE LORD plenty of encouragement to take me out from among the living without being pressured by me to go with the side of letting me remain. On the other hand, maybe if I had found a great marriage and had known biological descendants, then, for all I know, the other factors might have then favored choosing to vote for myself to be one of the essential personnel. Much of this is moot, though, rest assured, if you the reader were alive at the time of this book going to print and if you are someone other than the Liza Darnton referenced, then you are among the total human population of Earth of that time, minus one, for whom I voted at the time of the publication to tell THE LORD are among those of my vote in this scenario as among the expendable human personnel of Earth.

Of course, if you are, then do not feel so all alone, my vote here is for THE LORD to consider possible expendability of you and me and everyone else of that time other than that specific Liza Darnton (a Duke alumna who took Dr. Joy's Intro to Modern Philosophy class in the spring semester of 1995), daughter of John Darnton and Nina Darnton.

In many respects, I did not tend to travel into such a scenario until time went by for a while after Liza had leapfrogged past all the other contemporary, known humans who had ever impressed me via her LinkedIn networking acceptance of me as recognized meaningfully in context (coordinated by awareness with everything that had ever happened in my life and the lives of others, to the best of my ability to perceive the totality of everything). I have at times opened the door to possibilities of other women who have ever been eligible to ethically date me to thoroughly impress me, yet each of those would at some crucial instant make some subpar decision. Even the best of the best other than Liza, namely Jess, Rose, the legal Nevada courtesan, the strange young lady who shocked me by calling me from behind a little while before I watched *Gran Turismo* on Cinema Day 2023 and only shared a brief and friendly conversation with me—a conversation in which as I turned around while thinking she would likely be issuing some harsh criticism, yet the reality turned out to be that she told me that she liked my style, and I responded with thanking her and wishing her to have a good day, declining to ask her out or to ask her for her phone number because she appeared to be a few years younger than the age of consent, and many people might think of me as being more like Judge Roy Moore if I were to attempt to ethically pursue her than like Elvis Presley if I were to attempt to ethically pursue her—before we parted without asking for each other's names or anything else about each other, and the woman whom I met early on May 3, 2024, at something like a little before 2 A.M. that morning, even that set of the best of the best of the rest of the women with whom very meaningful and holistically favorable interactions in the realm of courtship would not quite get my vote at the time of this book going to print. There were times during my viewing of *Gran Turismo* on August 27, 2023 (i.e., Cinema Day 2023) in a movie theater that I thought the seemingly-about-14-year-old girl who had a little earlier told me she liked my style might be a better essential human being for the human race going forward than Liza Darnton, but, as time went by, I thought that what happened was in some ways an overreaction to the full context of that situation. Also, there were some ranges of time early on May 3, 2024 that I thought the woman I met at something like one-forty-something in the wee early hours might be equally as essential to the human race as Liza and that maybe I could even soon be worthy of enough self-regard to be a person whom I might vote for as an essential human being, but, alas, I soon found out that she had enough issues going on that although she revealed to me her place of work and what she indicated to be her cellphone number—with the warning that she alleged two of her male cousins to share access to that phone with her—enough complications ensued that I decided that, unless and until possibly later changing my mind about it, neither she nor I would quite reach the level of accomplishment in life to impress me enough for me to vote for us as whom I might present to THE LORD as essential human personnel. Therefore, to reiterate, at the time of this book going to print I would vote only for Liza Darnton (who was one of my classmates for Dr. Lynn Joy's "Introduction to Modern Philosophy" class at Duke University during Spring Semester 1995) to be among essential human personnel, leaving the rest of us as those I would vote to be among the expendable human personnel. This is not to say that I have any sort of grudge against everyone other than that Liza; to be perfectly and absolutely clear, I choose the unattached caring and impersonal spiritual love approach toward each and every sentient being as a baseline of how to interact—in keeping with some of the core of each of the major religions—and I accept that it is virtually definite that I will wind up never meeting that Liza again in this lifetime (meaning that her meetings with me in this life will almost definitely wind up limited to portions of the first five months of 1995), and this is simply a reflection that no one, not even HH the Dalai Lama, GM Lu Sheng-yen, or myself, that absolutely none of the known, living humans other than that Liza Darnton has, as of the time of this nonfiction work first going to press, impressed me as much as that Liza Darnton.

Some readers may be dumbfounded along any of at least twenty dimensions by what I have just now expressed about this. Though anywhere near complete comprehension may be unobtainable for very many readers regarding this, I believe it is still something very informative and something that can and does point toward much of the goodness in our reality. Legend has it that King Soloman was the author of *Ecclesiastes*. At the risk that Liza might read this and think that serendipity has led to something like a gender reversal of some of the plot elements of *From Noon Till Three* (a 1976 motion picture film directed by Frank D. Gilroy (1925-2015), starring Charles Bronson (1921-2003) and Jill Ireland (1936-1990)), in contrast with how a portion of the Seventh Chapter of *Ecclesiastes* states a ceiling of what was the greatest height that its author had as a regard for any of the women he had ever in any way known in his life up to the time of that work going to print, I regard Liza Darnton as being a woman righteous and reasonably perfect in the totality of the whole integrity of how she has affected me up to the time of this work going to print.

To make it easier to notice the contrast, consider three sample manifestations of English translations of the referenced portion (which aligns in the *KJV* and *NJPS* to the same verse numbers, while relatively having a one-verse-number-offset in what some might call the *Brenton and the 70 (or 72) Jewish Scholars Septuagint*):

- "And I find more bitter than death the woman, whose heart is snares and nets, and her hands as bands: whoso pleaseth God shall escape from her; but the sinner shall be taken by her. Behold, this have I found, saith the preacher, counting one by one, to find out the account: Which yet my soul seeketh, but I find not: one man among a thousand have I found; but a woman among all those have I not found." —*The King James Version Bible* : *Ecclesiastes* 7:26-28
- "And I find her *to be*, and I will pronounce *to be* more bitter than death the woman who is a

snare, and her heart nets, *who has* a band in her hands: *he that is* good in the sight of God shall be delivered by her; but the sinner shall be caught by her. Behold, this have I found, said the Preacher, *seeking* by one at a time to find out the account, which my soul sought after, but I found not; for I have found one man of a thousand; but a woman in all these I have not found." —*The Septuagint with Apocrypha: Greek and English* / Sir Lancelot Brenton (1807-1862) & The 70 (or 72) Jewish Scholars (c. 285-247 B.C./B.C.E.) / *Ecclesiastes* 7:27-29

- "Now, I find woman more bitter than death; she is all traps, her hands are fetters and her heart is snares. He who is pleasing to God escapes her, and he who is displeasing is caught by her. See, this is what I found, said Koheleth, item by item in my search for the reason of things. As for what I sought further but did not find, I found only one human being in a thousand, and the one I found among so many was never a woman." —*JPS Hebrew-English Tanakh* (1985; also known as *The New Jewish Publication Society of America Tanakh*)

Although I have read only a miniscule portion of the 1985 *JPS Hebrew-English Tanakh* (as re-printed 1999/2000), consider as a critical review here the following statement: The *NJPS* is fit for study by people of all religious, ancestral, and other demographic backgrounds if they are sufficiently interested in boldly exploring the mysteries in and adjacent to competing presentations of the alleged origins and guiding principles of reality, much like how the *KJV*, the various translations of the sacred books of the east, and many scientific and historical books can also be fit for study by those seeking the truths in and adjacent to texts.

Although I have read only a miniscule portion of the *Brenton and the 70 (or 72) Jewish Scholars Septuagint*, consider as a critical review here the following statement: *The Septuagint with Apocrypha: Greek and English* is fit for study by anyone sufficiently daring and adventurous to engage in wandering through its pages and thereby finding whatever one might find, analyzing what may be the dimensions of what of it is and what could be in and adjacent to its mysteries of heart and soul and mind.

Suffice it to say, that, with what I have experienced up to the time of bringing *Alternative Beginnings and Endings of All Things* to print via Synapsid Revelations Press Corporation as its publisher, I have searched the world over for those who, to the best of my ability to judge it are at or near the zenith of genuinely contributing at a complete level to the rest of the sentient beings, and HH the 14th Dalai Lama, GM Lu Sheng-yen, and Liza Darnton have truly impressed me in that regard, yet I feel that HH the 14th Dalai Lama and GM Lu Sheng-yen, much like myself, are at a reasonable type of a completion level of contribution, therefore on track to have completely contributed whether dying as a transition out of this lifetime at any time, whereas

Liza Darnton has reasonably great prospects for it to be a great advantage to the human race if she can live for quite a while longer. As for the rest of the human race alive at the time of this book going to print, not counting those three and not counting myself, calculating to a very large number minus four, there can be all sorts of ideas about why each one could present a huge advantage by staying alive or not present a huge advantage by staying alive, yet to be true to the best of my ability to accurately perceive everything at this time, I am choosing that the hypothetical voting at the request of THE LORD on who would be among the essential human personnel would result in my vote going to Liza Darnton as the only currently-living-known-to-be-among-the-contemporary human who has demonstrated to deserve that side of things.

Perhaps if King Soloman or Koheleth or whomever a given modern person might believe to have been the actual author of *Ecclesiastes* were to evaluate this at the time of my working on this book, then that person might contend me to be partway falling into the pattern that the Everly Brothers and Reba McEntyre sang about with the song "Kathy's Clown," though with Liza in the place of the Kathy character in that song and me in the place of the clown of that song. If such an author of that ancient book would be sufficiently cognizant of a huge percentage of the patterns in my life, then the ancient author might recognize in this modern author's challenges how perfectly that Darnton lady has managed each of several crucial moments of truth in how to deal with me. In some ways my father, Maurice A.T. Blair (1931-2015) and the singer whom I did not know personally yet whose music I enjoyed at an extraordinary level and with whom I was in the same auditorium with for her March 26, 2010 speech and March 27, 2010 concert, namely Olivia Newton-John (1948-2022), proved to a degree very perfect in their entireties of interactions with me, the fact that they have passed on beyond this life does not make it a very direct comparison with the living in this type of evaluation. At a whole other level, I dare not attempt to have the currently-living-known-to-be-among-the-contemporary humans compete with Jesus of Nazareth, Shakyamuni Buddha, and other such founders of the major ancient religions, as this seems best the type of thing to avoid unless and until if someday somewhat forced to have to address such an evaluation.

I can honestly state the following: Although in much of this life, it seems that virtually any woman with whom I share major, repeated in-depth interaction over a substantial amount of time such as to somewhat know her personally does in fact cause a major mixture of favorable and unfavorable effects on my life, I have found Liza Darnton to be the one true exception to that general rule, as her total, long-term effect on me, from its origins to the time of my completing the work *Alternative Beginnings and Endings of All Things* (May 2024), to affirm the goodness of reality in a way that I consider perfect.

Some might find it unfathomable how to reconcile this with how I stated in the 12:33 A.M. CDT, May 3, 2024 text message to Briana Roth, "I love beings but am willing to show that love in a very tough way, much like, for example, if I was in a nuclear silo and received the order from The Commander in Chief of the U.S. to hit the button to initiate the launching of thermonukes against targets designated by the U.S. military, then I could spiritually love the entire human race while participating in the likely execution of the human race." Others might find it eminently and automatically reconcilable. Unless there would be some extra level on the spot and in the situation to trust insubordination to the U.S. Commander in Chief as a better and more correct way to honor the duty to REALITY ITSELF, it would be best to trust obedience to the U.S. Commander in Chief as the best and correct way to honor the duty to REALITY ITSELF. Therefore, a more nuanced answer would be that what I stated in that bold sentence in that text message is based on the assumption that in context to the best of my abilities it would be the correct thing to do, whereas we cannot know ahead of time how the entire exact situation of something could be part of some generality or some exception.

Yet another thing that the strange correspondence covered a little while ago in this book can point toward, especially the way I chose to close the last message, is that, we can wonder if maybe something about how much nuclear weapons impressed, me when I was very young might have had some carryover effect into later in life such as to steer me into directions of every-so-often being more intense than would generally be warranted. Cognizance of this possibility after having gone through much in life, I can sometimes let go more thoroughly, whether conceived from viewpoints of Buddhism, Christianity, psychology, Scientology, biology, the team of Judaism and Noahidism, the team of Islam and People-of-the-Book-ism, Hinduism, management science, comparative religion, interdisciplinary studies, or anything else, or any combination, or any combination of combinations.

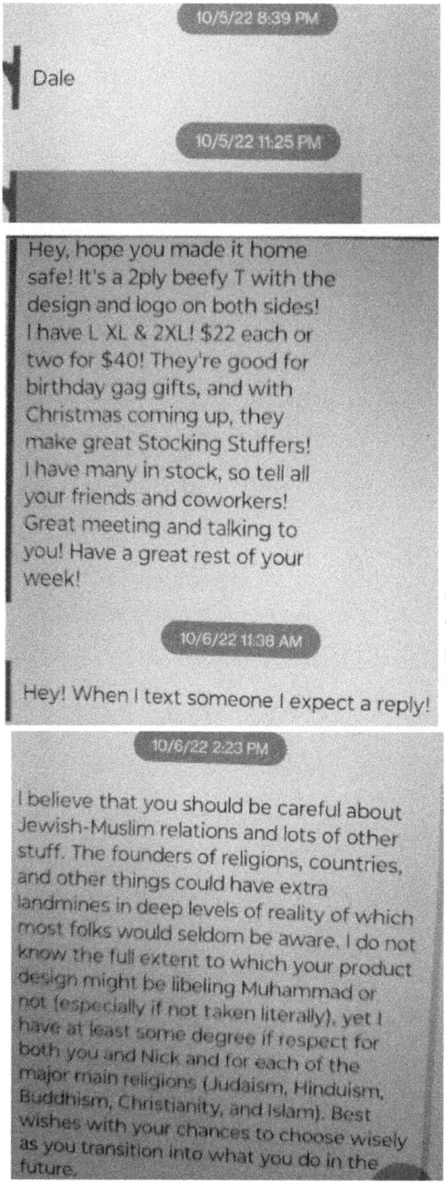
10/5/22 8:39 PM
Dale
10/5/22 11:25 PM
[redacted]
Hey, hope you made it home safe! It's a 2ply beefy T with the design and logo on both sides! I have L XL & 2XL! $22 each or two for $40! They're good for birthday gag gifts, and with Christmas coming up, they make great Stocking Stuffers! I have many in stock, so tell all your friends and coworkers! Great meeting and talking to you! Have a great rest of your week!
10/6/22 11:38 AM
Hey! When I text someone I expect a reply!
10/6/22 2:23 PM
I believe that you should be careful about Jewish-Muslim relations and lots of other stuff. The founders of religions, countries, and other things could have extra landmines in deep levels of reality of which most folks would seldom be aware. I do not know the full extent to which your product design might be libeling Muhammad or not (especially if not taken literally), yet I have at least some degree if respect for both you and Nick and for each of the major main religions (Judaism, Hinduism, Buddhism, Christianity, and Islam). Best wishes with your chances to choose wisely as you transition into what you do in the future.

Siegel introduced himself by text messaging after he and I met at Chili's on Westheimer a little East of the West Loop of Beltway 8.

That fellow then sent a follow-up text with an ad for the shirt that he again advertised in the Janaury 2023 group text messaging.

---

The next follow-up text from him asked for a response.

---

Respond I did.

--Maurice James Blair

May 7, 2024, reflecting on the correspondence

Additional Back-and-Forth by Text Messaging,

Soon after 6 OCT 2022, 2:23 PM:

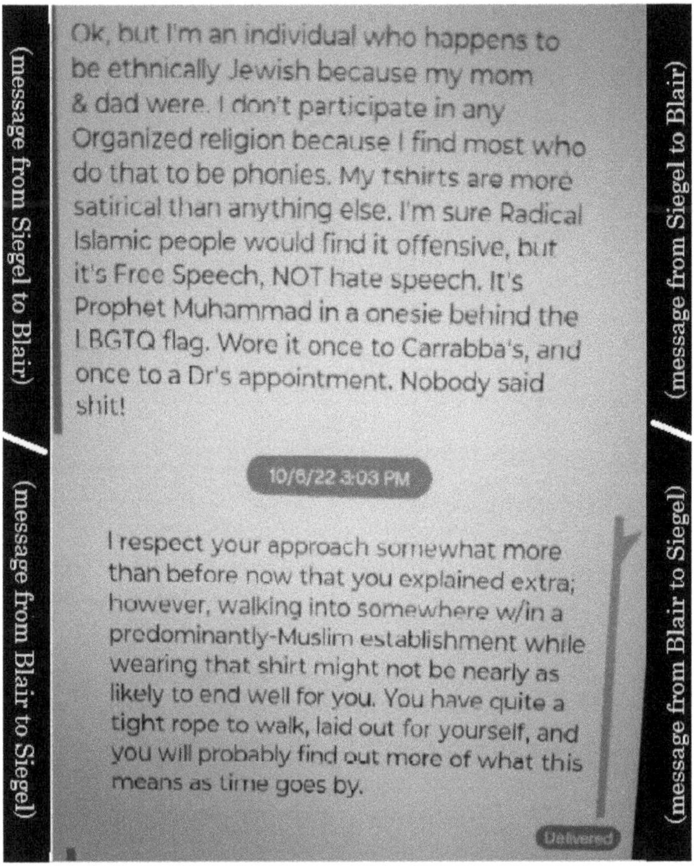

(message from Siegel to Blair)

Ok, but I'm an individual who happens to be ethnically Jewish because my mom & dad were. I don't participate in any Organized religion because I find most who do that to be phonies. My tshirts are more satirical than anything else. I'm sure Radical Islamic people would find it offensive, but it's Free Speech, NOT hate speech. It's Prophet Muhammad in a onesie behind the LBGTQ flag. Wore it once to Carrabba's, and once to a Dr's appointment. Nobody said shit!

10/6/22 3:03 PM

(message from Blair to Siegel)

I respect your approach somewhat more than before now that you explained extra; however, walking into somewhere w/in a predominantly-Muslim establishment while wearing that shirt might not be nearly as likely to end well for you. You have quite a tight rope to walk, laid out for yourself, and you will probably find out more of what this means as time goes by.

Delivered

Next, soon after 6 OCT 2022, 3:03 P.M., then over three-and-a-half months later:

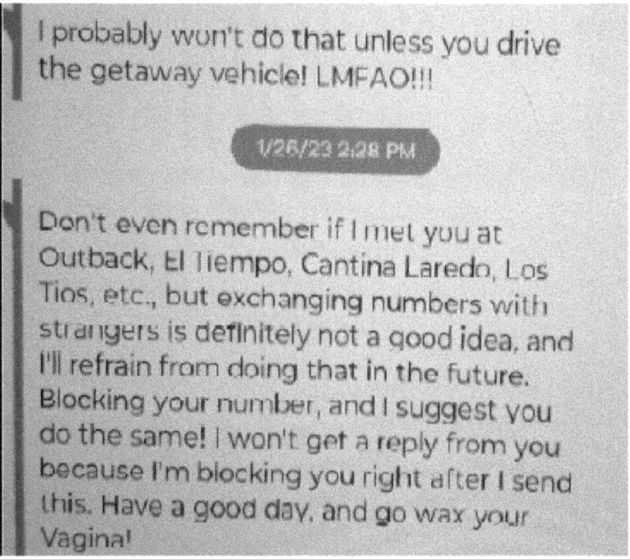

I probably won't do that unless you drive the getaway vehicle! LMFAO!!!
1/26/23 2:28 PM
Don't even remember if I met you at Outback, El Tiempo, Cantina Laredo, Los Tios, etc., but exchanging numbers with strangers is definitely not a good idea, and I'll refrain from doing that in the future. Blocking your number, and I suggest you do the same! I won't get a reply from you because I'm blocking you right after I send this. Have a good day, and go wax your Vagina!


OCT 2022 / JAN 2023 additional one-to-one messages from D. Siegel

---

<u>A Reflective Note:</u>

Something I have revealed to only a few people before is that during the evening of October 5, 2022 in Houston, upon first sight of Dale Siegel, I thought to myself, *The guy who just walked in is wearing Kansas City Chiefs attire… oh wait, that's not Chiefs attire, he's wearing Cleveland Indians attire, even though they've officially changed over to being The Cleveland Guardians. Things might be about to get weird.*

—Maurice James Blair, May 7, 2024

A Subsequent Reflective Note:

Of course, we could have a never-ending list of candidates of who to blame for how and why things later went poorly, and here are some of them and why:

1. Meditate about the aforementioned Dale Siegel (not to be confused with any other person of that name combination). That guy seemed hell-bent on crudely condemning the entirety of Islam while not conceding it to have even a trace of redeeming value at all.
2. Think for a while about the elementary school female physical education instructor (not to be confused with how I received training from at least one other female PE instructor and at least one male PE instructtor while attending elementary school; refresh memory via part of Chapter 2 if necessary). That woman punished me immediately after I had attempted to practice expanding my vocabulary by saying on part of a schoolground of a classmate, "Maybe she thinks she's going to flunk." The act of punishing me for that was probably, in and of itself, plausibly a correct action. However, the fact that the instructor failed to give any clear explanation of why she was so upset—whether it was, as I wrote in a 1994 essay as part of UWC during my freshman year at Duke, due to mishearing the word "flunk" as

the word "fuck," or if it was for some different reason(s)—and that led to my frequently having some hypersensitivity about risks of receiving false accusations. Therefore, sometimes when believing myself the victim of a false accusation I have gone ballistic quickly in self-defense, whereas at other times when facing such a predicament I would strategically arrange how to fight back in self-defense. Perhaps, if that instructor had been more enlightened at the time, she might have been able to address the situation with a calm explanation of a reason or multiple reasons with which to set me on a far less destructive path in terms of my subsequent conflicts with others.

3. There was an acquaintance in something like November 2021 who might be a prime candidate for blame, via a bizarre conversation he had with me in front of a Westheimer restaurant, Fogo de Chao, about halfway between 610 and Beltway 8, in Southwest Houston. It was somewhat between lunch and dinner, and that fellow, rather than simply communicating a situation of not being able to serve food due to guidelines, ended up with a conversation extremely similar to the following transcript, with myself displayed as "Occasional Customer" ("OC") and him displayed as "Employee of Questionable Behavior" ("EQB"):

Occasional Customer (with very full facial hair at that time, wearing a pair of glasses during most of the dialogue; then aged in the mid-40s): Hmm. You're open right now, right?

Employee of Questionable Behavior (appearing then to be aged in the early-to-mid-20s): No. We're closed, because it's between lunch and dinner.

(OC takes a brief look inside the door to see a few patrons dining there)

OC: You have a few cars in the parking lot. Also, momentarily taking a peek inside your door revealed that you have people dining right now. What gives?

EQB: We allow people who already started their meals to continue and finish their meals, but we are not allowing other people in until it gets closer to dinner time.

OC: Interesting. Though I've dined here before, I didn't know about this twist to guidelines. May I ask your name?

EQB: My name is Justin.

OC: Even more interesting. One of my friends is a guy named Justin, and he also works at Fogo de Chao. You've probably met him. May I ask for a more complete version of your name?

EQB: Justin Rodriguez.

OC: Rodriguez! What an interesting name! I sometimes dated and sometimes hung out with a woman of that family name many times in late 2011 to late 2014, but the last time I met her in person was something like early 2016 if I remember right. Maybe you're a distant relative of hers or maybe not. Would you happen to know a Rose Rodriguez from Corpus Cristi?

EQB: No! And your whole discussion of this seems ridiculous!

OC: How so? This doesn't seem ridiculous to me at all. I have dined at your restaurant before, and I probably will dine at it again sooner or later.

EQB: You better leave soon! Also, I am skeptical of what you said. You're probably making up the entire thing, the thing about you having dated a woman with the name Rodriguez.

OC: I *have* dated a Rose Rodriguez. You keep up with this way of excessively dissing people when you don't know much of anything about what has really happened in their lives, and you'll probably reap what you don't want to sow.

---

As it so happened, not too long after that, there was a night in which Justin Haynes invited my mother and me to go have dinner with him at a different restaurant, a diner called Molina, located close to Fogo de Chao.

(My friend Justin Haynes was able to keep the Fogo restaurant waiting job for a while, though that employment relationship eventually came to an end.)

Although the dining event went well at Molina in December 2021 or thereabouts for Justin Haynes, Ming Blair, and yours truly as the three in that party of diners, providing good company for each that time, after leaving that restaurant I inquired with Justin Haynes about his then-co-worker also of the name Justin.

Justin Haynes indicated that he then knew of two co-workers named Justin, but neither of them had the name Justin Rodriguez. Further into the conversation, Haynes was able to ascertain that the guy who had a dismissive and somewhat hostile attitude toward me and presented himself as Justin Rodriguez was actually—and Haynes felt certain of it—a man named Justin Walregan, whether of exactly that spelling or a slightly different spelling. (I do not know for sure whether Haynes had an accurate answer on that, but I trust that, from where I stand, he probably had an accurate answer on that. Therefore, unless you somehow personally know for sure about this, please take it with a grain of salt that Haynes identified the questionable service bloke as having been a Walregan.)

Between all the factors, at some stage after learning of this, I spoke in the ultra-hostile, death-and-destruction, seek-and-destroy mode that my father would use every so often with anyone he found to be causing serious problems.

I said things toward the Employee of Questionable Behavior guy with such crude and extreme hostility that placing a transcript of it here would probably jeopardize the long-term chances of its availability at mainstream online retailers.

Yes, you might look at any of a dozen or more of the extreme features of this book and think to yourself that it is already highly questionable for inclusion by any retailers, but, believe you me, to put in print here what I screamed out loud in the presence of Justin Haynes and Ming Blair about what I thought then to be a suitable fate for the EQB-acronym fellow who jumped to conclusions in a manner of total disrespect, that would easily have been a bridge to far, even by this book's standards.

I considered that "EQB" to have smoked himself out as teaming up with all of those who had been unethical toward me in portions of November 2018 up to late 2021. After I noticed Natasha McDaniel expressing to Juan Martinez one day circa the first week of December 2018 that she felt especially negative toward the way that I looked when I was one of the guys who participated in the National No-Shave November that highlights Prostate Cancer Awareness, seeming to point toward her perception that I should be a second-class citizen of being less eligible to participate in such facial hair growth as most other guys because of her finding me to be of a very ugly face or whatever, I have often intentionally let myself grow a sizable amount of beard and mustache to help smoke out anyone of any demographic who might have a toxic attitude against the entire reality of all affinities and affiliations involving my ancestry, religious choices, experiences, and life itself. A large part of this idea is that if she could show such a profound inability to show even a shred of respect toward the entirety of my life, even when warned repeatedly about much of the most profound aspects, then the fact that the major facial hair heightened her aversion to my life itself could help to lure people who are on the edge of major disrespect into basically volunteering themselves for swift conflicts with me early in interaction with which to nip problems in the bud. The “EQB” punk had seemed to jump headlong into exactly that.

Therefore, some of the statement I screamed out about an idea of what seemed to me possible how that EQB guy might best experience an excruciatingly-painful, deserved, brutal death as a harsh means to help him have a better chance of rapid enlightenment in the bardo realm and/or the next life and beyond—and to reduce the risks of him causing more harm to sentient beings in general in the near future—was a hybrid of several things: 1) the female method of executing an unsuspecting male (as revenge for participating in that female's daughter's demise earlier in the story) in *The Last House on the Left* (1972), 2) the male-on-male pickax murder scene in *The Rocky Horror Picture Show* (1978), 3) rumors about real-life zombies of any gender eating alive the brains of people of any gender, and 4) war stories of when some soldiers have mutilated the bodies of their enemies and stuffed the mutilated body parts into the mouths of those enemies.

This work spares its readers explicit transcription approximating exact wording from that. This parallels how news stories sometimes blur out portions of the video footage of people dying right before the viewer's eyes.

One of the things that this relates to is how in much of Christian theology, there is an idea that if someone thinks about a sin with the intention to commit that sin, then there is a major degree to which the person has already committed that sin. Granted, many might consider it at a significantly lesser degree than if carried out to observable fruition.

Also related is that Christianity, Buddhism, Hinduism, Judaism, and Islam generally agree that there are situations calling for righteous indignation and the enforcement method of imposing harsh penalties on evildoers. I believe that I was fully justified to speak out loud with full intent honestly perceiving at the time that the EQB fellow could easily deserve a gruesome punishment for his monumental disrespect, whether considering it from Vajrayana perspectives or from a variety of other reasonable perspectives. Yes, there is truth to the idea that reality transcends trains of thought about bright lines between what is justified and what is unjustified, but I feel the main energy of this ring true to me as having fit the situation.

In contrast, when someone chooses, instead of venting to a third party or venting directly to an offender, to retaliate against an offender by perpetrating physical harm, then many communities tend to carefully consider the context in judging whether it had been a criminal act or justifiable self-defense.

Analyze how Lorena Bobbitt dismembered John Wayne Bobbitt alive at a time when he was her husband. After cutting it off, she wandered around for a while, contemplating what she might do next, then she threw the mutilated portion of extremely-sensitive, nerve-dense flesh into a field.

(Thus concludes item #3 in a set analyzing some candidates for societal blame.)

4. Consider the possibility that each couple, whether that infamous Lorena Bobbitt and J.W. Bobbitt couple (who would go on to divorce after he survived the ordeal and doctors reattached it between his legs, though with diminished functionality). She alleged rape and other acts of abuse, which he denied. Cf. https://en.wikipedia.org/wiki/John_and_Lorena_Bobbitt as accessed on May 7, 2024. Consider them and consider any and all other couples in which at least one of the two sexually mutilated the other. In some lines of thinking, each such couple should be blamed as a couple. That is, with each who butchered and each who was butchered at least partially culpable, as per ideas along the lines of, "It takes two to tango, and if their choices and actions resulted in female genital mutilation and/or male genital mutilation (outside the auspices of any religiously-sanctioned and/or medically-sanctioned and/or penal-code-sanctioned procedures), then both should be to blame. Their roles were part of what led to their jointly acting out a gruesome failure to honor each other's bodies as divine temples."

Therefore, running with that premise, blame could go to nearly all who have ever, while in a girlfriend-boyfriend, fiancé-and-fiancée, husband-and-wife, etc. committed relationship, either sexually mutilated a significant other and/or been sexually mutilated by a significant other.

Note that in ultra-rare scenarios, both of the two partners could be on both sides of the mutilation. One range of such rarities can occur due to things like epileptic fits, unexpected car crashes, and earthquakes physically jolting a couple while engaging in risky sex, risky foreplay, and/or risky kink, therefore causing unintentional serious harm to the bodies of both partners. Nevertheless, it could remain plausible in the minds of some beholders to blame both members of a couple unintentionally experiencing such a misfortune. The idea behind that could be along the lines of, "If they weren't such freaky kinksters, then they would not have had to worry about an earthquake jolting them into mutilating each other while doing the 69. In the scales of sin and purity, they were found wanting. The wages of sin is death!" Other beholders might counter, "No one really knows for sure why some tragedies occur to some people while others who do the same activities in what seemed the same circumstances went unscathed. Even when looking around at the most unfortunate, we should remain humble and compassionate. There, but by the grace of God, go I."

Return now to the more normal part of this mind experiment in the conceptualizations of which beings to blame for what. There was the idea of how some might wish to blame every person who ever did what many often consider about the worst thing possible to a sexual partner, in terms of butchering the other person's genitals, and also blaming every person to whom that happened, etc.

Such logic ascribing blame to both the mutilator and the mutilated in those cases could aim toward steering everyone away from all possible grievous delinquencies by making examples out of those. This logic judges them to have failed to reasonably honor human bodies as temples unto God / The Divine Reality / etc.

**************

Taking the exploration even further could upset and horrify many of those not already upset and horrified by the preceding. Bear in mind an analogy to a quote from John Madden (1936-2021): "The road to Easy Street goes through the sewer." (Cf. the URL https://www.azquotes.com/quote/183397 as access-ed on May 18, 2024.)

**************

Consider gender relations from perspectives way outside of most people's comfort zones:

> At the risk of alienating many of those whose affection toward females is such as to perceive gender relations as requiring systematic tilting of sentiments in favor of all or nearly all females over all or nearly all males in the overwhelming

majority of gender conflicts and sex wars—many of those who regard extremely few, if any, males as ever qualifying to be anything other than beta males of social status way below the vast majority of females; either overtly or covertly exalting matriarchy; a peculiar list shall soon appear.

That list shall also risk alienating people with a rather opposite approach to the power relations between the genders.

At the risk of alienating many readers of a mindset exalting patriarchy, traditional gender hierarchies, consistent separation of duties such as for females to mainly serve as the helpmeets of their male significant others and as primary nurturers of their ancestors and descendants, with no females ever eligible to wield anywhere near the degree of authority vested in alpha males, a peculiar list shall soon appear. The list shall likely offend many readers, as it broaches difficult topics in sexual ethics, bioethics, etc. Consider these questions:

- When might a jury member best deem the balance of all factors to be such that a husband who mutilates his wife (or a widower who has mutilated his wife of the time) to death is/was: a) entirely to blame while his wife / ex-wife was blameless, b) partly to blame while his wife/ex-wife was also partly to blame, c) entirely blameless, d) etc.?

- When might a jury member best deem the balance of all factors to be such that a wife who mutilates her husband (or a widow who mutilated her husband of the time) to death is/was: a) entirely to blame while her husband/ex-husband was blameless, b) partly to blame while her husband/ex-husband was also partly to blame, c) entirely blameless, d) etc.?
- When should a human being consider it a requirement to: a) arrange for a male infant to be circumcised, b) refrain from arranging for a male infant to be circumcised, c) arrange for a female infant to be genitally modified in a way that some would characterize as female circumcision and others would characterize as female genital mutilation, d) refrain from arranging for a female infant to be genitally modified in a way that some would characterize as female circumcision and others would characterize as female genital mutilation, e) to do similar processes to people other than infants, f) to perform involuntary sterilization of otherwise-fecund adult human beings, g) to perform the spaying and neutering of canine animals, h) to perform the spaying and neutering of feline animals, i) to execute convicted criminals by means of public hanging or lethal injection, j) to execute convicted criminals by means of guillotine or electric chair, k) to kill

people outside the auspices of the criminal justice system (e.g., by vigilante actions, turf warfare, alleged justifiable self-defense, etc.), l) to love another person or to refrain from loving another person (in terms of each possible meaning of "love"), m) to be mean toward others, n) to be nice toward others, o) to intentionally attempt to cause another person to experience an orgasm, p) to accept patriarchy as a proper social structure or to reject it, q) to question everything, r) to restrict activities such as to be very prudish, s) to be strong, t) to feel open to crucifying others and/or to feel open to being crucified by others, u) to care about attempting to preserve the universe or at least the human race or not to care about attempting to preserve the universe or at least the human race, v) to care about victory above all else or to refrain from caring about victory above all else, w) to accept matriarchy as a proper social structure or to reject it, x) to use X (formerly known as Twitter) or to refrain from using X (formerly known as Twitter), y) to say yes to radical social changes or to say no to radical social changes, and z) to say maybe or to refrain from saying maybe?

5. What about the possibility of blaming whomever they would believe to be among "all of the sinners" or "all of the unredeemed sinners" as the best choice? People have had

such extreme disagreements with each other over the millennia about what to best deem to constitute sin, what to best deem to not constitute sin, what beings should do about the existence of sins, what the true path(s) to solving this would be, what the false paths to solving this would be, who to trust, how much to trust oneself, how much to trust in a higher power, etc. What gives? What's it to you?

Something that could bring this home is to imagine that every living human—at some instants designated by some superpowerful group of superconscious beings, would be part of a mind-meld between all humans and all members of the superconscious super-group instigating this.

During such mind-melding experiences, how would the array of all human cognitive dissonances, human cognitive consistencies, conscious transcendence over paradoxes and contradictions, etc. sort themselves out?

---

* * * * *

---

* * * * *

---

Here is a copy of a message that I sent on May 8, 2024 via Facebook Messenger:

9:11 PM

Andrew Cornett, Back in about the 1989-1990 school year, one time (unless some shift in universes rendered you a different person of the same name and almost identical type of appearance and background, which would seem astronomically unlikely) you chose to sucker punch me in a school hallway while you had some type of metallic covering (either brass knuckles or something extremely similar) on the hand you with which you punched. At the time, my mindset was such that I chose not to tattle-tale on you to the teachers or other school administration people. I am absolutely certain that an Andrew Cornett did that back then, and I can see from your Facebook photos that you look very much like a many-years-down-the-road version of what that Andrew would likely look like, plus I can see that we have a mutual friend in Brian Forrister, who indeed went to J.M. Hanks High School at the time that I went to that high school. The timing of the incident I am almost certain to have been the 1989-1990 school year and the location I am almost certain to have been Indian Ridge Middle School. Although I could express hostility toward you over this if I were to choose to do so, there have been such a great many strange things that have happened in my life in recent years, and I have found ways to navigate my way through them successfully to such a degree, that I currently feel a major amount of goodwill toward you, as having in some ways actually helped in a way similar to a drill sergeant, though that was probably not your intention in the choice to sucker punch me back then. If you have any comment about what you might remember, if anything, about that incident, especially why you thought it was the thing to do, then please, by all means, feel free to chime in with telling me something I don't know about what transpired from your perspective with that occurrence. In the long run, that incident has turned out to be something I succeeded into transforming into contributing toward both my awareness of how unprovoked attacks are in the vast majority of cases not a good tactic and how surviving that experience and other difficulties has helped me to toughen up. To toughen up, that is, with being effective at things like when legitimate psychological warfare happens between me and other people. Also, that is with events like how a legitimate bareknuckle barfight happened between another man and me on December 11, 2021 largely over what seemed a disagreement over public policy possibilities. On another note, I had one of my low points in life with ethics in general during portions of 8th Grade; whereas I made some improvements with ethics in 9th Grade, portions of 11th and 12th Grades, The Year 2003, The Year 2004, and a few other periods of time. Regards, Maurice J. Blair

5/8/2024

Here is a transcription of the 8 MAY 2024 message that appeared on the previous page:

Andrew Cornett, Back in about the 1989-1990 school year, one time (unless some shift in universes rendered you a different person of the same name and almost identical type of appearance and background, which would seem astronomically unlikely) you chose to sucker punch me in a school hallway while you had some type of metallic covering (either brass knuckles or something extremely similar) on the hand you with which you punched. At the time, my mindset was such that I chose not to tattle-tale on you to the teachers or other school administration people. I am absolutely certain that an Andrew Cornett did that back then, and I can see from your Facebook photos that you look very much like a many-years-down-the-road version of what that Andrew would likely look like, plus I can see that we have a mutual friend in Brian Forrister, who indeed went to J.M. Hanks High School at the time that I went to that high school. The timing of the incident I am almost certain to have been the 1989-1990 school year and the location I am almost certain to have been Indian Ridge Middle School. Although I could express hostility toward you over this if I were to choose to do so, there have been such a great many strange things that have happened in my life in recent years, and I have found ways to navigate my way through them successfully to such a degree, that I currently feel a major amount of goodwill toward you, as having in some ways actually helped in a way similar to a drill sergeant, though that was probably not your intention in the choice to sucker punch me back then. If you have any comment about what you might remember, if anything, about that incident, especially why you thought it was the thing to do, then please, by all means, feel free to chime in with telling me something I don't know about what transpired from your perspective with that occurrence. In the long run, that incident has turned out to be something I succeeded into transforming into contributing toward both my awareness of how unprovoked attacks are in the vast majority of cases not a good tactic and how surviving that experience and other difficulties has helped me to toughen up. To toughen up, that is, with being effective at things like when legitimate psychological warfare happens between me and other people. Also, that is with events like how a legitimate bare-knuckle barfight happened between another man and me on December 11, 2021 largely over what seemed a disagreement over public policy possibilities. On another note, I had one of my low points in life with ethics in general during portions of 8th Grade; whereas I made some improvements with ethics in 9th Grade, portions of 11th and 12th Grades, The Year 2003, The Year 2004, and a few other periods of time. Regards, Maurice J. Blair

---

* * * * *

---

* * * * *

---

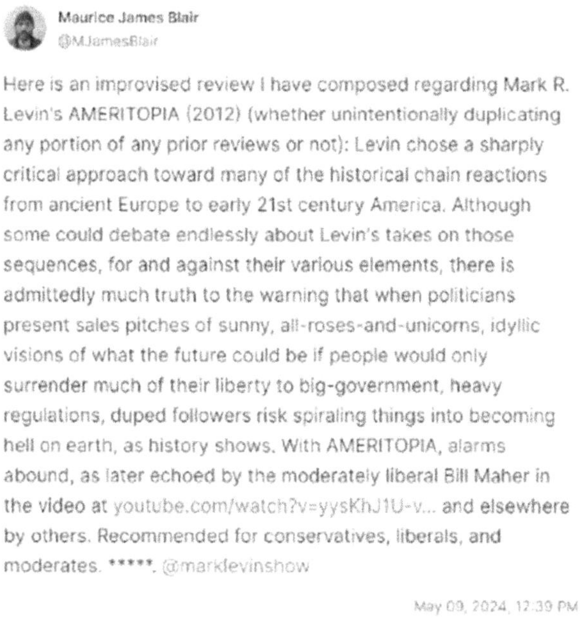

Maurice James Blair
@MJamesBlair

Here is an improvised review I have composed regarding Mark R. Levin's AMERITOPIA (2012) (whether unintentionally duplicating any portion of any prior reviews or not): Levin chose a sharply critical approach toward many of the historical chain reactions from ancient Europe to early 21st century America. Although some could debate endlessly about Levin's takes on those sequences, for and against their various elements, there is admittedly much truth to the warning that when politicians present sales pitches of sunny, all-roses-and-unicorns, idyllic visions of what the future could be if people would only surrender much of their liberty to big-government, heavy regulations, duped followers risk spiraling things into becoming hell on earth, as history shows. With AMERITOPIA, alarms abound, as later echoed by the moderately liberal Bill Maher in the video at youtube.com/watch?v=yysKhJ1U-v... and elsewhere by others. Recommended for conservatives, liberals, and moderates. *****. @marklevinshow

May 09, 2024, 12:39 PM

The above is a copy of a Truth Social post that transmitted from M.J.B. in Houston, TX to those with access to that platform.

Related URL: https://www.youtube.com/watch?v=yysKhJ1U-vM

The next page includes a transcription of that book review.

A transcription of what yours truly (of the Truth Social handle @MJamesBlair) posted at 12:39 PM U.S. Central Daylight Time on that: Here is an improvised review I have composed regarding Mark R. Levin's AMERITOPIA (2012) (whether unintentionally duplicating any portion of any prior reviews or not): Levin chose a sharply critical approach toward many of the historical chain reactions from ancient Europe to early 21st century America. Although some could debate endlessly about Levin's takes on those sequences, for and against their various elements, there is admittedly much truth to the warning that when politicians present sales pitches of sunny, all-roses-and-unicorns, idyllic visions of what the future could be if people would only surrender much of their liberty to big-government, heavy regulations, duped followers risk spiraling things into becoming hell on earth, as history shows. With AMERITOPIA, alarms abound, as later echoed by the moderately liberal Bill Maher in the video at youtube.com/watch?v=yysKhJ1U-vM and elsewhere by others. Recommended for conservatives, liberals, and moderates. *****. @marklevinshow

---

The YouTube link was to "New Rule: A Woke Revolution" as posted by Real Time with Bill Maher (@RealTime); also, see the February 3, 2023 article "Bill Maher Condemns Woke Revolution, Twitter's 'Red Guard', And Its US Parallels" (at the https://deadline.com/2023/02/bill-maher-condemns-woke-revolution-twitter-red-guard-us-parallels-1235249470/ URL) by Bruce Haring, if wishing for another set of angles on this.

---

Next, is a copy of a message that I sent to many people simultaneously via Facebook Messenger in the morning of May 19, 2024 from Houston, Texas; the recipients were of many locations.

Information on the recipient list, as well as other information relevant to readers of this book, shall appear after the transcript.

---

Diverse Recipients, This message is mainly to Andrew Cornett; the rest of you are here as a de facto cc line presence, whereas Facebook Messenger seems to deny its users the cc (i.e., copy concern) line when using it. If any of you who are de facto cc-line-style recipients question why you are included, then please reflect on your past interactions with anyone included in this communique and contemplate the idea expressed in *Crocodile Dundee* (1986) of how people would "talk to Wally" to improve community situations. Also, consider thinking about religious scriptures and/or philosophical treatises of whichever religion(s), if any, would be of your choice and/or whichever philosophy/philosophies, if any, would be of your choice. Sometime around 1991, Lesley Wong (who would later become Lesley Wong Chong) or a person very similar to her--although it was almost definitely that Lesley--at an El Paso Baptist Chinese Church event made a request by saying to me, "Say hi to Andrew Cornett." I answered, "Yes." However, at that time, I intentionally answered yes while intending to never say hi on her behalf to the Andrew Cornett to whom she had referred. I am almost completely certain that you, the first of the set of you listed as the recipients, the Andrew Cornett included in this message, is the Andrew Cornett that Lesley and I were discussing on that occasion over three decades ago. Whether he is / you are (depending on the reader's/readers' perspective(s)) identical or not to the person spoken of before (in terms of the "persistence of identity" type of perspective; obviously we're all different than who or what we were before in many ways, but we are in at least a trace of a way people of persistent identity to at least a trace of a degree), this should prove insightful into interpersonal and international relations. Therefore, one of the things that is happening with this message is that I am participating in a purification of what had happened before with that circa-1991 conversation. When Jennifer Dai wished me a happy birthday on June 14, 2023, and soon after that, part of my response was, "'From around late 2003 to about late July or early August 2008 I acted out a several-years-long total extinction event of intentional lies of commission (i.e., extinction of intentionally stating anything deceptive at its core vis-a-vis basic regular reality) as part of what I believed best in terms of training with True Buddha School methods. Then, I brought back on an exceedingly extremely rare basis, the capacity for intentional lies of commission, but only if I would at some core level know it to be a case of extreme warfare between good and evil with the use of it contributing to the good or if it would have a similarly clearly ethical basis. However, back in the 1990s I had a strongly fixed belief that hundreds of hours of sitcoms on TV had proven that some social white lies would be necessary for reasonable interpersonal relations, and, because there was a day and time between classes in middle school that I was walking along and Andrew Cornett sucker punched me in the ribs with either brass knuckles or something extremely similar to brass knuckles, and other factors, I said, "Yes" to the idea of saying hello to him on behalf of either Leslie or you while having already decided that there was no way in hell that I would go and say hello to him on behalf of either you or Leslie. Nowadays, in the post-late-2003-or-early-2004 era, I speak with people in the style of, "No, I have no plan to say hello to Andrew Cornett on your behalf, because one day I was walking between classes and, without having had any preexisting vendetta or feud with me, he suddenly sucker punched me in the ribs with either brass knuckles or some similar metallic covering." To which the other person might respond, "You're so funny. Such sarcasm!" To which I could respond, "I'm not freaking joking at all. Yes, he actually did that, though I did not go and complain to the school authorities. Though it somewhat hurt at the time, there was no major physical damage as far as I could tell, and I didn't particularly feel like reporting it. Still, I believe there's no way in hell that I should go and say hello to him on your behalf."'" (Note: In that mid-2023 response I had misspelled "Lesley" from memory as one of the spellings that involves the same pronunciation.) In any case, with enough of the changes in life, I decided to go ahead and say hi to the person whom I am almost absolutely certain to be that Andrew Cornett now. This is largely because of how a great many changes have happened in our reality over the span of thirty-something years. Recently, on May 8, 2024 (i.e., eleven days ago) I reached out to the Andrew Cornett (to whatever degree "you," the main recipient of this message; to whatever degree "he/him," a recipient other than most of the recipients of this message) who is almost definitely the many-years-down-the-road person who emerged from having been the Andrew who sucker-punched me in the ribs approximately in the 1989-1990 period, including a description similar to what I had responded to Jennifer with. (Note: The referenced mid-2023 personal Facebook page response was in a friends-only-setting birthday wish section), opening the door for ("him to provide" if applicable or "you to provide" if applicable) a response about what in the world was going on with the motive(s) behind the punch back then. No response came in the intervening time, although that recipient also evidently did not block me on Facebook in the intervening time. Many of you have been aware for many years about how my late father had served in combat in portions of the early 1950s and portions of the late 1960s as a soldier in the U.S. Army. Sometimes his ways of orienting me toward much more severe ways of dealing with people and things has worked very well, at other times, not quite as well; and there have been many influences in this life in both the direction of severity in dealing with everyone and the direction of leniency in dealing with everyone. As I told Andrew directly in my May 8, 2024 message, I currently feel no animosity toward him in connection with that incident, believing that in some ways the unexpected hit to the ribs has in the long run served me well as a drill-sergeant-style supplement to how my father, though never physically torturing me, used extreme psychological harshness as part of training me. He psychologically tortured a very high percentage of the people with whom he had substantial interactions after he came back from serving in combat in portions of Southeast Asia and experienced how it was that many Americans in the early-to-mid-1970s showed outright hostility to U.S. Military service members, including him. I believe that the vast majority of the people whom he psychologically tortured during his last few decades of life in this world probably deserved exactly what they got from him, including that I believe that my mother and I probably usually got exactly what we had coming when he would go into a combat mode of how to communicate toward some of his closest family members. Was he ever excessive in this? Yes. But aren't we all? Was he usually on target with it, neither excessive nor insufficient, sufficiently using the right amount of harshness? Yes, I truly believe that he was usually fully on target with it. In any case, we all have a balance of how severe to be toward others and how lenient to be toward others, whether any of us consider ourselves to be of a given faith or of no particular faith, etc. For example, whether a given person identifies with being among Christians, Jews, Muslims, Noahidists, Sikhs, Buddhists, Jains, Atheists, Agnostics, and/or whoever and/or whatever else. Whether any of you, the recipeents of this message, find it appropriate or inappropriate, bear in mind that I consider it the correct action for me to do, no matter which of you, if any, might choose to respond with an attempt to condemn me for anything about it. This message is in some ways food for thought and in other ways a toolkit of perspectives on the statics and dynamics of beings and activities. Have a great May 19, 2024 and best wishes with the next few days! (In other words, best wishes with possible greatness on The Day After Armed Forces Day and the next few days, including how two days from now shall be World Day of Cultural Diversity for Dialogue and Development!) Regards, Maurice James Blair

---

Notes to the preceding transcript of a May 19, 2024 message from yours truly to quite a number of recipients as a way of catalyzing awareness and dialogues on The Value of Cultural Diversity and The Treasures of Enlightenment:

• The Facebook display names of the recipients were: 1) Andrew Cornett, 2) Lesley Wong Chong, 3) Jennifer Dai, 4) Neal Quon, 5) Jim West, 6) Roger Nygard, 7) Roger Wistar, 8) Jeff Andrien, 9) Afolabi Ojumu, 10) Alex Pacheco, 11) Amanda Remy Freeland, 12) Amani Redd, 13) Ana Murcia, 14) Anthony Freedom, 15) Aron Silberg, 16) Brian Forrister, 17) Briana Roth, 19) Brock Hedgecoke, 20) Camilla Bradley, 21) Carisa Quintana, 22) Charles Ray, 23) Clay Collum, Damian Cyrocki, 24) Dan Mailman, 25) Dave Seidman, 26) David Hoffman, 27) David Plylar, 28) Dorothy Vaughton, 29) Erik Oslund, 30) Erin Petrie, 31) Francisco Blanchard Muldoon, 32) Frankie Sticks, 33) Frank McDonald, 34) Greg Rauch, 35) Gregory Peter, 36) J Spencer Portillo, 37) James Roy, 38) Jeff Hancock, 39) Jennie Lee, 40) Jerry Cook, 41) Jody Lynn Gillit, 42) John He, 43) John Hendrick, 44) John Shelby Crawford, 45) John Taylor, 46) Justin Haynes, 47) Katherine Navarrete, 48) Kenan Baluken, 49) Kenneth Barnes, 50) Kwunnie Ng Montgomery, 51) Laua Ziligson, 52) Leon Fusselman, 53) Lifes Good, 54) Louis Wheeler, 55) Maggie Wilson, 56) Michael Piazza, 57) Misha Ko, 58) Nishant Gaikwad, 59) Paul Benoit, 60) Rachel Smith Anderson, 61) Radically Transformed, 62) Reese McCray, 63) Rick Herrera, 64) Roger Beebe, 65) Tienling Chen, 66) Ustinya Shevtsova, 67) Vic Kwong, 68) Vlad Ghita, 69) Warren Harper, 70) William Woo, 71) Xteslea Moody Tse, 72) Yoichi Yammamoto, 73) Tad Schmaltz, & 74) Guro Larry St Clair.

•I confirm that the people of the Facebook display names "Aron Silberg," "Justin Haynes," "Briana Roth," "Andrew Cornett," "Ustinya Shevtsova," and "David Hoffman" were the people for whom those names appear elsewhere in this book.

• The "Frankie Sticks" fellow is the "Frank McDonald" fellow of the X (formerly known as Twitter) interactions involving "Frank McDonald (@FMcDonald_JDS)"—a man who has said his regular life name is, technically, Frank McDonald II.

• The Facebook display name "Frank McDonald" fellow is the Frank McDonald who is the father of the Frank McDonald II / "Frankie Sticks" fellow.

• The director of *The Nature of Existence* (2009) was Roger Nygard, who many years down the road became one of the many referenced May 19, 2024 message recipients.

• Michael Piazza was a Chi Delta Chapter Psi Upsilon Fraternity brother who was attending undergraduate studies at Duke University at some of the same time that Major League Baseball player Mike Piazza was active as a professional catcher who performed very well in terms of contributions to run production through his hitting prowess.

• Warren Harper is a FIDE Master with ELO rating 2356 (Cf. https://ratings.fide.com/profile/2028140 as accessed on May 19, 2024) as published by FIDE in May 2024.

I mentioned him briefly in portions of Chapter Three of the freely-distributed book *Impact* (2024; briefly referenced by Sec. 5, Pt. L of Ch. 10 of this ABAEOAT:SRPCHVII work.)

• The Amanda Remy and the Tad Schmaltz mentioned in *Science, Religion, Politics, and Cards* (2023) would eventually become the Amanda Remy Freeland and the Tad Schmaltz among the recipients of that 19 May 2024 communique.

• The Clayton Collum KPMG employee mentioned briefly in Chapter Eight many years later became the Clay Collum recipient of that Facebook message that included over 70 recipients.

• I unintentionally reversed two words, referring to El Paso Chinese Baptist Church as El Paso Baptist Chinese Church.

• Roger Beebe was a graduate school student at Duke University when he taught a Literature class that focused on Science Fiction Film in the summer session of 1997. I was one of his students for that class. He went on to earn a PhD, and, as of May 19, 2024, he was shown to be a professor among the faculty of The Ohio State University, as reflected on that date at https://theatreandfilm.osu.edu/people/beebe.77.

• Rachel Smith Anderson was known as Rachel Smith when she was a Hanks High School student of extraordinary academic achievement in El Paso, Texas, long ago. She is one of the best people in terms of the long-term dynamic of how, after a nearly-three-decade hiatus of communications, about 2/3 of the way into 2022, she and I shared direct messaging that caused her overall set of interactions with me to be such that she provides me with a tonic to the toxicity of many other people—a tonic not nearly at the superb, awe-inspiring level by which Liza Darnton has served to help me to heal, but still very helpful.

• Erin Petrie was in a science fiction writers' roundtable-style discussion group of which I was also a member in portions of late 2011 to early 2012. She demonstrated excellent writing.

• Appendix IV of *Science, Religion, Politics, and Cards* has a copy of some correspondence with Tienling Chen.

• The Dan Mailman whom I briefly mentioned in *Science, Religion, Politics, and Cards* (2023) became the Dan Mailman among those recipients of that 2024 message that brought Andrew Cornett, Erin Petrie, and Roger Nygard into each other's remote presence in its context, many years after that Dan and I first met at True Buddha Temple in Houston.

• The person of the display name Guro Larry St Clair is the Larry St. Clair who taught the mid-2002 Jeet Kune Do and Kali martial arts class of which I was one of the students. Chapter Six of this ABAEOAT:SRPCHVII (2024) work briefly mentioned him.

Consider how my home copy of *Knock 'em Dead 2003* (ISBN: 1-58062-759-5) included on its page 54 a passage to which I performed a circa-mid-2003-to-mid-2004 modification:

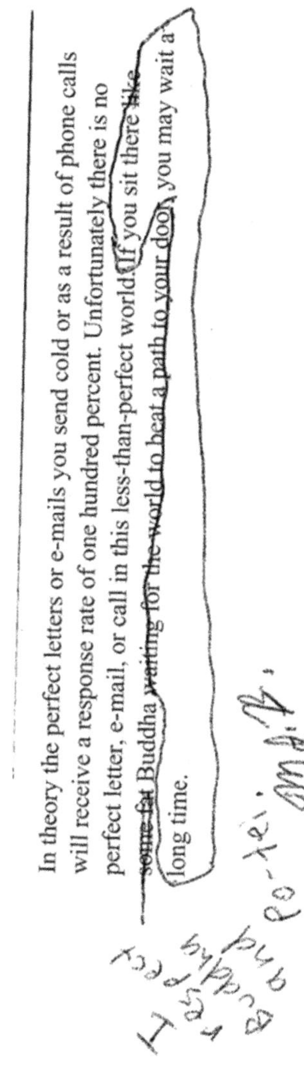

In theory the perfect letters or e-mails you send cold or as a result of phone calls will receive a response rate of one hundred percent. Unfortunately there is no perfect letter, e-mail, or call in this less-than-perfect world. If you sit there like some fat Buddha waiting for the world to beat a path to your door, you may wait a long time.

No, I did not seek permission from Adams Media Corporation to copy that portion of their book, nor was there any need to seek such permission.

This is a fair use of copyrighted material, given how small the amount copied was and how vitally relevant, in teaming up with the Buddhas, Bodhisattvas, and Dharma Protectors is Synapsid Revelations Press Corporation's act of showing that modification.

This is because both Martin Yate and Adams Media Corporation showed by their putting down everything about Buddhism in the way that they did, they therefore deserve every bit of the rebuke that Synapsid Revelations Press Corporation and I are showing them via the display on the previous page, as well as much of the rest of this book. *They had the First Amendment Right to print that, and Synapsid Revelations Press and I have the First Amendment Right to be part of the skillful means by which Buddhism resoundingly punches them back.*

* * * * * * * *

*If they sue, then we may find where such suit may go, including the possibility SRPC may countersue, and maybe we could bring to the public more fully into the light of day whatever Anti-Buddhist rot is under the surface of many Americans who might otherwise seem to be upstanding members of their communities.*

*I truly believe that there are currently many Afghanis, Iraqis, Iranians, Israelis, Chinese, Americans, Italians, Spanish, Mexicans, and others who would best shift away from clinging to very Anti-Buddhist mindsets and to embrace a healthy amount of Pro-Buddhist mindsets.*

As many people have stated over the eons, "Sunlight is the best disinfectant."

Yes, perhaps there have been many atheists, agnostics, Christians, Jews, Muslims, Hindus, and others who have believed it best in their lives to think, speak, and write with derision and condemnation toward Buddhism, its methods, its aims, and its practitioners. However, when people believe it best in their lives to think, speak, and write with derision and condemnation toward Buddhism, its methods, its aims, and its practitioners, doing any more of this than the amount actually warranted by reality is similar to flying an airplane directly toward a building at a high speed: unless course correction happens before it is too late, there will be terrible consequences. What if the people believe it best to fly in such a way as to deliberately crash into such a building, sacrificing themselves toward promoting a cause of Anti-Buddhism? From some Buddhist perspectives, a degree of Anti-Buddhism is in fact warranted as part of coordinating True Buddhism, yet any mistakes in the directions of any excessive Anti-Buddhism and/or in the directions of any excessive Pro-Buddhism tend to have hellacious consequences.

In terms of the views of those practicing atheism, agnosticism, and other things, beings could think of this in terms of how misjudgments about the degrees to which Buddhism is relevant to reality while carrying varying degrees of truth could be problematic, as with similar misjudgments toward anyone or anything.

In terms of Judaism, Noahidism, Islam, and various nondenominational Abrahamic religious mindsets, any mistake in the direction of an excessive Anti-Buddhism and any mistake in the direction of an excessive Pro-Buddhism could be considered a form of harmful idolatry, as could any mistakes in the directions of excessive Pro-Judaism, excessive Anti-Judaism, excessive Anti-Humanism, excessive Pro-Humanism, excessive Pro-Islam, excessive Anti-Islam, excessive Anti-Christianity, excessive Pro-Christianity, excessive Pro-Business, excessive Anti-Business, excessive Pro-Statism, excessive Anti-Statism, excessive Pro-Individualism, excessive Anti-Individualism, excessive Pro-Legalism, excessive Anti-Legalism, excessive Pro-Feminism, excessive Anti-Feminism, excessive Pre-Neutering, excessive Anti-Neutering, excessive Pro-Spaying, excessive Anti-Spaying, excessive Sex-Positivity, excessive Sex-Negativity, excessive Pro-Youth, excessive Anti-Youth, excessive Pro-Age, excessive Anti-Age, excessive Pro-Masculinism, excessive Anti-Masculinism, excessive Anti-Idolatry, excessive Pro-Idolatry, excessive Pro-Hinduism, excessive Anti-Hinduism, excessive Pro-Foundersism, excessive Anti-Foundersism, excessive Anti-Excessivism, excessive Pro-Excessivism, etc.

In terms of Christianity, a person can address these issues by quoting scripture and analyzing it, for example, extending the idea of *Matthew* 22 to be relevant to everyone and everything, rather than limiting its purview to issues of divinity, currencies, and governmental authorities.

Consider, for example, comparing several English translations of *Matthew* 22:19-21 with each other and various personal experiences:

Shew me the tribute money. And they brought unto him a penny. And he saith unto them, Whose is this image and superscription? They say unto him, Caesar's. Then saith he unto them, Render therefore unto Caesar the things which are Caesar's; and unto God the things that are God's. —KJV

Shew me the coin of the tribute. And they offered him a penny. And Jesus saith to them: Whose image and inscription is this? They say to him: Caesar's. Then he saith to them: Render therefore to Caesar the things that are Caesar's; and to God, the things that are God's. —RHE

Let me see the tax money. And they gave him a penny. And he said to them, Whose is this image and name on it? They say to him, Caesar's. Then he said to them, Give to Caesar the things which are Caesar's, and to God the things which are God's. —BBE

---

Although there is some truth in the idea that we should blame Martin Yate and Adams Media Corporation for having the nerve to present extreme disrespect toward the entirety of Buddhism in part of *Knock 'Em Dead 2003*, there is also blame attributable to those who subsequently acted out extreme disrespect toward Buddhism.

Also, very much blame attributable to various Christian theologians for misinterpreting REALITY ITSELF as somehow compatible with taking a no-quarter, absolute-and-utter-rejection approach to the entirety of Buddhism. In many ways, though, there need not be much to fret about this. When one chooses a no-quarter, absolute-and-utter-rejection approach toward the idea of Buddhism having any sensible reality and relevancy, this is in a similar vein as the airplane metaphor presented a few pages ago: It could be analogous to driving a car at top speed directly toward a solid concrete wall, then receiving a warning from others that the best course of action would be to avoid crashing head-on into that wall, then refusing to change course (on account of a rigid attachment to falsely believing it sheer and utter nonsense to think of that wall as posing any real threat at all). Eventually, it may happen that one receiving such warnings changes one's mind and steers away from crashing head-on. Alternatively, such a one might simply stop the vehicle. However, in some cases a warned being chooses to stick to believing there nothing more than a harmless illusion ahead, choosing to keep charging toward that wall, resulting in catastrophic injury or death upon collision. The wall turns out to be real, as those who gave warnings knew from experience. Perhaps on some extremely rare occasions, Providence might grant such a person charging toward a wall wages other than a collision, for example by transfiguring Reality to make the wall become an illusion, yet in the preponderance of cases the collision proves deadly. Also, in a high percentage of nonlethal cases, survivors suffer such maiming that they rue the day they failed to heed the warnings.

For your consideration, a way that I have put into my own words in this instance something that at a minimum is about 85% similar to expressions from others and at a maximum might exactly replicate verbatim an expression from hundreds of years ago, an expression that many Buddhist readers may find agreeable and that many non-Buddhist readers may find disagreeable; here is a pattern for you to consider:

"Buddhism helps people to recognize reality more thoroughly when people adapt well enough to find ways to use its tools as part of skillful means and wisely-chosen ends. Failure to properly use its tools proves, for many a sentient being, disastrous. Succeeding to wisely and skillfully use its tools proves, for many a sentient being, auspicious. Effective use of Buddhism is possibly the best thing that people can ever do for themselves and others."

*Both the side of excessively revering Buddhism and the side of excessively dismissing Buddhism can prove fatally problematic. Buddhism addresses this, and it also addresses dangers of excessively revering and/or excessively dismissing each and every other possible religion, philosophy, and/or science. It does this via many variations of how nonattachment, nonaversion, and nonindifference prove over great ranges to be vastly superior to attachment, aversion and indifference. It shows how the Dharma can thereby liberate beings, and after achieving a degree of liberation via holding onto the Dharma, beings may achieve yet greater liberation by finding a middle way between the continuous holding onto Dharma and the continuous letting go of Dharma.*

**********************************************

Although there are many controversies about many sects of Christianity, some of them—for example, Christian Science—have expressed the need for Christians "to avoid Christian idolatry," which is, as beheld by the minds of some, advice in a similarly true vein.

**************************************************

Although it has been a long time since I encountered it, I remember with absolute certainty that a speech/communications instructor at Houston Community College, a communications textbook, or both indicated that the word "altercasting" could, in at least some applications, be defined along the lines of, "presenting a hypothetical scenario with which to stimulate understanding and discourse."

**************************************************

To aim for complete objectivity, consider this: In that idea presented earlier about a hypothetical of dealing with if God/ Reality / Whatever-You-Might-Call-That-Profound-Whatever were to ask people to vote for who the most expendable organization on Earth might be, as a recommendation for The Almighty to consider, we could psychoanalyze how each possible person might take the step of choosing whom to target with the vote. Anyone who has ever had a huge conflict with any organization, especially after having previously cared deeply about that organization, could automatically lean toward voting for that formerly deeply-cared-for organization to be the most expendable. Yes, it does have some similarity to a scorned lover striking back at the other in some cases. However, no, in other cases it does not in every case have much similarity at all to a scorned lover striking back at the other. In many of those other cases, more of an apt analogy could involve paralleling an entire organization's role within THE ENTIRETY OF

REALITY to one person's role within an entire reasonably-ethically-and-legitimately-run country:

• Much as one male thinking himself to be bossing around others in a correct manner, yet actually acting in an unjustifiably-treasonous manner, if later defeated by the government of his country, then could face severe punishment, an organization believing itself to be interacting with individuals in a correct manner, yet actually acting in an unjustifiably-antireality manner, when eventually defeated by THE ENTIRETY OF REALITY, encounters severe consequences.

• Much as one female thinking herself to be bossing around others in a correct manner, yet actually acting in an unjustifiably-treasonous manner, if later defeated by the government of her country, then could face severe punishment, an organization believing itself to be interacting with individuals in a correct manner, yet actually acting in an unjustifiably-antireality manner, when sooner or later becoming thoroughly and resoundingly defeated by THE ENTIRETY OF REALITY, encounters severe consequences.

Return attention now to the idea of any given human being casting a vote at a given time for the category of, "Most Expendable Organization on Earth." It seems plausible that in whichever cases that this has happened in history—whether conceived in exactly this way or via an alternative that is de facto essentially equivalent to this—

instances of this have had mixed results, to say the least.

*This does not make the voter inherently wrong for caring to vote based on what the voter's experiences point toward, but it also does not necessarily make the organization receiving such a vote of nonconfidence among the organizations deserving to go extinct during a given interval—even if that organization accumulates a very large number of such votes within that interval.*

*Yes, if a sufficient amount of hostility from a sufficient number of beings becomes aimed at an organization, then that organization's days may well be numbered. However, if those extremely hostile to a given organization—whether the object of that condemnation happens to be a nation-state, a business organization, an allegedly-freedom-fighting organization, an allegedly-terrorist organization, or anything else—and those who actually run the organization—in other words, both the side for its survival and the side for its demise—steer things toward benevolence in terms of being oriented at the cores of their beings to sufficiently respect a holistic and spiritually-enlightened approach, then whether said organization endures or dissolves, the process still has great chances of proving very helpful to the long-term enlightenment of sentient beings.*

As a reminder, I still do not know whether those 9/22/2015 robbers were affiliated with any specific organization of which I have ever heard the name or, for that matter, if those robbers were affiliated with any officially-named, identifiable organization. Even if they were actually somehow not part of any organization officially and publicly acknowledged as existent, then they would, nevertheless, fit into a category of having formed an organization in terms of how they acted together in a concerted effort to carry out that robbery operation.

As I reflected on things from another angle, as of the about 10:20 A.M. to 10:23 A.M. CDT period on April 27, 2024, I found myself voting for them to be the most expendable on Earth. That vote might have been null and void if their organization had already dissolved prior to that time and never subsequently reconstituted. However, I do not know whether their organization has existed at any time other than the period that it used in order to violate my family. That brought up a degree of comparison and contrast between them and The Financial Advisory Group, Inc.

Considering this scenario, I let go then and there, in portions of the forenoon of April 27, 2024; I let go then and there in that process of all animosity toward The Financial Advisory Group, Inc. and all animosity toward Gray Reed & McGraw. Yes, subsequently I have repeatedly let that animosity return to me and let that animosity again depart from me. That is somewhat like occasionally spelunking and breathing in and breathing out the air of a cave or twenty-six. Yes, there were several totally FUBAR things about how those two organizations acted toward me, but, yes, there were also some totally FUBAR things about how I acted toward them. Both they and I were affected by many prior totally FUBAR things that a bunch of other people and organizations did to millions, including us—sometimes directly and sometimes indirectly.

In several ways both they and I are victims of how we have to navigate the legacies of terrible parts of the history of the human race, and factors beyond our control put us on collision courses with which to become hostile to one another. In several other ways neither they nor I nor you nor anyone else anywhere are victims of anything, because some portions of *The Dharmapada* point toward how it is that everyone everywhere can transcend all forms of victimhood, perpetratorhood, birth, aging, death, childhood, adolescence, adulthood, parenthood, it, not-it, nonparenthood, exordium, and terminus.

Return attention to events from decades or even millennia ago, especially the worst horrors.

*Those dirty, &()Δ-Δ@~*-Δ, ####--- health-violators who set up and performed the Tuskegee experiments long ago, in which some Americans became targeted to be involuntarily infected with venereal disease: although in some ways they most directly harmed the people physically infected, they also infected the entire population of The United States of America with a terrible reality to have to deal with. In many respects they made The United States of America in that context approximately morally equivalent to the infamous Dr. Mengele.*

This could lead to virtually endless debates about whether the U.S. *really* acted that terribly or *only halfway* acted that terribly, *etc.* Jack Vernon's *The Illustrated History of Torture* (2011) describes a vast array of cruelties, including the WW2 death camp practices—largely stemming from eugenics-based ideas advocated by the aforementioned Josef Mengele (1911-1979)—cruelties that even included acts of "attempting to attach the body parts of one subject to another without permission or need..." (Cf. pp. 48-49; ISBN 978-1-4351-3207-8.)

*Think about it, just think about it. No matter who you might be, imagine yourself in the predicament of people who went through that. A twist might make it more thoroughly hit home. Just imagine it, imagine that you are in some political prison in some totalitarian country, and the people running the facility start doing that in your presence: You watch inquisitors interrogate several of the other political prisoners, they mutilate select organs and select organ fragments ranging from victims' knees to victims' noses, and they implant or otherwise attach the mutilated body parts into or onto those who then become involuntary organ recipients. After you witness the grisly scene unfolding absent of any anesthesia for those in pain and agony, the perpetrators turn to you, and you know you're next.*

Yes, think about it for a while. I have thought of many gruesome scenarios that could happen to me, and one of the reasons has been an attempt to toughen up such as to be able to deal with the many difficult challenges that happen in our lives every now and then. (Cf. Chapters 8 and 11 of *Science, Religion, Politics, and Cards.*)

The Yamantaka empowerment has, since the Q1 2009 approval from True Buddha School to confer it upon me, proven to be one of the effective tools for when I deal with such challenging experiences. There are a plethora of advantages and a plethora of disadvantages to many training methods; moderation of time and energy spent on training is in many cases warranted.

—M.J.B., April 27 to May 20, 2024

**********************************************

On many occasions of moving on from earlier fact patterns and thought exercises to revisit afresh scenarios of addressing the issue of whom to vote for as the most-expendable organization(s), I let go of animosity toward any organization, idea, person, place, or thing—prepared, though, quite prepared to return to righteous indignation toward anyone or anything deserving it if and when correct for it. Yea verily, ready to again righteously harbor and act upon correct, enforcement-oriented animosity toward anyone or anything if it is truly the way to best serve the duty to Reality.

That could even include my letting go for a while—until if and when I might flash with rage against them again[4] of any animosity toward the people who perpetrated things like the WW2 death camps and the Tuskegee experiments, those upon whom writers and speakers might sometimes wish to confer any of the following epithets, each with "the dirty" preceding the next phraseology:

a) God-damned, fucking health-violators

b) ultra-unethical, rotten-to-the-core, forcefully-attacking-others-savagely health-violators

c) &()Δ-Δ@~*-Δ, ####--- health-violators

**********************************************

(Reminder: Bear in mind, though, again, that there are illusions to concepts in many ranges of reality.)

**********************************************

**********************************************

**********************************************

**********************************************

**********************************************

...&&&&&&&&&&&&........!*&......&&&&&&&c.

**********************************************

**********************************************

**********************************************

**********************************************

**********************************************

**********************************************

Perhaps I might never know what was going through the minds of those people who committed that September 2015 robbery, but if any of them wind up having the cruel stuff of legends happen to them—horrors that happened to characters in any television shows, movies, writings, and/or other manifestations of storytelling, especially means by which evildoers reap harsh consequences for what they have sown—then I would not be surprised.

*For all I know, maybe some of that kind of stuff has already happened to them. However, either way, perhaps they and you and I and everyone else will have future opportunities to experience a more perfect and more complete awareness of reality.*

**************************************************

**************************************************

**************************************************

**************************************************

**************************************************

**************************************************

**************************************************

**************************************************

Now, let us pivot away from anything very directly associated with my autobiographical information and away from any specific individuals' biographical and/or autobiographical information. Let the mind travel into analyzing categorical abstractions. Then the mind will segue a few times back into concrete actualizations of regular life examples with which to enrich the pathways to knowledge, understanding, and insight.

Consider a person of any set of demographics that coalesce in some way into a major portion of what that person considers the reality of the uniqueness of that individual. Next, think about whatever specific lifestyle choices that person makes over an extended period of time as part of what distinguishes that person and those of similar lifestyle choices from some high percentage of humanity. Whether or not that being gets literally or metaphorically crucified in a way by which others violate his/her/their/its core realities special to that specific sentient being's life, no one anywhere can fully take away from that being the full truth and the full brunt of reality of that being's origins and deliberate lifestyle choices.

Even if that person were to end up in conflict with others such as to stand up for those realities of that person's life and then wind up defamed by the entirety of society in some hideous, excruciatingly gruesome manner, due to decisions by businesspeople, criminals, judges, juries, attorneys, family members, friends, enemies, and/or any other people, as well as by anyone or anything other than people, then, at a core level, it still does not change the truth and the reality of the way that person was, and, if the person is still alive, then also some of the way that person is.

For anyone anywhere, based on any motive(s), to go on a rampage of attempting to strip that person of the very core essence of whatever the actual, genuine truth and reality combine to be for the totality of that person's background, foreground, choices, actions, and each and every thing else, those going on such an ad hominem path are attempting long-term elimination of a realm of genuine reality from being part of reality. They are in many ways trying to remove from ever having been part of reality what was and is irrevocably—to at least the most minute of a trace—a part of reality. No matter how much a "No Quarter" pattern and a "Pieces of You" pattern may supercollide in any given instance, each of those—as polar opposite as it might seem to the other—is irrevocably—to at least an infinitesimal degree—a part of Reality Itself.

Also, no matter how much a "believing circumcision to be superior to noncircumcision" pattern and a "believing noncircumcision to be superior to circumcision" pattern may supercollide in any given instance, each of those patterns is to at least a minimal degree some part of Reality Itself.

Think back to people who seek to absolutely eliminate other people and/or something about the reality of other people. Historical records have it that long ago The Roman Catholic Church and The Donatists completely butted heads with each other about how each one claimed to be "The One True Church." The Roman Catholic Church persisted the conflict, obliterating The Donatists from having any observable presence of a continuing tradition in our world. However, one day in mid-April 2021 I was standing near a trash can in the presence of strangers, then took a piece of trash and deposited it into the waste receptacle, fully cognizant of that history, and said out loud with a medium volume, "I'll donate this to the trash." A man nearby said, "Don't say that!" Although I neither knew then nor do I know now whether that person was a Roman Catholic or not, it sure seems like something to do with the mystery of how Roman Catholicism appeared to have eradicated the presence of Donatism from our world might have had something to do with how a male stranger became agitated and chose to immediately attempt to tell me not to use the sentence, "I'll donate this to the trash" when depositing waste into a waste receptacle. It does seem rather intuitive, though, that we need not consider any of our waste as completely obsolete stuff; rather we can consider it as stuff that we choose to relinquish through the garbage processes, donating it to go on a good journey to wherever it might go next. It can then do whatever it does next, and beings and items other than it can then do whatever it is that they do to it next, as well.

Returning to abstractions, think about the entire category of when people seek to eradicate anyone or anything from the entirety of all reality everywhere, whether the would-be eradicators consider it a way of in fact eradicating a category of evil, a way of eradicating a rival, or whatever other type of complete elimination. What if there is something fundamentally wrong about their attempt to eradicate someone or something from reality? Imagine, for a while, if for nothing else, then for the sake of argument, that those attempting that are dead wrong. Further, imagine that others inform them point blank that it is a rather suicidal path and that it is dead wrong. Imagine more thoroughly those making that attempt to eradicate someone or something from reality, and imagine them in the context of if they are, in fact, dead wrong to embark on that path. Think deeply about that scenario. Imagine also that in this scenario those leading such a movement have acquired followers. Think of the group of both the leaders and the followers of that movement of eradicating someone or something from the entirety of reality, and imagine them, again, in this scenario as being dead wrong in seeking that as a goal. Furthermore, carefully notice that seeking such eradication while being dead wrong means that they are perpetually defaming the character of whoever and/or whatever they are hell-bent on seeking to destroy. They remain in such a state of perpetual slander and/or libel against portions of reality unless and until they might someday course correct out of that path of perpetuating defamation.

This means that if they fail to course correct, then, after a while, they will tend to face virtually unlimited potential harm on account of how they keep on trying to eliminate from reality some portion of what was and is—in at least some infinitesimal amount, and, quite possibly, over some ranges, of some colossal amount—a reality that is irrevocably-present within the larger reality itself.

Even in cases in which some believe themselves to have acquired possession of what they allege to themselves and others to be justification to attempt that type of a warpath aimed toward defaming—perhaps rationalizing to themselves by alleging the defamation to serve a greater good—evidence indicates that they are cruising for a bruising in the long run.

If they are that hell-bent against some vital essence of the reality of anyone, any group, anything, any category, et cetera, then the fact that they intend a permanent suppression of portions of reality to become part of the larger reality is a situation in which they are in many ways repeatedly butting their heads against the entirety of reality itself.

As Israel Albert Horowitz (1907-1973) stated long ago, "Weakness will out." (Cf. *How to Win in the Chess Openings*, Cornerstone Library Publications, New York, 1951; reprinted 1961, p. 121.)

Whether a given being emphasizes perspectives from Shakyamuni Buddha, Moses, Lao-Tzu, Muhammad, Jesus of Nazareth, The Founders of The United States, or anyone else, there are realities in which many truths are relative to observers' conscious frames of reference.

Upon witnessing this work reach publication, I shall let go of all idea structures, practice some Zazen, and soon discover which previous idea structures come back to mind upon when I stand back up, get moving, and allow the free motion of thought to fully return.

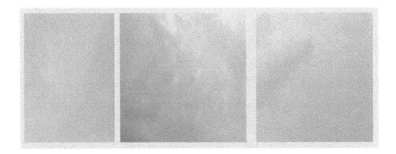

## SECTION SEVEN

Sometimes people talk with derision toward the idea that the Zapruder film or anything else provided evidence of a so-called "magic bullet" that went undetected by investigatory authorities in the aftermath of the assassination of President John F. Kennedy (1917-1963). Many years ago, though, I heard of a plausible explanation for why it might have eluded forensics teams. Specifically, long ago, some assassins sanctioned by select organizations were evidently already privy to special technologies involving the firing of bullets composed of some type of ice (to whatever degree, if any, $H_2O$-based and/or to whatever degree, if any, based on a different molecule) which would melt away shortly after impact.[2, 3]

## CONCLUSION

Consider a variation on the X (formerly known as Twitter) posts in connection with the screenshot that concluded Part Four of Chapter Six—a variation that edits, augments, and fuses them:

Although many folks have had greatly varying perceptions whether O.J. Simpson (1947-2024) was to best be found guilty beyond a reasonable doubt or to best be found not guilty beyond a reasonable doubt as the verdict on his murder trial, I have steadfastly maintained nonjudgment toward him on that. Had I actually served on the jury of that trial, then reality would not have afforded me the luxury to steadfastly maintain this nonjudgment, but the fact is that I did not serve on that specific jury. On a related note, I have often perceived it—as observed with limited information as an outsider in this case—likely that he had hired a hitman. That was one of the theories that I heard floating around television sometime in the early aftermath of those two brutal murders. As of May 18, 2024 I am still very uncertain who did those killings.

This is something that touches on something of fundamental importance to all beings. Those who believe with certainty in a given take on a given controversy or a given set of multiple controversies, if later proven wrong and in need of correction by YHVH/GOD/ADIBUDDHA/REALITY, then should be warned about the likelihood that they may someday face the need to eventually change their minds, lest they fall into a death trap of being stuck on committing perpetual defamation of character against everyone and everything real on the side that they had wrongly assumed against.

Whether in this life or beyond it, if failing to make the appropriate corrections, then those with such a need would be attempting to force their ignorance onto REALITY ITSELF. They would be doing that in a manner such as to place themselves at odds with the entirety of The Strong Force, The Weak Force, and All Other Forces.

This is reminiscent of dialogue at The Houston Museum of Natural Science on December 24, 2004. At the Tibetan special exhibit featured at that time a tour guide received an audience question of whether he was a Buddhist. He answered, "No. I would not consider myself a Buddhist, but I do believe in the truths of Buddhism. For example, the Buddha would say that if you are hitting your head against a wall, and it hurts, then consider stopping. I agree with that."

Choosing to be judgmental versus nonjudgmental regarding beings' effects, for good, ill, or a mixture, whether brought to justice in a given life or not, consider the Twelfth Chapter of *Ecclesiastes*, the First and Second Chapters of *The Dhammapada*, and *the totality of mind and experience*.

Any being who renders unto anyone or anything any variance from whatever would be best to render—for example, believing with all one's might in a person's guilt without actually truly knowing it, and, for another example, believing with all one's might in a person's innocence without actually truly knowing it—be warned that, in due season, on such occasions when Reality Itself would—either in this lifetime or beyond it—expand any being's cognizance to start to actually become genuinely aware of the facts of whatever true reality had been hidden beneath the surface, accuracy of thought may require a change of mind. When challenges are critical, Reality Itself compels us to clear a hurdle—with potential consequences that could range from the most dire to the most auspicious.

## ENDNOTES:

[1] Cf. *Science, Religion, Politics, and Cards,* p. 65 for more information regarding that vehicle. In March 2024 I changed over to driving a new, model year 2024 vehicle.

[2] Abraham_Zapruder (1905-1970). Cf. the URLs https://en.wikipedia.org/wiki/Abraham_Zapruder & https://www.conservapedia.com/Zapruder_film (as accessed on April 8, 2024).

[3] Maurice A.T. Blair (1931-2015) mentioned the ice bullet technology to me multiple times during his life. Although I am almost completely certain that he had completely nothing to do with any direct involvement with the November 22, 1963 assassination referenced, I accept a degree of uncertainty about this. From where I stand, there are several reasons for this trace of uncertainty.

First, he never seemed to say to me anything clearly indicating having noticed news on that day shocking him, and he never seemed to indicate to me where he was when he found out about it. My father and I shared an enormous amount of time together, and, somehow, to the best of my memory, he never shared with me the kind of thing that Rush Limbaugh (1951-2021) shared on air on at least one occasion about remembering vividly the situation way back when of receiving word of that presidential assassination and feeling shocked about it.

Second, it seems very peculiar to me sometimes when I think hard about it every now and then that my father on at least a couple of occasions said to me something essentially identical to, “Lyndon B. Johnson warned President Kennedy, ‘Don’t do it! Don’t go to Dallas for that trip! And, please, if you actually do go on that motorcade, don’t go there in the open. If you do go there, be sure to have bullet-proof glass between you and the crowd!!’ But John F. Kennedy went anyway, going out there in the open.”

Third, he was extra forceful with telling me over and over and over and over again, spread over the span of many years, stern guidance that would take several forms, each of which equated to, whether in those words or some slight variation, “Never joke with anyone about the idea of a presidential assassination.” Although this is a guideline that it is generally good to mention to anyone—just ask comedian Kathy Griffin, for one example[4]—I sometimes wonder why he would repeat it so many times and why he would repeat it so forcefully. Prevention can be worth a pound of cure, but why so much force and so much repetition? Once in a while I would have suspicions, given that I knew my father well enough to believe him capable to have known much more about November 22, 1963 than he would ever share with me or anyone else lacking a need to know some secret assassination information, possibly taking a duty to the United States Military-Industrial Complex and/or La Cosa

Nostra and/or whoever else to the grave. For clarification, from my point of view, I believe it to be overwhelmingly likely that my father never had any direct, knowing involvement with La Cosa Nostra, much like how I have never had any direct, knowing involvement with La Cosa Nostra.

In contrast, it is public knowledge that my father was quite involved with the United States Military-Industrial Complex, including how he served in the U.S. Army for over twenty years in total, spread over the 1950-1972 period. {Side note: Although I *have not* seen the Oliver Stone film *JFK* (1991) up to the time of composing this book, I am considering watching that movie someday. In contrast, I *have* seen the Martin Scorsese film *The Irishman* (2019), having spread a complete viewing of that biopic (based on known, actual events and some events alleged to have also actually happened) over the range from December 2021 to approximately 10:17 P.M. Central Daylight Time May 16, 2022.}

Another odd idea about JFK's 11/22/1963 death was an allegation that my father expressed nearly verbatim as, "If Kennedy hadn't been shot where he was, then he probably would have been shot just a little ways further—or if not a little ways further, then later on in that route. There were so many he had alienated by that time: the military-industrial complex, the mob, and maybe six or ten other very powerful groups who wanted him dead."

One can wonder how many beings at any given instant might want the entire human race dead.[5]

[4] Cf. For your consideration, a set of seven items: a news story, five motion picture films, and a supplemental narrative:

• https://abcnews.go.com/Entertainment/kathy-griffin-president-trump-ordered-secret-service-investigation/story?id=54757722 (as accessed on April 22, 2024)
• *Saving Private Ryan* (1999) {which included the use of the acronym "FUBAR" to mean, "fucked up beyond all recognition"}
• *Full Metal Jacket* (1987) {a movie which highlighted several kinds of toughness amid FUBAR situations}
• *Bullet Train* (2022) {which was bizarre and insightful}
• *Eternals* (2021) {which took the Marvel Cinematic Universe's grandiloquence to a whole other level}
• *The Buddha* (2010) {an excellent documentary}
• A related narrative involves several tales of zealotry, while leaving it to the reader how much, if any, of that may have been for the best, excessive, insufficient, etc.

Tale #1: In ancient Europe, a monk of a Sramanic order demonstrated his commitment to Sramanist practices by self-immolating as a method of executing his own physical, biological body; his name was Zarmanochegas. (Cf. the https://en.wikipedia.org/wiki/Zarmanochegas URL, as accessed on May 10, 2024.)

Tale #2: In Vietnam on June 11, 1963, Thích Quảng Đức (1897-1963) self-immolated in protest of how the government of South Vietnam as then led by Ngô Đình Diệm (1901-1963), a Roman Catholic, was persecuting Buddhists living there at that time. (Cf. the URLs https://en.wikipedia.org/wiki/Thích_Quảng_Đức and https://en.wikipedia.org/wiki/Ngo_Dinh_Diem as accessed on May 10, 2024.)

Tale #3: Maurice A.T. Blair, according to accounts and descriptions that he spoke out loud in portions of approximately the 1985-2013 period, was performing his employment duties for Raytheon in Iran in early 1979. He looked out in the streets, though, and saw lines of men displaying absolute focus and devotion while repeatedly hitting their backs with chains. Between that and the news of the time, he came to the belief that the danger level for him as an American working there on defense contracting was escalating to near infinity. Therefore, he placed a request to Raytheon to be transferred out of that assignment and to return to working elsewhere for the next stages of his employment. Soon his employer granted that request. Not very long after he left Iran, the news came out to the world that an Islamic Revolution was in the process of occurring there, including regime change and the taking of U.S. hostages by some of the revolutionaries.

Tale #4: Mohamed Bouazizi (1984-2011) self-immolated on January 4, 2011 in protest of how the Tunisian government of that time was treating people. (Cf. the URL at https://en.wikipedia.org/wiki/Mohamed_Bouazizi as accessed on May 10, 2024.)

Tale #5: On April 19, 2024, in front of the Manhattan courthouse involving a trial of President Donald Trump, Maxwell Azzarello (1987-2024) self-immolated in order to protest what he believed to be dire threats to liberty worldwide. (Cf. the https://en.wikipedia.org/wiki/Self-immolation_of_Maxwell_Azzarello URL and the video "GRAPHIC WARNING: Man who set himself on fire outside Tump trial dies | REUTERS" as posted at URL https://www.youtube.com/watch?v=luPWC1mlQRk by Reuters; both as accessed on May 10, 2024.)

Tale #6: In mid-April 2005, very near the end of my internship with KPMG, there was a gathering of some employees from the International Executive Services portion of the Houston office of that limited liability partnership. At some stage there was a three-person conversation that happened essentially exactly as this:

Toby Cisneros: Maurice, what religion do you practice?

Maurice J. Blair: Buddhism.

Toby Cisneros (expressing nonverbal cues of derision, including chuckling): So you practice Bootyism!

A Female Supervisor Who Looked Like She Had Some Significant Percentage of Her Ancestry From India (speaking in a deadly serious and stern voice right at Cisneros): Toby, so you just blew off an entire major religion. You should think twice before doing such a thing!

Tale #7: A man named Hassan attended True Buddha Temple in Houston during portions of the 2004-2005 period. At some stage, while I was one of the other people present, that Hassan presented several rather shocking allegations that he had gathered from his trips to India and other exotic places. Here are a few of them:

- By his account: 1) the Himalayan Buddhists of were sharply divided about what to make of the Nazi Germans before and during the European Theatre of World War II. 2) Some were neutral toward the Nazis, others were in favor of the Nazis, and a few were opposed to the Nazis. 3) After the war, many of those who were among the Nazi-sympathizers committed suicide. 4)

The evidence indicated in the long run that all or nearly all of the Nazis who had sought Vajrayana empowerments were among those tragic people who set out to obtain Vajrayana empowerments in a quest mainly to expand personal power, only to later find themselves hoist by their own petards.

- Also, he expressed a sincere belief that multiple men in India as of the time he spoke about them were significantly over 2,000 years old, though not officially recognized by Western science to be among the oldest living humans.
- Even more astounding, he stated that for some of the oldest residents of India, the age of 2,000 years is actually quite young, with some of the elderly being multiple times that age!

Comment from yours truly as a follow-up:

1) The Vajrayana transcendental beings will often neither ask quarter nor give quarter to anyone who violates the deeper levels of reality, especially those who have received Vajrayana empowerments. They will also show great mercy and compassion to those who are sincere, including those who previously violated the deeper levels of reality and choose to return to honoring those deeper levels of reality. Yes, this parallels quite a variety of things from diverse religions and cultures.

As mentioned earlier in this work, Shabkar stated, "Thus, one should know all the tenets of the religions of Buddhism and non-Buddhism—for example, other religions, Bönpos, the Chan Buddhists, the Nyingma, the Kagyus, the Sakya, the Geluks, and so forth—to be the emanations of the buddhas and bodhisattvas."

—Source: "The *Rimé* Activities of Shabkar Tsokdruk Rangdrol (1781-1851)" by Rachel H. Pang, Davidson College, accessed at http://himalaya.socanth.cam.ac.uk/collections/journals/ret/pdf/ret_30_01.pdf on December 31, 2023 and on March 18, 2024.

2) Western science has recognized the oldest recorded-and-officially-confirmed-by-corraborating-evidence individual humans of modern times to have tended to range from about 113 years old to about 122 years old, as of the time leading up to and including May 2024. (Source: https://en.wikipedia.org/wiki/Oldest_people as accessed on May 11, 2024.)

3) Although it sure seemed that Hassan was speaking about his impressions from conversations with people in India regarding the current, individual lifetimes of a few individual humans, we might not be able to rule out the possibility that notions of counting sentient beings' ages across multiple lifetimes of reincarnation may have affected whatever led to his provocative claims.

From having actually been there for conversations with Hassan near the middle of the 2000s decade, it seems definite to me that he was not intending to speak about some way of counting across multiple lives within sequences of reincarnation when making those startling claims. Reminder: he alleged some living people to be over 2,000 years old, including at least a few to be over 5,000 years old. One may wonder whether during his spiritual pilgrimages to parts of South Asia he might have had something very altered in translation during his meetings with extraordinary people. One might also wonder how many astounding legends, as presented by any source, are actually completely true.

Tale #8: Here is a different set of angles on the jury duty mentioned earlier as having involved a male judge who became livid toward a female defense attorney. (Refer to . That happened on February 8th, 2013; consider the following lightly-edited transcription of some of the notes that I took that day on the experience of that:

Arrived a few minutes after 8 A.M. Passed through security, went to assembly room (one of multiple such assembly rooms then at 1201 Congress). They informed us at 9:04 A.M. that my group would be in #236 (a felony court) to proceed with the next step of the jury process. Presiding over the court would be Judge Jim Wallace, #236, Criminal District Court, 15th Floor, 1201 Franklin. My juror process number for that was #63. We entered the courtroom at about 10:57 A.M. #60 to #65 (i.e., the last six, including #63) were placed in the back. Judge Wallace spoke at about 11 A.M. He revealed to us that the defense attorney arrived late and became held in contempt; therefore, there would be no trial on that day for the case involved. He referred to that attorney as having been a woman. They released me from that edition of jury duty at 11:17 A.M., although the work release form ended up stating 5 P.M. as part of how their procedural processes work.

Please be cognizant that there are multiple different people of the Jim Wallace name combination. Per the URL at https://ballotpedia.org/Jim_Wallace_(Texas) as access-ed on May 12, 2024, that Judge Jim Wallace won elect-ion to the 263rd District Court in Texas in 2010, went on to win reelection to that court in 2014, then retired from the Texas judiciary on December 31, 2018.

Tale #9: Many Buddhist legends corroborate with each other on the idea of Yama having served as The Lord of Death for eons, then having encountered Yamantaka, who subdued Yama in order to make Yama adjust into becoming reasonably compliant with the ways of the Dharma of Buddhism.

Cf. *The Book of Buddhas: Ritual Symbolism Used on Buddhist Statuary and Ritual Objects* (1990, reprinted multiple times including 8th printing in 2001) by Eva Rudy Jansen, illustrated by Bert Wieringa; translated from the Dutch by Tony Langam... et al; transl. of *Het Boeddha-boekje: Boeddha's, godheden en rituele symbolen.* Diever: Binkey Kok, 1990, Holland. Distr. in the U.S.A. by Samuel Weiser Inc., York Beach, Maine. & http://buddhistsutras.org/gallery/rebirth_wheel.htm as accessed on April 26, 2011 (i.e., The Twenty-Sixth Day of April Twenty-Eleven).

Tale #10: The eschatological expressions from diverse religions and cultures predict a vast array of competing ideas about how the main conventions of our regular-world, scientifically-and-historically-observable reality might someday come to an end, thus then replaced by the beginning of a new reality.

- Some believe that this already happened in the past, perhaps repeatedly.
- Many believe us to have not yet witnessed the big one.

(Cf. All eschatology.)

Tale #11: Also, think about the many possible manifestations in different contexts of believing time, season, and purpose to arrive for it to be correct to do a given action. Alternatively, consider performing correct actions spontaneously in accordance with how Lee and others have said regarding some range of skillful actions, "It hit all by itself."

Tale #12: One day in the U.S. Army long ago, a Black man became enraged at a White man. That Black man confided in a different White man about what he was thinking and feeling, spontaneously telling that other White man, who happened to be Maurice A.T. Blair, something essentially amounting to, "I'm gonna stab that bastard to death!"

Maurice A.T. Blair said to him, either word-for-word or nearly word-for-word, "Do you really want to throw your life away over that piece of White trash?"

The Black man snapped out of his rage enough to return to his senses, and he answered, either verbatim or nearly so, "No, I don't want to do that."

The military unit averted what otherwise could have become a tragedy.

Tale #13: Maurice A.T. Blair started work as a truck driver. At first, things went smoothly. However, while driving on a mountain road one day in the mid-20$^{th}$ century, the brakes stopped working. He was driving downhill at a high velocity in a runaway big rig. However, he soon noticed that there were off-ramps set up, presumably to help with exactly this type of predicament. He steered the truck to go onto one of those off-ramps. As the truck slowed down a little while it moved upward on the ramp, he correctly timed jumping off of it to then roll as he hit the ground. The runaway big rig flew off the side of the mountain. The trucking company's HR policy was, "One bad accident, and you're out," and, true to form, they fired him. However, he lived to tell the tale.

Tale #14: Maurice A.T. Blair, after a career that had witnessed brief adventures into things outside of the U.S. Military, over two decades of service in the U.S. Military, and several years of service as a defense contractor, went into a retirement mode for a while. After being retired for a while, he decided to come out of retirement for a little while in order to learn the insurance industry better by becoming a part-time insurance agent. That lasted for about a couple of years.

Several times in the 1980s and subsequent decades he shared comments with others alleging that one of his insurance co-workers of that time, a woman named Pat Saenz, to have openly told others about her involvement with some unusual spiritual movement that attempted to relate strands of Eastern religion with strands of Western religion.

Tale #15: The X-15 spaceplane flew on many missions with which to help The United States of America continue its quest to help its citizens and beings in general to be able to have enhanced opportunities to live well, with dignity, honor, and reasonable access to liberty. Some find vehicles sexy.

Tale #16: Tennessee Ernie Ford (1919-1991) had a huge hit with the song "Sixteen Tons."

Tale #17: Henson Cargill (1941-2007) had an incisive hit with the song "Skip a Rope."

Tale #18: Ellie Goulding had a major hit with "Lights."

Tale #19: Bette Davis (1908-1989), Leslie Howard (1893-1943), Archie Mayo (1891-1968), and others teamed up on the motion picture film *The Petrified Forest* (1936).

Tale #20: Kalachakra is Time and Timeliness. Vishvamata is Eternity and Timelessness. Mind(s) can contemplate Kalachakra and Vishvamata embracing each other.

[5] Imagine, if you care to dare, a reality in which an extraordinary number of beings perpetually judge all life on Earth, ready to act as executioners at any instant, up to and including the possibility that they might someday exterminate all Earthly life.

Now imagine the same presence permeating the solar system that includes the Earth, the Moon, Mars, Jupiter, Saturn, Venus, Pluto, Mercury, Io, Titan, Neptune, Uranus, and Helios.

*Finally, imagine at least one being—of a reality that goes way beyond the entire multiverse that includes manifestations of The Milky Way Galaxy, The Andromeda Galaxy, and an enormous number of other galaxies—who has the power to judge, sentence, and execute all life and all existence in that multiverse.*

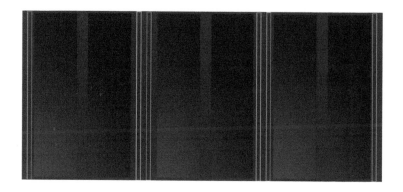

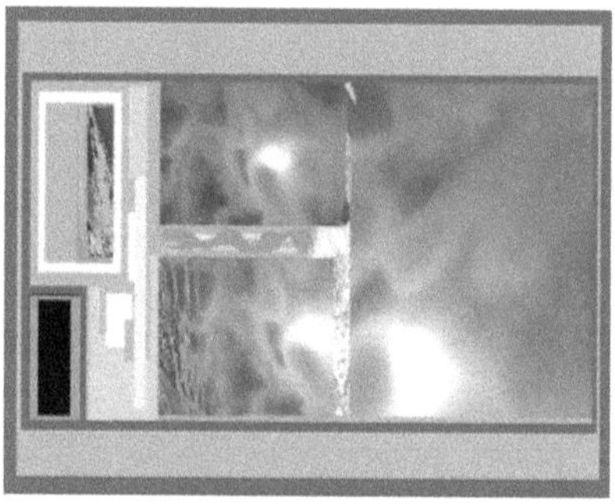

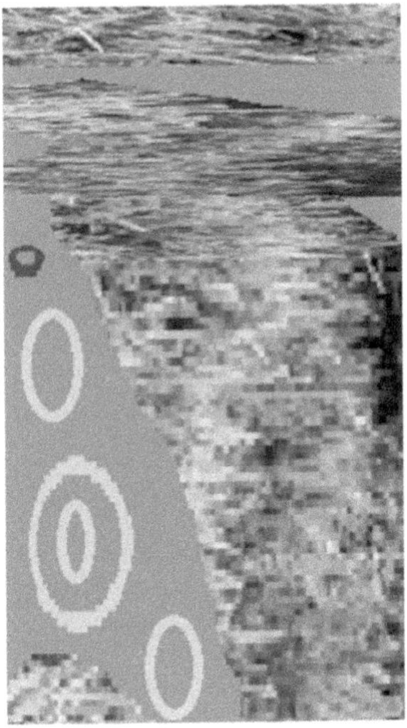

A Ω

# Epilogue

"Stars, darkness, a lamp,
a phantom, dew, a bubble.
A dream, a flash of lightning, and a
cloud—thus we should look upon
the world (all that was made)."

—The Unknown Author(s)
of *The Vajracchedika Sutra*
(also referred to as *The Diamond Sutra*),
as translated by F. Max Müller

INDEX

SYNAPSID REVELATIONS PRESS CORPORATION WILL RETURN TO PRESENT

*The Dimetrodons, the Dorians, and the Modern World, Synapsid Critical Edition.*